KU-013-071

Contents

How to use this book

Assessment and You!

This Evidence Guide has been specially designed to help you gather evidence of the right knowledge and skills for your portfolio, in order for you to achieve the L2 Diploma in Health and Social Care.

Each separate assessment criterion is one page. It explains in simple terms the knowledge and skills you will need to know and demonstrate, and how you might go about generating evidence.

This book is your constant companion and a source of reference whenever your assessor is not available! It covers all the mandatory and 12 optional units.

Key features of the book

The L2 Evidence Guide will help you to understand:

Learning Outcome 1: Understand why communication is important in the work setting

Assessment Criterion 1.1: Identify the different reasons people communicate

What does AC1.1 mean?

- The lead word identify means that you must make clear the reasons why people communicate.
- Your list must make clear the different reasons why people communicate with others.
- For the key word people, you can think about all those whom you come into contact with in your work setting such as the individuals you provide care and support to, their families and friends, your colleagues, senior, manager and other external professionals you liaise with such as GPs, social workers, speech therapists, interpreters and advocates.

The meaning of each assessment criterion

Understand all the requirements of the qualification with clearly stated learning outcomes and assessment criteria fully matched to the specification

The key words included in each assessment criterion

Enhance your understanding of Assessment criteria and key terms, and what you will need to do to evidence each AC

Real Work Setting

Name: Maxwell
Job Role: Support Worker in a residential care home for adults who have learning disabilities
Maxwell has been working as a Support Worker for one year. His responsibilities include supporting individuals to lead fulfilling lives, enabling individuals to achieve their goals and aspirations, and enabling individuals to access the community and participate in activities.
Communicating with staff: Maxwell works as part of a team and always ensures he attends team meetings and handovers.
Communicating with individuals: Maxwell communicates with individuals on a daily basis to ascertain what they would like to do and how they would like to do it.
Communicating with families and others: Maxwell assists the Senior at individuals' support meetings and shares information, when required to do so by the Senior or Manager, with individuals' families, friends, advocates and other professionals involved in their lives.

Evidencing AC1.1 to your assessor:

For AC1.1 you must evidence your understanding of the different reasons why people communicate

Assessment Methods:

Oral or **Written** Questioning or **Discussion** or a **Spidergram**

- You can **tell** your assessor the different reasons why people communicate.
- *Or*, you can **talk** to your assessor about the different reasons why people communicate.
- *Or*, you can complete a **spidergram** of the different reasons why people communicate.

REMEMBER TO:

- Provide the different reasons **why** people communicate.
- Include **varied** reasons why people communicate.
- Think about your **own work setting** and **why** communication is necessary.
- Think about the different **people** you come into contact with in your **own work setting** and communicate with.

How each assessment criterion relates to your work setting

See how concepts are applied in settings with real life scenarios. Each AC has a different role, description and case study that links to the AC so you can reflect and apply the scenario to your own role and setting

The range of assessment methods that you can use to gather evidence

Helpful suggestions for how you can evidence your understanding of assessment criteria including oral, written and discussion assessment methods as well as ways to show your understanding and skills in competence based units

How to ensure that each assessment criterion is fully addressed

Helpful tips and guidance including points to cover in your evidence. Points to remember to help you in the work setting and develop your professional skills are also included.

SHC21 Introduction to communication in health, social care or children's and young people's settings

Learning Outcome 1: Understand why communication is important in the work setting

Assessment Criterion 1.1: Identify the different reasons people communicate

What does AC1.1 mean?

- The lead word **identify** means that you must **make clear** the reasons why people communicate.
- Your **list** must make clear the **different reasons** why people communicate with others.
- For the key word **people**, you can think about all those whom you come into contact with in your work setting such as the individuals you provide care and support to, their families and friends, your colleagues, senior, manager and other external professionals you liaise with such as GPs, social workers, speech therapists, interpreters and advocates.

Read the following **Real Work Setting** scenario and think about how it relates to your work setting and role:

Real Work Setting

Name: Maxwell
Job Role: Support Worker in a residential care home for adults who have learning disabilities
Maxwell has been working as a Support Worker for one year. His responsibilities include supporting individuals to lead fulfilling lives, enabling individuals to achieve their goals and aspirations, and enabling individuals to access the community and participate in activities.
Communicating with staff: Maxwell works as part of a team and always ensures he attends team meetings and handovers.
Communicating with individuals: Maxwell communicates with individuals on a daily basis to ascertain what they would like to do and how they would like to do it.
Communicating with families and others: Maxwell assists the senior at individuals' support meetings and shares information, when required to do so by the senior or manager, with individuals' families, friends, advocates and other professionals involved in their lives.

Evidencing AC1.1 to your assessor:

For AC1.1 you must evidence your understanding of the different reasons why people communicate.

Assessment Methods:

Oral or **Written** Questioning or **Discussion** or a **Spidergram**

- You can **tell** your assessor the different reasons why people communicate.
  Or
- You can **talk** to your assessor about the different reasons why people communicate.
  Or
- You can complete a **spidergram** of the different reasons why people communicate.

REMEMBER TO:

- Provide the different reasons **why** people communicate.
- Include **varied** reasons why people communicate.
- Think about your **own work setting** and **why** communication is necessary.
- Think about the different **people** you come into contact with in your **own work setting** and communicate with.

Learning Outcome 1: Understand why communication is important in the work setting

Assessment Criterion 1.2: Explain how effective communication affects all aspects of the learner's work

What does AC1.2 mean?

- The lead word **explain** means that you must **make clear** how communication affects all aspects of the learner's work.
- Your **account** must make clear the **different ways** in which effective communication can have an impact on all aspects of the learner's work.
- For the key words **effective communication**, you can think about how **good** communication affects all aspects of your work.
- For the key word **aspects**, you can think about the different ways that effective communication can impact on different areas related to your job role and responsibilities such as: the way you work with others; the team you work in; the quality of the service provided; as well as how you carry out your work role.

Read the following **Real Work Setting** scenario and think about how it relates to your work setting and role:

Real Work Setting

Name: Maxwell

Job Role: Support Worker in a residential care home for adults who have learning disabilities (See page 1 for a description of the role)

Effective communication: Maxwell has recently participated in a team meeting where he shared his positive experience of working at the home including how this was, in the main, due to everyone being committed to working together as a team, respecting and supporting each other to enable all individuals to have the support required for them to lead fulfilling lives. Maxwell reflected on his first week at the home and remembers how welcomed he was made to feel by everyone and how clearly everyone communicated with him when he had questions about working with individuals and others involved in their lives he did not know.

Evidencing AC1.2 to your assessor:

For AC1.2 you must evidence your understanding of how effective communication affects all aspects of your work.

Assessment Methods:

Oral or **Written** Questioning or **Discussion** or a **Personal Statement** or **Reflection**

- You can **tell** your assessor how effective communication affects all aspects of your work.
  Or
- You can **talk** to your assessor about how effective communication affects all aspects of your work.
  Or
- You can write a **personal statement** or **reflection** about your experience of how effective communication affects all aspects of your work.

REMEMBER TO:

- Provide an **account** and explain **how**.
- Include the impact of **effective** communication.
- Include the **effects** on different aspects of your work role.
- Think about **effective communication** in your **work setting**.
- Think about how effective communication affects all aspects of your job role in your **work setting**.

Learning Outcome 1: Understand why communication is important in the work setting

Assessment Criterion 1.3: Explain why it is important to observe an individual's reactions when communicating with them

What does AC1.3 mean?

- The lead word **explain** means that you must make clear the reasons why it is important to observe an individual's reactions when communicating with them.
- Your **account** must make clear the **different reasons** why.
- For the key word **observe**, you can think about the importance of taking note of how an individual reacts when communicating with them.
- For the key word **reactions**, you can think about the different feelings that could be experienced by an individual and the different ways individuals may react to different communications, as well as the reasons for this.

Read the following **Real Work Setting** scenario and think about how it relates to your work setting and role:

Real Work Setting

Name: Maxwell

Job Role: Support Worker in a residential care home for adults who have learning disabilities (See page 1 for a description of the role)

Observing an individual's reactions: Maxwell is meeting with Craig today, one of the individuals who lives in the home, to find out which activity he would like to participate in this evening. Craig has said to another support worker that he wouldn't mind taking part in the football game outside but doesn't know whether he might prefer to do something else. Maxwell begins by sharing with Craig the activities planned for this evening, which include football outside, cooking, or choosing and watching a DVD. Craig shrugs his shoulders and says to Craig that he doesn't know. Maxwell explains to Craig a little more about what each activity involves and observes Craig's body language and facial expressions while doing so.

Evidencing AC1.3 to your assessor:

For AC1.3 you must evidence your understanding of why it is important to observe an individual's reactions when communicating with them.

Assessment Methods:

Oral or **Written** Questioning or **Discussion** or a **Personal Statement** or **Reflection**

- You can **tell** your assessor why it is important to observe an individual's reactions when communicating with them.
  Or
- You can **talk** to your assessor about why it is important to observe an individual's reactions when communicating with them.
  Or
- You can write a **personal statement** or **reflection** about why it is important to observe an individual's reactions when communicating with them.

REMEMBER TO:

- Provide an **account** and explain **why**.
- Include evidence of the **importance of** observing an individual's **reactions.**
- Include evidence of the importance of observing both **positive and negative reactions**.
- Think about the reasons why it is important to observe an individual's reactions when communicating in **your work setting**.

Learning Outcome 2: Be able to meet the communication and language needs, wishes and preferences of individuals

Assessment Criterion 2.1: Show how to find out an individual's communication and language needs, wishes and preferences

What does AC2.1 mean?

- The lead word **show** means that you must **be able to demonstrate through your work practices** how to find out an individual's communication and language needs, wishes and preferences.
- Your **observations of your work practices** must include **different ways** of establishing an individual's communication and language needs, wishes and preferences.
- For the key words **find out**, you can think about the different ways to establish individuals' needs in relation to their communication and language needs, wishes and preferences.
- For the key word **preferences**, you can think about the different ways to establish individuals' communication preferences, such as how they want to communicate with you and others in line with their beliefs, values and culture.

Read the following **Real Work Setting** scenario and think about how it relates to your work setting and role:

Real Work Setting

Name: Lisa
Job Role: Support Worker in an independent living scheme for adults who have mental health needs
Lisa has been working as a Support Worker for two years. Her responsibilities include promoting individuals' independence, supporting individuals with daily living skills, contributing to a therapeutic environment and recovery model approaches, and enabling individuals to maintain links with their communities, families and friends.
Finding out an individual's communication needs: Lisa assists the senior with finding out about individuals' communication needs by working closely with the individual and reading through information provided from others involved in the individual's life and recorded in the individual's support plan.
Finding out an individual's language needs: Lisa ensures she checks with the individual at their first meeting the language the individual uses to communicate.
Finding out an individual's preferences: Lisa and her colleagues work together to find out from the individual and others involved in their lives what communication preferences they have and how they can ensure these are met.
Finding out an individual's wishes: Lisa explains to each individual that part of her role involves finding out the communication wishes of each individual, including any support or aids they would like to make themselves understood.

Evidencing AC2.1 to your assessor:

For AC2.1 you must evidence your skills of how to find out an individual's communication and language needs, wishes and preferences.

Assessment Method:

Direct Observation of your work practices

- You can **show** your assessor, or an expert witness, how you find out an individual's communication and language needs, wishes and preferences.

REMEMBER TO:

- Make arrangements for **observation** of your **work practices**.
- Include evidence of your work practices with different **individuals**.
- Include evidence of **communication and language** needs, **wishes and preferences**.
- Think about how you find out in your **work setting** how different individuals communicate.
- Think about different individuals in **your work setting**, their **different backgrounds, cultures and beliefs**.

Learning Outcome 2: Be able to meet the communication and language needs, wishes and preferences of individuals

Assessment Criterion 2.2: Demonstrate communication methods that meet an individual's communication needs, wishes and preferences

What does AC2.2 mean?

- The lead word **demonstrate** means that you must **be able to show through your work practices** how you use **different** communication methods to meet individuals' needs.
- Your **observations of your work practices** must include the use of **different communication methods** to meet an individual's communication needs, wishes and preferences.
- For key words **communication methods**, you can think about the different verbal and non-verbal ways you use to communicate with individuals **in your work setting**, including eye contact, touch, physical gestures, body language, behaviour, vocabulary, linguistic tone and pitch, and any communication aids that you use.

Read the following **Real Work Setting** scenario and think about how it relates to your work setting and role:

Real Work Setting

Name: Lisa

Job Role: Support Worker in an independent living scheme for adults who have mental health needs (See page 4 for a description of the role)

Demonstrating communication methods: Lisa will support two individuals this morning with their daily living skills. Lisa begins by supporting Jen with her laundry. Lisa knows that Jen likes to first see the items she plans to wash, so Lisa ensures that she supports Jen taking out each item in turn and then makes brief eye contact with her after each item is returned back to her laundry basket. Jen also prefers not to speak with her support worker while she places her items in the washing machine but does enjoy a discussion about what she has done after she has completed the task. Lisa will then support Gregory to collect his prescription from the GP's surgery. Prior to going out, Lisa is aware that Gregory likes to be reminded an hour beforehand of the task he is about to complete and talk through what he is going to do and how he is going to be supported to achieve it.

Evidencing AC2.2 to your assessor:

For AC2.2 you must evidence your skills of how to use communication methods to meet an individual's communication needs, wishes and preferences.

Assessment Method:

Direct Observation of your work practices

- You can **show** your assessor how you use communication methods to meet an individual's communication needs, wishes and preferences.

REMEMBER TO:

- Make arrangements for **observations** of your **work practices.**
- Include evidence of your work practices with **different individuals**.
- Include evidence of using **different communication methods**.
- Think about the **ways** you communicate in your **work setting** with different individuals.
- Think about **different individuals** in your work setting, their **different backgrounds, cultures and beliefs.**

Learning Outcome 2: Be able to meet the communication and language needs, wishes and preferences of individuals

Assessment Criterion 2.3: Show how and when to seek advice about communication

What does AC2.3 mean?

- The lead word **show** means that you must **be able to demonstrate through your work practices** how and when to seek advice about communication.
- Your **observations of your work practices** must include you seeking advice about communication.
- For the key word **advice**, you can think about the procedure you must follow in your work setting for seeking further clarification or information about communication, including the people or services you can approach.

Read the following **Real Work Setting** scenario and think about how it relates to your work setting and role:

Real Work Setting

Name: Lisa
Job Role: Support Worker in an independent living scheme for adults who have mental health needs (See page 4 for a description of the role)
Seeking advice about communication: While Lisa was supporting Gregory to collect his prescription from the GP's surgery, she noted how he communicated with the receptionist using a combination of key words and facial expressions that she hadn't seen him use before. Lisa, again, noted Gregory's use of these when he met with his GP. On her return to the work setting, Lisa recorded in Gregory's support plan full details of the key words and facial expressions he had used with both the receptionist and the GP and reported her observations to the senior on duty. After talking these through with the senior they decided that it will be also important to share this information with other members of the team, as well as Gregory's advocate.

Evidencing AC2.3 to your assessor:

For AC2.3 you must evidence your skills of how and when to seek advice about communication.

Assessment Method:

Direct Observation of your work practices

- You can **show** your assessor, or an expert witness, how and when to seek advice about communication.

REMEMBER TO:

- Make arrangements for **observations** of **your work practices.**
- Include evidence of you **seeking advice** about **communication.**
- Include evidence of you showing **both how and when** to seek advice about communication.
- Think about how and when you seek advice about communication in your **work setting**.

Learning Outcome 3: Be able to reduce barriers to communication

Assessment Criterion 3.1: Identify barriers to effective communication

What does AC3.1 mean?

- The lead word **identify** means that you must **make clear** what the barriers to effective communication are.
- Your **list** must make clear the **different** barriers to effective communication.
- For the key word **barriers**, you can think about how these can arise out of the **physical environment**, the **psychological attitude** of those communicating, as well as **cultural and language differences** that may exist.

Read the following **Real Work Setting** scenario and think about how it relates to your work setting and role:

Real Work Setting

Name: Saad

Job Role: Support Worker to people who have learning disabilities and live in their own homes

Saad has been working as a Support Worker for seven months. His responsibilities include providing personalised care and support to individuals living in their own homes, promoting independence and full participation in all daily living and personal care tasks, and enabling individuals to participate in their communities.

Barriers to effective communication: Saad provides support to different individuals, each of whom communicates with him in different ways. Sometimes, during his visits Saad finds that communicating with individuals is difficult and this may be due to a variety of reasons including, in relation to the individual, what has occurred either before or during the visit, the involvement of others such as an individual's family, friends or other professionals, as well as how he is carrying out his job role and associated duties during the visit.

Saad has experienced that when an individual is feeling worried or concerned this can affect how the individual communicates with him and others. For example, Saad remembers providing support to an individual who seemed more emotional than usual, and it was only at the end of his visit to him that the individual apologised for being tearful, as he was concerned about whether his benefit application was going to be accepted or not. Saad remembers how this concern affected the individual's body language, facial expressions and verbal communication.

Evidencing AC3.1 to your assessor:

For AC3.1 you must evidence your understanding of the barriers to effective communication.

Assessment Methods:

Oral or **Written** Questioning or **Discussion** or a **Spidergram**

- You can **tell** your assessor about the barriers to effective communication.
  Or
- You can **talk** to your assessor about the barriers to effective communication.
  Or
- You can complete a **spidergram** of the barriers to effective communication.

REMEMBER TO:

- Provide a list of **different** barriers.
- Include the barriers to **effective** communication.
- Think about your **own work setting** and the **different** barriers that there are to effective communication.
- Think about your **own work setting** and the different staff, individuals, families and others with whom you communicate.

Learning Outcome 3: Be able to reduce barriers to communication

Assessment Criterion 3.2: Demonstrate how to reduce barriers to communication in different ways

What does AC3.2 mean?

- The lead word **reduce** means that you must **be able to show through your work practices** how to lessen barriers to effective communication.
- Your **observations of your work practices** must include how you reduce **different barriers** to communication that may arise.
- For the key word **reduce**, you can think about how you successfully minimise barriers to communication that arise in your work setting.
- For the key word **barriers**, you can think about how these can arise out of the **physical environment**, the **psychological attitude** of those communicating and **cultural and language differences** that exist.

Read the following **Real Work Setting** scenario and think about how it relates to your work setting and role:

Real Work Setting

Name: Saad
Job Role: Support Worker to people who have learning disabilities and live in their own homes (See page 7 for a description of the role)
Reducing physical barriers: Saad will support Rafael to attend a conference for the first time and has arranged to show him the venue, including how to get there and what it feels like to be in a room with a large group of people.
Reducing psychological barriers: Saad ensures that when he is communicating with individuals he empowers them to feel confident about expressing what they want and prefer in ways that they feel comfortable with. Saad believes that it is important to do this so that each individual is understood and develops their own preferred ways of communicating with others.
Reducing cultural and language barriers: Saad always tries to find out as much information as he can about an individual's culture and language so that he can use methods that are suitable and respectful towards each individual, while taking into account individuals' cultural and language needs.

Evidencing AC3.2 to your assessor:

For AC3.2 you must evidence your skills of how to reduce barriers to effective communication.

Assessment Method:

Direct Observation of your work practices

- You can **show** your assessor, or an expert witness, how you reduce barriers to effective communication.

REMEMBER TO:

- Make arrangements for **observations** of **your work practices**.
- Include evidence of **your work practices** of how to minimise **different barriers** to communication.
- Think about the **ways** you reduce barriers to communication in **your work setting**.

Learning Outcome 3: Be able to reduce barriers to communication

Assessment Criterion 3.3: Demonstrate ways to check that communication has been understood

What does AC3.3 mean?

- The lead word **demonstrate** means that you must **be able to show through your work practices** different ways to check that communication has been understood.
- Your **observations of your work practices** must include how you use **different ways** to check that communication has been understood.
- For the key word **ways**, you can think about how you use different methods of checking that communication has been understood.

Read the following **Real Work Setting** scenario and think about how it relates to your work setting and role:

Real Work Setting

Name: Saad

Job Role: Support Worker to people who have learning disabilities and live in their own homes (See page 7 for a description of the role)

Ensuring communication is understood: Saad uses a variety of methods of confirming whether communication has been understood by individuals and others he works with. When working alongside his colleagues, Saad continuously checks whether his communications with them have been understood by asking if they understand his written and verbal communications and by clarifying any comments that do not appear to have been understood.

When supporting individuals, Saad uses a variety of methods of checking whether communications with him and others have been understood, depending on the individual and their communication needs and preferences. For example, Saad will encourage Sam to repeat back to him what he has agreed to. When supporting Jim, Saad will wait and see whether Jim gives him eye contact, or not, when he asks him if he has understood what they have talked about. Saad uses thumbs up and thumbs down signs to support Abi to confirm whether he has understood what has been communicated.

Evidencing AC3.3 to your assessor:

For AC3.3 you must evidence your skills of demonstrating ways to check that communication has been understood.

Assessment Method:

Direct Observation of your work practices

- You can **show** your assessor how you use different ways to check that communication has been understood.

REMEMBER TO

- Make arrangements for **observations** of **your work practices**.
- Include evidence of **your work practices** of how to use **different ways** to check that communication has been understood.
- Think about the different **ways** you check that communication has been understood in **your work setting**.

Learning Outcome 3: Be able to reduce barriers to communication

Assessment Criterion 3.4: Identify sources of information and support or services to enable more effective communication

What does AC3.4 mean?

- The lead word **identify** means that you must **make clear** the sources of information and support or services to enable more effective communication.
- Your **list** must make clear the **different** sources of information and support or services.
- For the key word **support**, you can think about the different communication aids, people and professionals that can be accessed to enable individuals to communicate effectively.
- For the key word **services**, you can think about the different specialist external agencies that can be accessed to enable individuals to communicate effectively, such as translation, interpreting, speech and language and advocacy services.

Read the following **Real Work Setting** scenario and think about how it relates to your work setting and role:

Real Work Setting

Name: Saad

Job Role: Support Worker to people who have learning disabilities and live in their own homes (See page 7 for a description of the role)

Sources of information and support or services: Saad is meeting with his manager to discuss sources of information and services that are required for an individual he supports. Saad begins by explaining that he feels he has recently seen a deterioration in the use of language by this individual and has noticed that the individual no longer speaks in sentences and seems to confuse the meanings of his words. Saad has also observed how the individual feels quite frustrated when he can't express what he wants to say; Saad states that this may be signs of dementia and suggests the Alzheimer's Society as a good source of information. It is agreed at the meeting that a referral to this individual's GP will be made in the first instance to check whether there are any causes for this deterioration and seek his advice on this.

Evidencing AC3.4 to your assessor:

For AC3.4 you must evidence your understanding of sources of information and support or services to enable more effective communication.

Assessment Methods:

Oral or **Written** Questioning or **Discussion** or a **Spidergram**

- You can **tell** your assessor about the sources of information and support or services to enable more effective communication.

  Or
- You can **talk** to your assessor about the sources of information and support or services to enable more effective communication.

  Or
- You can complete a **spidergram** of the sources of information and support or services to enable more effective communication.

REMEMBER TO:

- Provide a list of **different sources of information and support or services**.
- Include sources that enable more **effective** communication.
- Think about **your own work setting** and the **different** sources of information and support or services to enable more effective communication that exist both within and outside your work setting.

Learning Outcome 4: Be able to apply principles and practices relating to confidentiality at work

Assessment Criterion 4.1: Explain the term 'confidentiality'

What does AC4.1 mean?

- The lead word **explain** means that you must **make clear** the meaning of the term 'confidentiality'.
- Your **account** must make clear the meaning of confidentiality.
- For the key word **confidentiality**, you can think about how to keep safe personal information that is held, discussed and written about individuals.

Read the following **Real Work Setting** scenario and think about how it relates to your work setting and role:

Real Work Setting

Name: Ben

Job Role: Care Assistant to older people

Ben has been working as a Care Assistant for three years. His responsibilities include assisting individuals with personal care tasks, serving meals and drinks and assisting individuals to eat and drink, working closely with the senior to maintain good working relationships with individuals and others involved in their lives, including their families, friends, advocates and professionals, and understanding and maintaining confidentiality at all times.

Confidentiality: Ben is working towards his L2 Diploma in Health and Social Care. As part of Unit SHC21: Introduction to communication in health, social care or children's and young people's settings, he will need to generate evidence towards the 'Be able to' Learning Outcome, 5. Ben and his assessor have agreed to meet and discuss the assessment of this learning outcome. They agree that for AC5.1 Ben will need to provide an explanation about what the term 'confidentiality' means; both discuss how this explanation needs to be written in Ben's own words and reflect his understanding of the term. Ben's assessor suggests to him that he begins by thinking about how confidentiality is relevant to his job role, responsibilities and work setting. Ben thinks about how this affects the way he reports and records on a daily basis, how this applies to information shared about individuals, as well as information that may relate to others involved in individuals' lives. Ben's assessor reminds him to ensure he includes examples in his explanation that show his understanding of this term.

Evidencing AC4.1 to your assessor:

For AC4.1 you must evidence your knowledge of the term 'confidentiality'.

Assessment Methods:

Oral or **Written** Questioning or **Discussion** or a **Personal Statement** or **Reflection**

- You can **tell** your assessor about what the term 'confidentiality' means.
  Or
- You can **talk** to your assessor about what the term 'confidentiality' means.
  Or
- You can write a **personal statement** or **reflection** about your experience of the meaning of the term 'confidentiality' in your work setting.

REMEMBER TO:

- Provide an **account** and explain with examples.
- Include the **meaning** of the term 'confidentiality'.
- Include how confidentiality applies to your work role and work setting.
- Think about what confidentiality means in **your work setting**.

Learning Outcome 4: Be able to apply principles and practices relating to confidentiality at work

Assessment Criterion 4.2: Demonstrate confidentiality in day-to-day communication, in line with agreed ways of working

What does AC4.2 mean?

- The lead word **demonstrate** means that you must **be able to show through your work practices** how you maintain confidentiality in day-to-day communication, in line with agreed ways of working.
- Your **observations of your work practices** must include different ways of how you maintain confidentiality in day-to-day communication.
- For the key word **confidentiality**, you can think about personal information that is held, discussed and written about individuals and how your work setting's policies and procedures state how you must maintain confidentiality in day-to-day communication.
- For the key words **agreed ways of working**, you can think about how you maintain confidentiality, in line with your work setting's policies, procedures, guidelines and working practices.

Read the following **Real Work Setting** scenario and think about how it relates to your work setting and role:

Real Work Setting

Name: Ben
Job Role: Care Assistant to older people (See page 11 for a description of the role)
Confidentiality: Ben and his assessor next discuss how Ben plans to generate evidence towards AC5.2 in Unit SHC21, which requires Ben to show his assessor how he maintains confidentiality in day-to-day communication. Ben and his assessor agree that as maintaining confidentiality is applicable to all aspects of his job role and responsibilities, this evidence can be observed naturally and over a period of time as part of his day-to-day responsibilities in his work setting. Ben and his assessor agree on the type of evidence that might be observed, such as communications with individuals and others in the work setting; these may include both spoken and written communications. Ben's assessor asks him to ensure also that he refers to his work setting's confidentiality procedure before being observed so that he is aware of its content and how this applies to his job role.

Evidencing AC4.2 to your assessor:

For AC4.2 you must evidence your skills of how to demonstrate confidentiality in day-to-day communication, in line with agreed ways of working.

Assessment Method:

Direct Observation of your work practices

- You can **show** your assessor how you demonstrate confidentiality in day-to-day communication.

REMEMBER TO:

- Make arrangements for **observations** of **your work practices**.
- Include evidence of **your work practices** of how to maintain confidentiality in day-to-day communication.
- Ensure the evidence you provide is in line with your work setting's agreed ways of working.
- Think about the **ways** you maintain confidentiality in day-to-day communication in **your work setting**, in line with agreed ways of working.

Learning Outcome 4: Be able to apply principles and practices relating to confidentiality at work

Assessment Criterion 4.3: Describe situations where information normally considered to be confidential might need to be passed on

What does AC4.3 mean?

- The lead word **describe** means that you must **make clear** the situations where information normally considered to be confidential might need to be passed on.
- Your **account** must make clear the different situations.
- For the key word **situations**, you can think about occasions that require you to pass on confidential information such as when there may be concerns about an individual's safety and well-being.
- For the key word **confidential**, you can think about personal information that is held, discussed and written about individuals and occasions that may require this to be passed on to others.

Read the following **Real Work Setting** scenario and think about how it relates to your work setting and role:

Real Work Setting

Name: Ben

Job Role: Care Assistant to older people
(See page 11 for a description of the role)

Passing on confidential information: Ben and his assessor are having a discussion today about confidentiality and specifically about when information normally considered to be confidential may need to be passed on to generate evidence towards AC5.3 for unit SHC21. Ben and his assessor begin by discussing the meaning of confidential information and how it applies to his job role. Ben then tells his assessor how, having read his work setting's procedure, he is aware that there are occasions where information normally considered to be confidential may need to be passed on and in his own words provides full details of these.

Evidencing AC4.3 to your assessor:

For AC4.3 you must evidence your knowledge of situations where information normally considered to be confidential might need to be passed on.

Assessment Methods:

Oral or **Written** Questioning or **Discussion** or a **Personal Statement** or **Reflection**

- You can **tell** your assessor about situations where information normally considered to be confidential might need to be passed on.
  Or
- You can **talk** to your assessor about situations where information normally considered to be confidential might need to be passed on.
  Or
- You can write a **personal statement** or **reflection** about your experience of situations where information normally considered to be confidential might need to be passed on in your work setting.

REMEMBER TO:

- Provide an **account** and detail the situations.
- Include examples of **different** situations.
- Include **evidence** of where information normally considered to be confidential might need to be passed on.
- Think about how situations where information normally considered to be confidential might need to be passed on in **your work setting**.

Learning Outcome 4: Be able to apply principles and practices relating to confidentiality at work

Assessment Criterion 4.4: Explain how and when to seek advice about confidentiality

What does AC4.4 mean?

- The lead word **explain** means that you must **make clear** how and when to seek advice about confidentiality.
- Your **account** must make clear the process of seeking advice about confidentiality.
- For the key word **confidentiality**, you can think about how to keep safe personal information that is held, discussed and written about individuals and the procedure that must be followed in your work setting when you need to seek advice about confidentiality.

Read the following **Real Work Setting** scenario and think about how it relates to your work setting and role:

Real Work Setting

Name: Ben
Job Role: Care Assistant to older people (See page 11 for a description of the role)
Seeking advice about confidentiality: Further to discussing situations where information normally considered to be confidential might need to be passed on, Ben explains to his assessor that he has also familiarised himself with what the confidentiality procedure in his work setting states about how and when to seek advice about confidentiality. Ben explains in full, and using his own words, the process he must follow for this procedure including the actions he must take, from whom he needs to seek advice and how he needs to record and report.

Evidencing AC4.4 to your assessor:

For AC4.4 you must evidence your knowledge of how and when to seek advice about confidentiality.

Assessment Methods:

Oral or **Written** Questioning or **Discussion** or a **Personal Statement** or **Reflection**

- You can **tell** your assessor about how and when to seek advice about confidentiality.
  Or
- You can **talk** to your assessor about how and when to seek advice about confidentiality.
  Or
- You can write a **personal statement** or **reflection** about your experience of how and when to seek advice about confidentiality in your work setting.

REMEMBER TO:

- Provide an **account** and explain with **examples**.
- Include evidence of **how** to seek advice about confidentiality.
- Include evidence of **when** to seek advice about confidentiality.
- Include details of the **procedure** you must follow to seek advice about confidentiality.
- Think about how and when to seek advice about confidentiality in **your work setting**.

SHC22 Introduction to personal development in health, social care or children's and young people's settings

Learning Outcome 1: Understand what is required for competence in your work role

Assessment Criterion 1.1: Describe the duties and responsibilities of your role

What does AC1.1 mean?

- The lead word **describe** means that you must **make clear** the range of duties and responsibilities you have.
- Your **account** must make clear both the duties and responsibilities you have at work.
- For the key word **duties** you can think about the **activities** you are expected to carry out as part of your job role.
- For the key word **responsibilities** you can think about the different **approaches** and **qualities** you use to carry out your work activities.

Read the following **Real Work Setting** scenario and think about how it relates to your work setting and role:

Real Work Setting

Name: Katarina
Job Role: Care Assistant to adults who have dementia
Katarina has been working as a Care Assistant in the community for two years. Katarina's responsibilities include supporting individuals who have dementia to: live in their own homes safely; lead fulfilling and active lives; be an active part of their local communities; and maintain links with their families, friends and others involved in their lives.
Duties: Katarina's duties include: assisting individuals with daily activities as stated in their individual plan of care; assisting with personal care tasks; assisting individuals with household and laundry tasks; providing individuals with emotional support; assisting individuals with attending appointments and other activities in their local communities; and recording and reporting any changes in individuals.
Responsibilities: Katarina's responsibilities include acting in individuals' best interests at all times, dealing calmly and positively with different types of situations that may arise, encouraging individuals' families and friends to be involved in their lives, having a caring and respectful attitude to work.

Evidencing AC1.1 to your assessor:

For AC1.1 you must evidence your understanding of the duties and responsibilities of your work role.

Assessment Methods:

Oral or **Written** Questioning or **Discussion** or a **Personal Statement** or **Reflection**

- You can **tell** your assessor the different duties and responsibilities you have at work.
  Or
- You can **talk** to your assessor about the duties and responsibilities you have at work.
  Or
- You can write a **personal statement** or **reflection** about your experience of the different duties and responsibilities you have in your work setting.

REMEMBER TO

- Provide an **account** and detail **both** your duties and responsibilities.
- Include **different examples** of the duties and responsibilities you have.
- Think about your **job description, person specification** and **your work setting.**

Learning Outcome 1: Understand what is required for competence in your work role

Assessment Criterion 1.2: Identify standards that influence the way your role is carried out

What does AC1.2 mean?

- The lead word **identify** means that you must **make clear** the standards that are relevant to your duties and responsibilities at work.
- Your **list** must make clear the **different** standards that are relevant.
- For the key word **expectations** you can think about your work **duties** and **responsibilities** and what your employer expects about how you carry these out.
- For the key word **standards** you can think about the different standards that are relevant to your job role such as codes of practice, regulations, minimum standards and national occupational standards.

Read the following **Real Work Setting** scenario and think about how it relates to your work setting and role:

Real Work Setting

Name: Katarina

Job Role: Care Assistant to adults who have dementia
(See page 15 for a description of the role)

Standards that influence your job role: Katarina is meeting with her supervisor today to discuss her allocated duties and responsibilities and any further training and support she may require to carry out her day-to-day work activities effectively. In preparation for this meeting, Katarina has been asked by her supervisor to think about how and why she is required to carry out her job role in the way she does, in terms of both the organisation she works for and the national standards that are in place for Care Assistants who provide support to individuals who live in their own homes and require care and support, including those individuals who have dementia.

Evidencing AC1.2 to your assessor:

For AC1.2 you must evidence your understanding of the standards that influence the way your role is carried out.

Assessment Methods:

Oral or **Written** Questioning or **Discussion** or a **Spidergram**

- You can **tell** your assessor about the different standards that influence the way your role is carried out.
  Or
- You can **talk** to your assessor about the different standards that influence the way your role is carried out.
  Or
- You can complete a **spidergram** about the different standards that influence the way your role is carried out in your work setting.

REMEMBER TO:

- Provide examples of **different** standards.
- Include **standards** that influence how you carry out your job role.
- Think about your **own work setting** and the standards that influence the way your job role is carried out.

Learning Outcome 1: Understand what is required for competence in your work role

Assessment Criterion 1.3: Describe ways to ensure that personal attitudes or beliefs do not obstruct the quality of work

What does AC1.3 mean?

- The lead word **describe** means that you must **make clear** the ways to ensure that personal attitudes or beliefs do not obstruct the quality of work.
- Your **account** must make clear the **different** ways.
- For the key words **personal attitudes or beliefs** you can think about how to ensure that what you believe to be of value and importance in life and your own experiences that you have had do not affect or get in the way of the quality and standard of your work.

Read the following **Real Work Setting** scenario and think about how it relates to your work setting and role:

Real Work Setting

Name: Katarina
Job Role: Care Assistant to adults who have dementia (See page 15 for a description of the role)
Ensuring that personal attitudes or beliefs do not obstruct the quality of work: Katarina is a Christian and believes that attending church regularly and living her life according to Christian values and principles is very important. At work Katarina works with a range of individuals and work colleagues who all have different personal attitudes and beliefs to her. Katarina ensures she treats each person with respect and according to how they like to be addressed, supported and worked with, irrespective of their personal attitudes or beliefs. Most importantly, Katarina remains non-judgemental of each person she meets and works with.

Evidencing AC1.3 to your assessor:

For AC1.3 you must evidence your understanding of the ways to ensure that personal attitudes or beliefs do not obstruct the quality of work.

Assessment Methods:

Oral or **Written** Questioning or **Discussion** or a **Personal Statement** or **Reflection**

- You can **tell** your assessor about the different ways to ensure that personal attitudes or beliefs do not obstruct the quality of work.
  Or
- You can **talk** to your assessor about the different ways to ensure that personal attitudes or beliefs do not obstruct the quality of work.
  Or
- You can write a **personal statement** or **reflection** about your experience of the different ways to ensure that personal attitudes or beliefs do not obstruct the quality of work in your work setting.

REMEMBER TO:

- Provide an **account** and detail **different ways**.
- Include **different examples** of how to ensure that neither personal attitudes nor beliefs obstruct the quality of work.
- Think about **your work setting** and the different ways to ensure that personal attitudes or beliefs do not obstruct the quality of work.

Learning Outcome 2: Be able to reflect on your work activities

Assessment Criterion 2.1: Explain why reflecting on practice is an important way to develop knowledge, skills and practice

What does AC2.1 mean?

- The lead word **explain** means that you must **make clear** the reasons why reflecting on practice is an important way to develop knowledge, skills and practice.
- Your **account** must make clear the reasons why reflecting on practice is important.
- For the key words **reflective practice** you can think about how you develop your knowledge and skills and improve your working practices and the quality of services provided.

Read the following **Real Work Setting** scenario and think about how it relates to your work setting and role:

Real Work Setting

Name: Hayley
Job Role: Support Worker to people who have physical disabilities and live in their own home
Hayley has been working as a Support Worker in the community for five years. Hayley's responsibilities include promoting independent living skills on a daily basis, supporting and assisting with personal care tasks, enabling individuals to access their local communities and go shopping, meet with friends and family, attend appointments and education and/or work placements.
Importance of reflective practice: Hayley takes time out at the end of each working week to sit down and think back over what has happened during the week at work, including what has worked well and what requires further improvement; she finds this is a useful way to keep her mind focused on maintaining high standards at work, as well as to further develop her own working practices and her understanding and knowledge around a number of different areas that are relevant to her job role.

Evidencing AC2.1 to your assessor:

For AC2.1 you must evidence your knowledge of why reflecting on practice is an important way to develop knowledge, skills and practice.

Assessment Methods:

Oral or **Written** Questioning or **Discussion** or a **Personal Statement** or **Reflection**

- You can **tell** your assessor about why reflecting on practice is an important way to develop knowledge, skills and practice.
  Or
- You can **talk** to your assessor about why reflecting on practice is an important way to develop knowledge, skills and practice.
  Or
- You can write a **personal statement** or **reflection** about your experience of why reflecting on practice is an important way to develop knowledge, skills and practice in your work setting.

REMEMBER TO:

- Provide an **account** and **explain the reasons why** reflecting on practice is important.
- Include **different** reasons why.
- Ensure your evidence relates to **developing knowledge, skills** and **practice.**
- Think about **your work setting** and the different reasons why reflecting on practice is an important way to develop knowledge, skills and practice.

Learning Outcome 2: Be able to reflect on your work activities

Assessment Criterion 2.2: Assess how well your knowledge, skills and understanding meet standards

What does AC2.2 mean?

- The lead word **assess** means that you must **be able to show through your work practices** how you judge how well your knowledge, skills and understanding meet standards.
- Your **observations of your work practices** must include you making a judgement about your knowledge, skills and understanding.
- For the key word **standards** you can think about the different national occupational, minimum and quality standards that are relevant to your job role and how you judge how well your knowledge, skills and understanding meet these.

Read the following **Real Work Setting** scenario and think about how it relates to your work setting and role:

Real Work Setting

Name: Hayley

Job Role: Support Worker to people who have physical disabilities and live in their own home (See page 18 for a description of the role)

Assessing how well your knowledge, skills and understanding meet standards: Hayley's supervisor completed a professional practice observation with her at the beginning of this week and today both are discussing how this went, including discussing and assessing how well Hayley's knowledge, skills and understanding meet the organisation's and national standards that Hayley is required to work to. Both agree that Hayley works to a high standard and within the required and expected limits of her job role. One area that Hayley has identified with her supervisor that requires further development is around the promotion of individuals' independence when out in their local communities, as at times Hayley tends to not provide individuals with sufficient opportunities to enable them to make their own informed decisions and choices.

Evidencing AC2.2 to your assessor:

For AC2.2 you must evidence your skills in how to assess how well your knowledge, skills and understanding meet standards.

Assessment Method:

Direct Observation of your work practices

- You can **show** your assessor or an expert witness how to assess how well your knowledge, skills and understanding meet standards.
- You can also use as a **supporting piece of work product evidence** your personal development plan.

REMEMBER TO:

- Make arrangements for **observations** of you assessing how well your knowledge, skills and understanding meet standards.
- Include evidence of how you **assess** your knowledge, skills and understanding.
- Think about how to assess how well your knowledge, skills and understanding meet the standards in **your work setting**.

Learning Outcome 2: Be able to reflect on your work activities

Assessment Criterion 2.3: Demonstrate the ability to reflect on your work activities

What does AC2.3 mean?

- The lead word **demonstrate** means that you must **be able to show through your work practices** how you reflect on your work activities.
- Your **observations of your work practices** must include how you reflect on your work activities.
- For the key word **reflect** you can think about how you develop your knowledge and skills and improve your working practices.

Read the following **Real Work Setting** scenario and think about how it relates to your work setting and role:

Real Work Setting

Name: Hayley

Job Role: Support Worker to people who have physical disabilities and live in their own home (See page 18 for a description of the role)

Reflecting on your work activities: During Hayley's meeting with her supervisor, Hayley reflects on when her supervisor observed her earlier on in the week when supporting Simon to the gym. Hayley talks through with her supervisor the different ways she could have promoted Simon's independence in making his own informed choices and decisions. For example, Hayley could have spent some time reviewing with Simon the different gyms that were available to him to attend, rather than assume that Simon wanted to attend the same gym as last time. Once at the gym, Hayley declined the offer of one of the gym instructors to show Simon round as she was present; Hayley did not discuss this with Simon, or check if this was what he wanted. Doing so would have provided Simon with the opportunity to meet someone else and use the gym independently from Hayley.

Evidencing AC2.3 to your assessor:

For AC2.3 you must evidence your skills in reflecting on work activities.

Assessment Method:

Direct Observation of your work practices

- You can **show** your assessor or an expert witness how you reflect on work activities.
- You can also use as a **supporting piece of work product evidence** your personal development plan.

REMEMBER TO:

- Make arrangements for **observations** of you reflecting on your work activities.
- Include evidence of **how you reflect** on your work activities.
- Think about the **ways** you reflect on your work activities in **your work setting**.

Learning Outcome 3: Be able to agree a personal development plan

Assessment Criterion 3.1: Identify sources of support for your learning and development

What does AC3.1 mean?

- The lead word **identify** means that you must **make clear** the sources of support for your learning and development.
- Your **list** must make clear the **different** sources of support.
- For the key words **sources of support** you can think about the support available both within and outside your work setting that can help you to learn and develop in your work role, working practices and knowledge, such as informal and formal support, supervision and appraisal.

Read the following **Real Work Setting** scenario and think about how it relates to your work setting and role:

Real Work Setting

Name: Nick

Job Role: Residential Support Worker (Nights) to older people

Nick has been working as a Residential Support Worker for four years. Nick's responsibilities include: contributing to person-centred planning, care and reviews, supporting individuals' independence at all times, remaining attentive to individuals' needs to ensure these are fully met, observing, monitoring and recording the conditions of individuals and completing accurate records and reports.

Sources of support for own learning and development: Nick enjoys his job very much and feels that he is continuously learning and developing in his job role by working alongside others, encountering different and new situations and by furthering his knowledge and skills across a number of areas; this includes moving and positioning individuals safely, contributing to care plans, supporting individuals to manage continence, and maintaining the health and safety of the working environment.

Evidencing AC3.1 to your assessor:

For AC3.1 you must evidence your knowledge of sources of support for your learning and development.

Assessment Methods:

Oral or **Written** Questioning or **Discussion** or a **Spidergram**

- You can **tell** your assessor about the different sources of support for your learning and development.
  Or
- You can **talk** to your assessor about the different sources of support for your learning and development.
  Or
- You can complete a **spidergram** of the different sources of support for your learning and development.
- You can also use as a **supporting piece of work product evidence** your personal development plan.

REMEMBER TO:

- Provide the **different** sources of formal and informal support available to you.
- Include examples of support available both **within** and **outside** your work setting.
- Ensure your evidence relates to your learning and development.
- Think about the different sources of support available in and outside **your work setting**.

Learning Outcome 3: Be able to agree a personal development plan

Assessment Criterion 3.2: Describe the process for agreeing a personal development plan and who should be involved

What does AC3.2 mean?

- The lead word **describe** means that you must **make clear** the process for agreeing a personal development plan and who should be involved.
- Your **account** must make clear both **the process** and **who should be involved**.
- For the key word **agreeing** you can think about with whom you discuss your personal development plan and how you decide on the activities you plan to undertake.
- For the key words **personal development plan** you can think about how you evidence your personal development including how this is documented and will include agreed objectives for development, proposed activities to meet objectives and timescales for review.
- For the key words **who should be involved** you can think about others that may be involved in agreeing a personal development plan such as the individual, carers, advocates, supervisor, line manager, employer and/or other professionals.

Read the following **Real Work Setting** scenario and think about how it relates to your work setting and role:

Real Work Setting

Name: Nick

Job Role: Residential Support Worker (Nights) to older people
(See page 21 for a description of the role)

Agreeing a personal development plan and who should be involved: Nick will soon be meeting with his line manager to agree a personal development plan. As part of this process, both Nick and his manager will need to agree on his goals for development, how to prioritise these in terms of how soon they need to be achieved and when and how they will be monitored. Nick will also need to agree with his manager, and other relevant people, the activities and support that are required for him to achieve his development goals.

Evidencing AC3.2 to your assessor:

For AC3.2 you must evidence your knowledge of the process for agreeing a personal development plan and who should be involved.

Assessment Methods:

Oral or **Written** Questioning or **Discussion** or a **Personal Statement** or **Reflection**

- You can **tell** your assessor about the process for agreeing a personal development plan and who should be involved.

  Or
- You can **talk** to your assessor about the process for agreeing a personal development plan and who should be involved.

  Or
- You can write a **personal statement** or **reflection** about your experience of the process for agreeing a personal development plan and who should be involved in your work setting.

REMEMBER TO:

- Provide an **account** and detail the **process to follow.**
- Include details of the **steps to take** to agree a personal development plan.
- Include details of **who should be involved** and **how**.
- Think about **your work setting** and the process for agreeing a personal development plan and who should be involved.

Learning Outcome 3: Be able to agree a personal development plan

Assessment Criterion 3.3: Contribute to drawing up your personal development plan

What does AC3.3 mean?

- The lead word **contribute** means that you must **be able to show** how you work alongside other people to draw up your personal development plan.
- Your **observations of your work practices** must include how you **contribute** to your personal development plan.
- For the key words **drawing up** you can think about with whom you discuss your personal development plan and how you contribute to the activities you plan to undertake.
- For the key words **personal development plan** you can think about how you evidence your personal development including how this is documented and will include agreed objectives for development, proposed activities to meet objectives and timescales for review.

Read the following **Real Work Setting** scenario and think about how it relates to your work setting and role:

Real Work Setting

Name: Nick

Job Role: Residential Support Worker (Nights) to older people
(See page 21 for a description of the role)

Contributing to drawing up your personal development plan: Nick has prepared for his personal development meeting with his line manager by writing down his own development goals and thinking about how he could achieve these, and the timescales and support required for him to do so effectively. Nick will share this information with his line manager prior to their meeting and then discuss this with him while drawing up his personal development plan. Nick has also noted down the reasons why he would like to work towards these development goals, as well as the benefits to the individuals he works with and the overall service provision; Nick has also found out about the people that he would need to involve to achieve these.

Evidencing AC3.3 to your assessor:

For AC3.3 you must evidence your skills of how to contribute to drawing up your personal development plan.

Assessment Method:

Direct Observation of your work practices

- You can **show** your assessor or an expert witness how you contribute to drawing up your personal development plan.
- You can also use as a **supporting piece of work product evidence** your personal development plan.

REMEMBER TO:

- Make arrangements for **observations** of how you **contribute** to your personal development plan.
- Include evidence of how you work alongside others to **agree** your personal development plan.
- Think about how you contribute to drawing up your personal development plan in **your work setting**.

Learning Outcome 4: Be able to develop knowledge, skills and understanding

Assessment Criterion 4.1: Show how a learning activity has improved your knowledge, skills and understanding

What does AC4.1 mean?

- The lead word **show** means that you must **be able to demonstrate** how a learning activity has improved your knowledge, skills and understanding.
- Your **observations of your work practices** must include how a learning activity you have taken part in has improved your knowledge, skills and understanding.
- For the key words **learning activity** you can think about how a situation or training you have undertaken has improved your own knowledge, skills and understanding such as by giving you a greater insight, providing you with an opportunity to learn about new areas or develop different ways of working and applying the knowledge and skills you have gained.

Read the following **Real Work Setting** scenario and think about how it relates to your work setting and role:

Real Work Setting

Name: Chris
Job Role: Personal Assistant to an adult who has Asperger syndrome
Chris has been working as a Personal Assistant for six months. Chris's responsibilities include supporting John to interact with others in social situations to enable him to take part in activities he enjoys, such as playing golf and gardening, as well as organising these and taking part in these with him.
How a learning activity has improved your knowledge, skills and understanding: Chris is meeting with John's mother today, as planned, to provide her with feedback about the training session he organised for him to attend that focused on social relationships for those individuals with Asperger syndrome and, specifically, to consider the difficulties that John experiences in social situations and when interacting with others. Chris explains to John's mother that the training session improved his understanding of what it is like to live with Asperger syndrome, as well as his skills and understanding of different ways of working with John to enable him to overcome the difficulties he experiences when others interact with him.

Evidencing AC4.1 to your assessor:

For AC4.1 you must evidence how a learning activity has improved your knowledge, skills and understanding.

Assessment Method:

Direct Observation of your work practices

- You can **show** your assessor or an expert witness how a learning activity has improved your knowledge, skills and understanding.

REMEMBER TO:

- Make arrangements for **observations** of how a learning activity has improved your knowledge, skills and understanding.
- Include evidence of how your knowledge, skills and understanding have improved.
- Think about **your work setting** and how a learning activity has improved your knowledge, skills and understanding.

Learning Outcome 4: Be able to develop knowledge, skills and understanding

Assessment Criterion 4.2: Show how reflecting on a situation has improved your knowledge, skills and understanding

What does AC4.2 mean?

- The lead word **show** means that you must **be able to demonstrate** how reflecting on a situation has improved your knowledge, skills and understanding.
- Your **observations of your work practices** must include how you reflect on a situation.
- For the key word **situation** you can think about a real-life scenario that you have experienced that has improved your own knowledge, skills and understanding such as by giving you a greater insight, providing you with an opportunity to learn about new areas or develop different ways of working and applying the knowledge and skills you have gained.

Read the following **Real Work Setting** scenario and think about how it relates to your work setting and role:

Real Work Setting

Name: Chris

Job Role: Personal Assistant to an adult who has Asperger syndrome
(See page 24 for a description of the role)

How reflecting on a situation has improved your knowledge, skills and understanding: During Chris's meeting with John's mother he also reflects on the situation that occurred when he played golf with John. He explained how John became very distressed when a group of young adults told him that he was not a very good golf player. Chris remembers how difficult John found it to listen to these comments from other people and to deal with these and to continue playing golf. At the time, Chris thought it was in John's best interest to leave, which John agreed to. Upon reflection, however, Chris now believes that perhaps he should have supported John to manage this unplanned situation in a different way by, for example, providing him with suggestions of responses he could use for this situation and any others that may arise in the future.

Evidencing AC4.2 to your assessor:

For AC4.2 you must evidence how reflecting on a situation has improved your knowledge, skills and understanding.

Assessment Method:

Direct Observation of your work practices

- You can **show** your assessor or an expert witness how reflecting on a situation has improved your knowledge, skills and understanding.

REMEMBER TO:

- Make arrangements for **observations** of how reflecting on a situation has improved your knowledge, skills and understanding.
- Include **evidence** of a **situation** you have reflected on.
- Include evidence of how your knowledge, skills and understanding have improved.
- Think about **your work setting** and how reflecting on a situation has improved your knowledge, skills and understanding.

Learning Outcome 4: Be able to develop knowledge, skills and understanding

Assessment Criterion 4.3: Show how feedback from others has developed your knowledge, skills and understanding

What does AC4.3 mean?

- The lead word **show** means that you must **be able to demonstrate** how feedback from others such as the individuals you provide care and support to, your colleagues and your manager has developed your knowledge, skills and understanding.
- Your **observations of your work practices** must include how you use feedback that you have received from others.
- For the key word **feedback** you can think about the different people that provide you with feedback and how you use their comments and views to continue to develop your knowledge, skills and understanding.

Read the following **Real Work Setting** scenario and think about how it relates to your work setting and role:

Real Work Setting

Name: Chris
Job Role: Personal Assistant to an adult who has Asperger syndrome (See page 24 for a description of the role)
How feedback from others has developed your knowledge, skills and understanding: During Chris's meeting with John's mother, she provides Chris with some useful feedback about how she agrees that he should have tried some different strategies to enable John to learn the social skills required for managing situations like those that may arise, rather than removing him from the situation. She suggests that giving John a set of responses that he could think about and adapt for himself will be more useful for future situations that may arise so that he can feel he is responding in words that he would use. Chris agrees to have a meeting with John about this so that together they can discuss the situation that occurred when playing golf and different ways of how he could manage situations like this. Chris has also sought feedback from his line manager, who has agreed to provide him with some more training and support on working with John, including ideas for practical ways of managing any difficulties he may experience with social interactions.

Evidencing AC4.3 to your assessor:

For AC4.3 you must evidence your skills of using feedback from others to develop your knowledge, skills and understanding.

Assessment Method:

Direct Observation of your work practices

- You can **show** your assessor, or an expert witness, how you use feedback from others to develop your knowledge, skills and understanding.

REMEMBER TO:

- Make arrangements for **observations** of **you using feedback**.
- Include evidence of **feedback** you have obtained from others.
- Ensure your evidence relates to developing your knowledge, skills and understanding.
- Think about **your work setting** and how you use feedback from others to develop your knowledge, skills and understanding.

Learning Outcome 4: Be able to develop knowledge, skills and understanding

Assessment Criterion 4.4: Show how to record progress in relation to personal development

What does AC4.4 mean?

- The lead word **show** means that you must **be able to demonstrate** how to record progress in relation to personal development.
- Your **observations of your work practices** must include how to record your progress with achieving your personal development plan's goals.
- For the key word **progress** you can think about how to record how you are proceeding with achieving your goals for your personal development; including what has been achieved and how, what has not been achieved and why, as well as how you plan to achieve the goals that are still outstanding.

Read the following **Real Work Setting** scenario and think about how it relates to your work setting and role:

Real Work Setting

Name: Chris

Job Role: Personal Assistant to an adult who has Asperger syndrome
(See page 24 for a description of the role)

Recording progress in relation to personal development: Chris is meeting with his line manager today and, in view of the situation that has arisen with supporting John to participate in activities he enjoys, both will discuss and review Chris's personal development plan. They will document that Chris has attended a training session on Asperger syndrome but requires further training and support to work specifically with supporting John to manage situations and social interactions that he finds difficult. Both agree that this must be actioned quite soon and agree to a timescale of two weeks for this to be achieved. Chris also suggests to his line manager that he thinks it would benefit him to have John's mother present, if not for all, for part of the training to gain a personal insight into her son's needs and difficulties.

Evidencing AC4.4 to your assessor:

For AC4.4 you must evidence your skills of how to record progress in relation to personal development.

Assessment Method:

Direct Observation of your work practices

- You can **show** your assessor or an expert witness how you record progress in relation to personal development.
- You can also use as a **supporting piece of work product evidence** your personal development plan.

REMEMBER TO:

- Make arrangements for **observations** of **recording your progress**.
- Include evidence of the **progress you have made**.
- Ensure your evidence relates to **your personal development.**
- Think about **your work setting** and how to record progress in relation to personal development.

SHC23 Introduction to equality and inclusion in health, social care or children's and young people's settings

Learning Outcome 1: Understand the importance of equality and inclusion

Assessment Criterion 1.1: Explain what is meant by diversity, equality, inclusion and discrimination

What does AC1.1 mean?

- The lead word **explain** means that you must **make clear** the meaning of the terms diversity, equality, inclusion and discrimination.
- Your **account** must make clear the meaning of all four terms.
- For the key word **diversity** you can think about what makes individuals and others such as individuals' families, friends, your colleagues and other professionals different and unique.
- For the key word **equality** you can think about how this involves making opportunities available to all individuals.
- For the key word **inclusion** you can think about how this involves encouraging individuals and others to be full and active participants in their lives.
- For the key word **discrimination** you can think about how individuals and others can be treated unfairly or excluded.

Read the following **Real Work Setting** scenario and think about how it relates to your work setting and role:

Real Work Setting

Name: Matthew

Job Role: Carer in a residential care home for older people

Matthew has been working as a Carer for five years. His responsibilities include promoting the independence and dignity of all individuals, supporting individuals to have their personal and care needs met, supporting individuals to take part in social activities, accompanying individuals to appointments, and communicating with individuals, their families and friends positively and respectfully.

The meaning of diversity, equality, inclusion and discrimination: Matthew sees each person as a unique individual and enjoys finding out who they are, what they like, what they don't like, their background, their preferences, their wishes and goals. Approaching each person he meets in this way means that he is able to recognise and value each person's differences and make available a range of opportunities for them to choose from. Matthew also feels that he benefits an enormous amount from empowering individuals to be fully involved in their lives and ensuring that no one he supports and works with is treated unfairly or excluded in the work setting.

Evidencing AC1.1 to your assessor:

For AC1.1 you must evidence your understanding of what is meant by diversity, equality, inclusion and discrimination.

Assessment Methods:

Oral or **Written** Questioning or **Discussion** or a **Personal Statement**

- You can **tell** your assessor about the meaning of the terms diversity, equality, inclusion and discrimination.

  Or
- You can **talk** to your assessor about the meanings of all four terms.

  Or
- You can write a **personal statement** about the meanings of all four terms.

REMEMBER TO:

- Provide an **account** and explain the meaning of all four terms.
- Include **examples** to show your understanding of all four terms.
- Think about what is meant by diversity, equality, inclusion and discrimination in your **work setting**.

Learning Outcome 1: Understand the importance of equality and inclusion

Assessment Criterion 1.2: Describe ways in which discrimination may deliberately or inadvertently occur in the work setting

What does AC1.2 mean?

- The lead word **describe** means that you must **provide an account** that **details** ways in which discrimination may deliberately or inadvertently occur in the work setting.
- Your **account** must make clear the **different ways** that discrimination may deliberately or inadvertently occur at work.
- For the key word **discrimination** you can think about how individuals can be treated unfairly or excluded.
- For the key word **deliberately** you can think about how an employer may treat an employee unfairly, such as an employer that only promotes female members of staff into senior job roles, in spite of male members of staff being available for promotion too.
- For the key word **inadvertently** you can think about how an organisation may put in place a rule or condition that may be unfair to some employees, such as an employer that states that all male members of staff must be clean shaven, which may be unfair to some employees from different religions and cultures.

Read the following **Real Work Setting** scenario and think about how it relates to your work setting and role:

Real Work Setting

Name: Matthew

Job Role: Carer in a residential care home for older people
(See page 28 for a description of the role)

How discrimination can occur deliberately and inadvertently: During the training session Matthew attended, the participants were also asked to think about different ways that discrimination may occur deliberately or unintentionally in the work setting. Matthew found it interesting to listen to other participants' examples of how discrimination may occur in the work setting and this made him think more about how he needs to be more vigilant at work to ensure that discrimination does not occur deliberately or inadvertently. Matthew also decided that he will refer back to his work setting's procedure when he returns to work to see what it states about the different ways in which discrimination may occur.

Evidencing AC1.2 to your assessor:

For AC1.2 you must evidence your understanding of the ways in ways in which discrimination may deliberately or inadvertently occur in the work setting.

Assessment Methods:

Oral or **Written** Questioning or **Discussion** or a **Personal Statement** or **Reflection**

- You can **tell** your assessor about the ways in which discrimination may deliberately or inadvertently occur in the work setting.

  Or
- You can **talk** to your assessor about the ways in which discrimination may deliberately or inadvertently occur in the work setting.

  Or
- You can write a **personal statement** or **reflection** about your experience of the ways in which discrimination may deliberately or inadvertently occur in the work setting.

REMEMBER TO:

- Provide an **account** and include details.
- Include different **examples** of the **ways in which discrimination may deliberately or inadvertently occur in the work setting.**
- Think about **different ways**.
- Think about how discrimination may deliberately or inadvertently occur in your **work setting**.

Learning Outcome 1: Understand the importance of equality and inclusion

Assessment Criterion 1.3: Explain how practices that support equality and inclusion reduce the likelihood of discrimination

What does AC1.3 mean?

- The lead word **explain** means that you must **make clear** how promoting equality and inclusion reduces the likelihood of discrimination occurring.
- Your **account** must make clear **how** discrimination is reduced through practices that support equality and inclusion.
- For the key word **equality** you can think about how making opportunities available to individuals and others can reduce the likelihood of discrimination occurring.
- For the key word **inclusion** you can think about how encouraging individuals and others to be full and active participants in their lives can reduce the likelihood of discrimination occurring.
- For the key word **discrimination** you can think about how promoting equality and inclusion can reduce the likelihood of individuals being treated unfairly or excluded.

Read the following **Real Work Setting** scenario and think about how it relates to your work setting and role:

Real Work Setting

Name: Matthew
Job Role: Carer in a residential care home for older people (See page 28 for a description of the role)
Reducing the likelihood of discrimination: In the final part of the training session Matthew attended, the participants considered effective ways of reducing the likelihood of discrimination occurring at work. Matthew reflected on the group discussions he participated in and thought carefully about how the promotion of equality and inclusion is very important and crucial to ensuring that the work setting is a safe and comfortable environment, where everyone feels that they are included, treated fairly and in control of their lives and careers.

Evidencing AC1.3 to your assessor:

For AC1.3 you must evidence your understanding of how practices that support equality and inclusion reduce the likelihood of discrimination.

Assessment Methods:

Oral or **Written** Questioning or **Discussion** or a **Personal Statement** or **Reflection**

- You can **tell** your assessor about how practices that support equality and inclusion reduce the likelihood of discrimination.

  Or
- You can **talk** to your assessor about how practices that support equality and inclusion reduce the likelihood of discrimination.

  Or
- You can write a **personal statement** or **reflection** about your experience of how practices that support equality and inclusion reduce the likelihood of discrimination.

REMEMBER TO:

- Provide an **account** and explain **how.**
- Include different **examples** to show your understanding of **practices that support equality and inclusion.**
- Ensure your evidence relates to **how the likelihood of discrimination is reduced.**
- Think about how practices that support equality and inclusion reduce the likelihood of discrimination in your **work setting.**

Learning Outcome 2: Be able to work in an inclusive way

Assessment Criterion 2.1: Identify which legislation, codes of practice relating to equality, diversity, discrimination and rights apply to your work role

What does AC2.1 mean?

- The lead word **identify** means that you must **make clear** the legislation and codes of practice relating to equality, diversity and discrimination in your work role.
- Your **list** must make clear the **different** legislation and codes of practice that are relevant.
- For the key words **legislation** and **codes of practice** you can think about different laws and guidance that relate to equality, diversity and discrimination in your work role.
- For the key word **equality** you can think about the laws, guidance and agreed ways of working that relate to making opportunities available to individuals.
- For the key word **diversity** you can think about the laws, guidance and agreed ways of working that relate to respecting individuals' differences and uniqueness.
- For the key word **discrimination** you can think about the laws, guidance and agreed ways of working that relate to reducing the likelihood of individuals being treated unfairly or excluded.

Read the following **Real Work Setting** scenario and think about how it relates to your work setting and role:

Real Work Setting

Name: Millie

Job Role: Care Assistant for adults with physical disabilities

Millie has been working as a Care Assistant for one month. Her responsibilities include: supporting individuals with their daily living tasks such as cooking, shopping, housework, the laundry, personal care tasks, paying bills and going out to socialise with others.

Relevance of legislation and codes of practice: Millie has been asked to read through her work setting's codes of practice and legislation that are relevant to equality, diversity, and discrimination in her work role to further her knowledge of these and how they apply to her day-to-day work and responsibilities. Reading through these makes Millie realise how her work setting's codes of practice relate to the legislation in place.

Evidencing AC2.1 to your assessor:

For AC2.1 you must evidence your knowledge of the legislation and codes of practice relating to equality, diversity and discrimination in your work role.

Assessment Methods:

Oral or **Written** Questioning or **Discussion** or a **Spidergram**

- You can **tell** your assessor about the relevant legislation and codes of practice.

  Or
- You can **talk** to your assessor about the relevant legislation and codes of practice.

  Or
- You can complete a **spidergram** of the relevant legislation and codes of practice.

REMEMBER TO:

- Provide **different** examples of legislation and codes of practice.
- Ensure your evidence relates to equality, diversity and discrimination in your work role.
- Think about **your work setting** and the relevant legislation and codes of practice.

Learning Outcome 2: Be able to work in an inclusive way

Assessment Criterion 2.2: Show interaction with individuals that respects their beliefs, culture, values and preferences

What does AC2.2 mean?

- The lead word **show** means that you must **be able to demonstrate through your work practices** how your interactions with individuals respect their beliefs, culture, values and preferences.
- Your **observation of your work practices** must include how you respect individuals' beliefs, culture, values and preferences.
- For the key word **beliefs** you can think about how you can ensure that your interactions respect different individuals' faiths.
- For the key word **culture** you can think about how you can ensure that your interactions respect different individuals' ideas, customs and behaviours.
- For the key words **values and preferences** you can think about how you can ensure that your interactions respect different individuals' beliefs about what is important in life and to them.

Read the following **Real Work Setting** scenario and think about how it relates to your work setting and role:

Real Work Setting

Name: Millie

Job Role: Care Assistant for adults with physical disabilities
(See page 31 for a description of the role)

Millie has been working as a Care Assistant for one month. Her responsibilities include: supporting individuals with their daily living tasks such as cooking, shopping, housework, the laundry, personal care tasks, paying bills and going out to socialise with others.

Interactions that respect individuals: Millie has been observed by two Senior Care Assistants, who have given her some positive and constructive feedback on how she interacts with individuals. One of the Senior Care Assistants fed back to Millie that she thought the way she took into account one of the individual's wishes to use running water to wash was respectful and conducted in a sensitive manner. Both Senior Care Assistants also observed how Millie always asked first the support required by each individual when she visited and how they wanted her to support them; both fed back to Millie that not only did she do this consistently across all individuals she visited, but also she did this in a warm and respectful manner that took into account individuals' different beliefs, cultures, values and preferences.

Evidencing AC2.2 to your assessor:

For AC2.2 you must evidence your skills of how to show interaction with individuals that respects their beliefs, culture, values and preferences.

Assessment Method:

Direct Observation of your work practices

- You can **show** your assessor how you show interaction with individuals that respects their beliefs, culture, values and preferences.

REMEMBER TO:

- Make arrangements for **observations** of how **you interact** with individuals.
- Include evidence of how your **working practices** show that you respect individuals' beliefs, culture, values and preferences.
- Think about your **work setting** and interactions with individuals that respect their beliefs, culture, values and preferences.

Learning Outcome 2: Be able to work in an inclusive way

Assessment Criterion 2.3: Describe how to challenge discrimination in a way that encourages change

What does AC2.3 mean?

- The lead word **describe** means that you must provide **an account** that **details** how to challenge discrimination in a way that encourages change.
- Your **account** must make clear the **different ways** in which discrimination can be challenged in a way that encourages change.
- For the key word **challenge** you can think about positive actions you can take when discrimination occurs.
- For the key word **discrimination** you can think about how to challenge when you observe or hear that individuals and/or others have been treated unfairly or been excluded.

Read the following **Real Work Setting** scenario and think about how it relates to your work setting and role:

Real Work Setting

Name: Millie

Job Role: Care Assistant for adults with physical disabilities
(See page 31 for a description of the role)

Challenging discrimination in a way that encourages change: Millie has requested to speak with one of the Senior Care Assistants, as she wishes to report to her how she observed a Senior Care Assistant discriminate against an individual whom they were both supporting with cooking her lunch today. Millie begins by detailing to the Senior what happened at this individual's home. Millie explains how she observed the Senior Care Assistant treat Maggie unfairly when they were supporting her to cook her lunch; when Maggie requested to cook something different from what had been planned, the Senior refused her wish to do so because she said that it would take too long for her to decide and then cook something different. Maggie explained how she immediately asked to speak to the Senior on her own away from the individual and expressed her concerns over her refusing this individual her preference of what to cook. Maggie also added that she felt that she was treating the individual unfairly. As the Senior Care Assistant did not take her concerns seriously and refused to change her mind, Millie explained that she then felt she had to report this to someone else in a senior position and has also written down the incident using the work setting's incident form.

Evidencing AC2.3 to your assessor:

For AC2.3 you must evidence your knowledge of how to challenge discrimination in a way that encourages change.

Assessment Methods:

Oral or **Written** Questioning or **Discussion** or a **Personal Statement** or **Reflection**

- You can **tell** your assessor about how to challenge discrimination in a way that encourages change.
  Or
- You can **talk** to your assessor about how to challenge discrimination in a way that encourages change.
  Or
- You can write a **personal statement** or **reflection** about your experience of how to challenge discrimination in a way that encourages change.

REMEMBER TO:

- Provide an **account** and include details of **how.**
- Include different **examples** of how to challenge discrimination in a way that encourages change.
- Think about how discrimination is challenged in your **work setting** in a way that encourages change.

Learning Outcome 3: Know how to access information, advice and support about diversity, equality and inclusion

Assessment Criterion 3.1: Identify a range of sources of information, advice and support about diversity, equality and inclusion

What does AC3.1 mean?

- The lead word **identify** means that you must make clear the sources of information, advice and support about diversity, equality and inclusion.
- Your **list** must make clear the **different sources**.
- For the key word **sources** you can think about the places and people within your work setting and outside your work setting from which information, advice and support can be obtained.
- For the key word **diversity** you can think about sources of information, advice and support in relation to respecting individuals' differences and uniqueness.
- For the key word **equality** you can think about sources of information, advice and support in relation to making opportunities available to individuals and others.
- For the key word **inclusion** you can think about sources of information, advice and support in relation to encouraging individuals and others to be full and active participants in their lives.

Read the following **Real Work Setting** scenario and think about how it relates to your work setting and role:

Real Work Setting

Name: Sangan
Job Role: Personal Assistant to an adult who has a visual impairment
Sangan has been working as a Personal Assistant for two years. His responsibilities include supporting an individual with his daily living skills and with travelling to and from college on public transport.
Sources of information, advice and support: On his way back home after college, Ian tells Sangan that he did not enjoy his course this evening because the new tutor had not taken into account his visual impairment. Ian also tells Sangan that one of the other participants in the class told Ian that he should not be at college, as he is taking up too much of the tutor's time. Sangan thinks about the sources of information, advice and support that are available.

Evidencing AC3.1 to your assessor:

For AC3.1 you must evidence your knowledge of how to identify a range of sources of information, advice and support about diversity, equality and inclusion.

Assessment Methods:

Oral or **Written** Questioning or **Discussion** or a **Spidergram**

- You can **tell** your assessor about how to identify a range of sources of information, advice and support about diversity, equality and inclusion.
  Or
- You can **talk** to your assessor about how to identify a range of sources of information, advice and support about diversity, equality and inclusion.
  Or
- You can complete a **spidergram** of a range of sources of information, advice and support about diversity, equality and inclusion.

REMEMBER TO:

- Provide examples of **different** sources of information, advice and support.
- Ensure that the **examples** you provide relate to **diversity, equality and inclusion.**
- Think about your **work setting** and sources of information, advice and support about diversity, equality and inclusion available both in and outside your work setting.

Learning Outcome 3: Know how to access information, advice and support about diversity, equality and inclusion

Assessment Criterion 3.2: Describe how and when to access information, advice and support about diversity, equality and inclusion

What does AC3.2 mean?

- The lead word **describe** means that you must provide **an account** that **details** how and when to access information, advice and support about diversity, equality and inclusion.
- Your **account** must make clear how and when.
- For the key word **diversity** you can think about how and when to access information, advice and support in relation to respecting individuals' differences and uniqueness.
- For the key word **equality** you can think about how and when to access information, advice and support in relation to making opportunities available to individuals and others.
- For the key word **inclusion** you can think about how and when to access information, advice and support in relation to encouraging individuals and others to be full and active participants in their lives.

Read the following **Real Work Setting** scenario and think about how it relates to your work setting and role:

Real Work Setting

Name: Sangan

Job Role: Personal Assistant to an adult who has a visual impairment
(See page 34 for a description of the role)

Accessing information, advice and support: On their return home, Sangan agrees with Ian to sit down together and talk through what happened in Ian's college course this evening. Ian begins by telling Sangan that he feels very upset that the new tutor did not know he had a visual impairment. Ian then goes on and explains to Sangan that during break time Emma, one of the group participants, said to him that he shouldn't be there because he takes up too much of the tutor's time. Ian tells Sangan that he doesn't know whether he wants to go back to college next week. Sangan reassures Ian, records in full what Ian has told him and agrees to report this directly to his manager.

Evidencing AC3.2 to your assessor:

For AC3.2 you must evidence your knowledge of how and when to access information, advice and support about diversity, equality and inclusion.

Assessment Methods:

Oral or **Written** Questioning or **Discussion** or a **Personal Statement** or **Reflection**

- You can **tell** your assessor about how and when to access information, advice and support.
  Or
- You can **talk** to your assessor about how and when to access information, advice and support.
  Or
- You can write a **personal statement** or **reflection** about your experience of how and when to access information, advice and support.

REMEMBER TO:

- Provide an **account** and include details of **how and when.**
- Include different **examples** of **how to access** information, advice and support about diversity, equality and inclusion.
- Ensure your evidence details **the process to follow.**
- Think about your **work setting** and how and when to access information, advice and support about diversity, equality and inclusion.

SHC24 Introduction to duty of care in health, social care or children's and young people's settings

Learning Outcome 1: Understand the implications of duty of care

Assessment Criterion 1.1: Define the term 'duty of care'

What does AC1.1 mean?

- The lead word **define** means that you must **make clear** the meaning of 'duty of care'.
- Your **definition** must make clear **what is meant** by duty of care.
- For the key words **duty of care** you can think about how this relates to promoting individuals' rights and safeguarding individuals from danger, harm and abuse.

Read the following **Real Work Setting** scenario and think about how it relates to your work setting and role:

Real Work Setting

Name: Cynthia
Job Role: Residential Care Worker for people who have complex needs
Cynthia has been working as a Residential Care Worker for four years. Her responsibilities include providing individualised and quality care to eight individuals, enabling individuals to participate in daily activities and personal care, as well as promoting individuals' independence.
Duty of care: Cynthia has been asked by her manager to work with a new care worker who has never worked in the sector before; Cynthia agrees to this and is introduced to Sheila, the new care worker. Cynthia begins by asking Sheila about herself, including how long she has worked in the sector and why she has chosen to work in this work setting. Sheila explains that she has cared for her brother for 25 years and also her mother for 10 years before they both died but how she has never worked in a care setting before, such as this one. Sheila tells Cynthia that she has spent the first few days reading through the work setting's policies and procedures and is looking forward to attending the training organised for tomorrow. Cynthia asks Sheila what the training is about and she explains that it is about understanding more about her job role and the meaning of the term 'duty of care'. Cynthia explains to Sheila how the training should raise her awareness of the concept of duty of care in relation to her job role and the individuals she will be providing care and support to.

Evidencing AC1.1 to your assessor:

For AC1.1 you must evidence your understanding of the meaning of the term 'duty of care'.

Assessment Methods:

Oral or **Written** Questioning or **Discussion** or a **Spidergram**

- You can **tell** your assessor about the meaning of the term 'duty of care'.
  Or
- You can **talk** to your assessor about the meaning of the term 'duty of care'.
  Or
- You can complete a **spidergram** of the meaning of the term 'duty of care'.

REMEMBER TO:

- Provide the **meaning** of the term **duty of care**.
- Include details about what duty of care involves.
- Provide details that **relate** specifically to duty of care in your work setting.
- Think about **your work setting** and the meaning of duty of care.

Learning Outcome 1: Understand the implications of duty of care

Assessment Criterion 1.2: Describe how duty of care affects your work role

What does AC1.2 mean?

- The lead word **describe** means that you must provide an **account** that **details** how duty of care affects your work role.
- Your **account** must detail **how** duty of care affects the way you carry out your job role.
- For the key words **duty of care** you can think about how this affects your job role in terms of promoting individuals' rights and safeguarding individuals from danger, harm and abuse.

Read the following **Real Work Setting** scenario and think about how it relates to your work setting and role:

Real Work Setting

Name: Cynthia

Job Role: Residential Care Worker for people who have complex needs
(See page 36 for a description of the role)

How duty of care affects your work role: The day after Sheila attended the training that focused on understanding more about her job role and the meaning of the term 'duty of care', Cynthia asks Sheila about how this went and whether she has a better understanding now about the meaning of duty of care. Sheila tells Cynthia that the training was very useful and furthered her understanding of the meaning of duty of care and how it relates to working in health or social care settings. Cynthia then discusses with Sheila how their job roles and responsibilities are underpinned by duty of care of the individuals they support on a daily basis. Sheila asks Cynthia whether she can give her some examples of how duty of care affects their job roles. Cynthia agrees to provide Sheila with some examples and begins by asking her to tell her what her understanding of duty of care is and then together they discuss how this is relevant to their day-to-day working practices in supporting individuals who have complex needs.

Evidencing AC1.2 to your assessor:

For AC1.2 you must evidence your understanding of how duty of care affects your role at work.

Assessment Methods:

Oral or **Written** Questioning or **Discussion** or a **Personal Statement** or **Reflection**

- You can **tell** your assessor about how duty of care affects your role at work.
  Or
- You can **talk** to your assessor about how duty of care affects your role at work.
  Or
- You can write a **personal statement** or **reflection** about your experience of how duty of care affects your role at work.

REMEMBER TO:

- Provide an **account** and detail **how**.
- Include examples of how duty of care affects the way you carry out your job role.
- Think about **your work setting** and how duty of care affects the way you carry out your job role.

Learning Outcome 2: Understand support available for addressing dilemmas that may arise about duty of care

Assessment Criterion 2.1: Describe dilemmas that may arise between the duty of care and an individual's rights

What does AC2.1 mean?

- The lead word **describe** means that you must provide an **account** that **details** the dilemmas that may arise between the duty of care and an individual's rights.
- Your **account** must detail **different** dilemmas that may arise.
- For the key word **dilemmas** you can think about how duty of care may be at variance with an individual's rights and safety from danger, harm and abuse.
- For the key words **duty of care** you can think about the dilemmas that may arise between safeguarding individuals from danger, harm and abuse and an individual's rights.

Read the following **Real Work Setting** scenario and think about how it relates to your work setting and role:

Real Work Setting

Name: Ned
Job Role: Care Assistant for adults who have dementia
Ned has been working as a Care Assistant for seven years. His responsibilities include: supporting individuals with personal care, assisting individuals with their personal laundry and to maintain their rooms tidy, and supporting individuals with all aspects of daily living as indicated on their individual plans.
Dilemmas: While Ned assists Gladys this morning to tidy her room, Gladys says to Ned that she wants to go out and buy some new clothes but wants to go out on her own without any support staff so that she doesn't stand out in the local shops, where a lot of the owners know her as she has lived in the area for over 40 years. Gladys then shows Ned a bottle of whisky that she keeps safe at the bottom of her wardrobe, as she knows she is not supposed to drink alcohol because of her medication but enjoys having a drink in her room on her own from time to time.

Evidencing AC2.1 to your assessor:

For AC2.1 you must evidence your understanding of dilemmas that may arise between the duty of care and an individual's rights.

Assessment Methods:

Oral or **Written** Questioning or **Discussion** or a **Personal Statement** or **Reflection**

- You can **tell** your assessor about dilemmas that may arise.

  Or
- You can **talk** to your assessor about dilemmas that may arise.

  Or
- You can write a **personal statement** or **reflection** about your experience of dilemmas that may arise.

REMEMBER TO:

- Provide an **account** and include **details** of dilemmas.
- Include **examples** of different dilemmas that may arise between the duty of care and an individual's rights.
- Ensure your evidence makes it clear the reasons why these are dilemmas.
- Ensure your evidence relates to duty of care and an individual's rights.
- Think about dilemmas that have arisen between the duty of care and an individual's rights in **your work setting**.

Learning Outcome 2: Understand support available for addressing dilemmas that may arise about duty of care

Assessment Criterion 2.2: Explain where to get additional support and advice about how to resolve such dilemmas

What does AC2.2 mean?

- The lead word **explain** means that you must **make clear** where to get additional support and advice about how to resolve dilemmas that may arise about the duty of care.
- Your **account** must make clear the **different sources** of support and advice about how to resolve dilemmas, **how** to access these and **why**.
- For the key word **dilemmas** you can think about how the duty of care may be at variance with an individual's rights and safety from danger, harm and abuse.

Read the following **Real Work Setting** scenario and think about how it relates to your work setting and role:

Real Work Setting

Name: Ned

Job Role: Care Assistant for adults who have dementia
(See page 38 for a description of the role)

Resolving dilemmas: Ned listens carefully to what Gladys has told him with respect to her wishes to go clothes shopping on her own, as well as the bottle of whisky she has in her possession in her room. Ned asks to speak in private with the Senior on duty and shares with her the two dilemmas that have arisen while supporting Gladys this morning to tidy her room. Ned explains that he feels torn between upholding Gladys's rights to be independent while clothes shopping and to drink alcohol and his duty of care towards her with respect to safeguarding her from harm. The Senior advises Ned to speak with the manager.

Evidencing AC2.2 to your assessor:

For AC2.2 you must evidence your understanding of where to get additional support and advice about how to resolve such dilemmas.

Assessment Methods:

Oral or **Written** Questioning or **Discussion** or a **Personal Statement** or **Reflection** or a **Witness Testimony**

- You can **tell** your assessor about where to get additional support and advice about how to resolve dilemmas that may arise about duty of care.
  Or
- You can **talk** to your assessor about where to get additional support and advice about how to resolve dilemmas that may arise about duty of care.
  Or
- You can write a **personal statement** or **reflection** about your experience of where to get additional support and advice about how to resolve dilemmas that may arise about duty of care.
  Or
- Your supervisor or manager can write a **witness testimony** about an occasion where you got additional support and advice about how to resolve dilemmas that may arise about duty of care.

REMEMBER TO:

- Provide an **account** and explain **where**.
- Include examples of **different** sources of both support and advice, as well as **why** and **how** to access these.
- Ensure your evidence relates to resolving dilemmas that may arise about duty of care.
- Think about dilemmas about duty of care that have arisen in **your work setting** and the different sources of support and advice that are available to resolve these.

Learning Outcome 3: Know how to respond to complaints

Assessment Criterion 3.1: Describe how to respond to complaints

What does AC3.1 mean?

- The lead word **describe** means that you must provide **an account** that **details** the process to follow for responding to complaints.
- Your account must detail **the process** to follow.
- For the key word **complaints** you can think about how duty of care may be at variance with an individual's rights and result in an individual being dissatisfied.

Read the following **Real Work Setting** scenario and think about how it relates to your work setting and role:

Real Work Setting

Name: Shweta

Job Role: Personal Assistant

Shweta has been working as a Personal Assistant for three years and her responsibilities include: supporting individuals with preparing and cooking food, laundry and ironing, housework, shopping and going out.

Responding to complaints: While being supported by Shweta this morning, Patricia tells Shweta that she is not very happy with the Personal Assistant who visited her yesterday evening, because she did not spend the time agreed with her; this meant there was insufficient time left to support her to do the washing up after her evening meal, put the rubbish out and iron the clothes she was going to wear this morning, so the Personal Assistant did it all for her. Shweta asks Patricia whether she has informed the office about this; Patricia responds by saying that she hasn't because she does not want to cause any trouble for anyone.

Shweta reassures Patricia that it is her right to complain about the support that is provided if she is dissatisfied with it. Shweta asks Patricia whether she would like her to phone the office on her behalf and tell the manager in confidence about her experience with this Personal Assistant yesterday evening. Patricia agrees for Shweta to do this, so Shweta phones the office from Patricia's home, explains Patricia's complaint to the manager and agrees to return to the office to put this in writing.

Evidencing AC3.1 to your assessor:

For AC3.1 you must evidence your knowledge of how to respond to complaints.

Assessment Methods:

Oral or **Written** Questioning or **Discussion** or a **Personal Statement** or **Reflection** or a **Witness Testimony**

- You can **tell** your assessor about how to respond to complaint.
  Or
- You can **talk** to your assessor about how to respond to complaints.
  Or
- You can write a **personal statement** or **reflection** about your experience of how to respond to complaints.
  Or
- Your supervisor or manager can write a **witness testimony** about an occasion where you responded to a complaint.

REMEMBER TO:

- Provide an **account** and detail **the process** to follow.
- Include details about each stage of the process to follow.
- Provide details that relate to **responding** to complaints about duty of care.
- Think about complaints relating to duty of care that have arisen, or may arise, in **your work setting** and how to respond to these.

Learning Outcome 3: Know how to respond to complaints

Assessment Criterion 3.2: Identify the main points of agreed procedures for handling complaints

What does AC3.2 mean?

- The lead word **identify** means that you must **make clear** the main points of agreed procedures for handling complaints relating to duty of care.
- Your **list** must make clear the **main points** of agreed procedures for handling complaints.
- For the key words **agreed procedures** you can think about your work setting's procedures for handling complaints.
- For the key word **complaints** you can think about how duty of care may be at variance with an individual's rights and result in an individual being dissatisfied.

Read the following **Real Work Setting** scenario and think about how it relates to your work setting and role:

Real Work Setting

Name: Shweta

Job Role: Personal Assistant
(See page 40 for a description of the role)

Agreed procedures for handling complaints: After Shweta has spoken with the office, Patricia thanks Shweta for her help and asks her whether she could tell her what she thinks will happen next with her complaint. Shweta shows Patricia the complaint information leaflet included in her welcome pack and talks this through with her. In doing so, Shweta answers all of Patricia's questions in relation to the service's commitment to ensure all complaints are taken seriously, what happens to a complaint when it is received by the service, how long it takes to deal with complaints, how a response is communicated to complainants in different ways, as well as the possible outcomes that may arise from complaints made. Patricia tells Shweta that she has found it very useful to discuss the complaints process with her and how she is clear about what this involves and feels better in herself knowing that her concerns have been listened to. Before leaving, Shweta reminds Patricia of the name of the manager who will be responding to her complaint.

Evidencing AC3.2 to your assessor:

For AC3.2 you must evidence your knowledge of the main points of agreed procedures for handling complaints.

Assessment Methods:

Oral or **Written** Questioning or **Discussion** or a **Spidergram**

- You can **tell** your assessor about the main points of agreed procedures for handling complaints.
  Or
- You can **talk** to your assessor about the main points of agreed procedures for handling complaints.
  Or
- You can complete a **spidergram** of the main points of agreed procedures for handling complaints.

REMEMBER TO:

- Provide the **main points of agreed procedures** for handling complaints.
- Include a **list** of the main points of agreed procedures.
- Provide details that **relate** specifically to handling complaints.
- Think about **your work setting** and the main points of agreed procedures.

HSC024 Principles of safeguarding and protection in health and social care

Learning Outcome 1: Know how to recognise signs of abuse

Assessment Criterion 1.1: Define the following types of abuse: physical abuse, sexual abuse, emotional/psychological abuse, financial abuse, institutional abuse, self-neglect, and neglect by others

What does AC1.1 mean?

- The lead word **define** means that you must **make clear** the meanings of each of the following types of abuse: physical abuse, sexual abuse, emotional/psychological abuse, financial abuse, institutional abuse, self-neglect, and neglect by others.
- Your **definitions** must make clear what each of the seven types of abuse involves.
- For the key word **abuse** you can think about the danger and/or harm an individual may be at risk of having inflicted.

Read the following **Real Work Setting** scenario and think about how it relates to your work setting and role:

Real Work Setting

Name: Luke

Job Role: Support Worker to people who have diverse needs living independently

Luke works as a Support Worker and his responsibilities include: assisting individuals with applications for welfare benefits entitlements, supporting individuals with accessing employment and education, facilitating access to health and mental health services, and supporting individuals to maintain their well-being.

Types of abuse: Luke has attended a safeguarding adults training session to update his knowledge of how to recognise signs of abuse. He found it very interesting to think about the different types of abuse and what each type means. The training has helped to raise his awareness of what constitutes abuse and the different forms this can take.

Evidencing AC1.1 to your assessor:

For AC1.1 you must evidence your knowledge of the meanings of the following types of abuse: physical abuse, sexual abuse, emotional/psychological abuse, financial abuse, institutional abuse, self-neglect, and neglect by others.

Assessment Methods:

Oral or **Written** Questioning or **Discussion** or a **Spidergram**

- You can **tell** your assessor about the meanings of the following types of abuse: physical abuse, sexual abuse, emotional/psychological abuse, financial abuse, institutional abuse, self-neglect, and neglect by others.
  Or
- You can **talk** to your assessor about the meanings of the following types of abuse: physical abuse, sexual abuse, emotional/psychological abuse, financial abuse, institutional abuse, self-neglect, and neglect by others.
  Or
- You can complete a **spidergram** of the meanings of the following types of abuse: physical abuse, sexual abuse, emotional/psychological abuse, financial abuse, institutional abuse, self-neglect, and neglect by others.

REMEMBER TO:

- Provide **the meanings** of each of the seven types of abuse.
- Include details about what **each type of abuse involves**.
- Provide details that **relate** specifically to **each type of abuse**.
- Think about **different types of abuse** that you have received training on in **your work setting** and the meanings of these.

Learning Outcome 1: Know how to recognise signs of abuse

Assessment Criterion 1.2: Identify the signs and/or symptoms associated with each type of abuse

What does AC1.2 mean?

- The lead word **identify** means that you must **make clear** the signs and/or symptoms associated with each of the following types of abuse: physical abuse, sexual abuse, emotional/psychological abuse, financial abuse, institutional abuse, self-neglect, and neglect by others.
- Your **list** must make clear the signs and/or symptoms for each type of abuse.
- For the key word **signs** you can think about the visible changes that may be seen and/or noticed in individuals who are being, or have been, abused.
- For the key word **symptoms** you can think about how individuals who are being, or have been, abused may feel and how this may be expressed in a variety of ways.
- For the key word **abuse** you can think about the danger and/or harm an individual may be at risk of having inflicted.

Read the following **Real Work Setting** scenario and think about how it relates to your work setting and role:

Real Work Setting

Name: Luke

Job Role: Support Worker to people who have diverse needs living independently
(See page 42 for a description of the role)

Signs and/or symptoms of abuse: In the safeguarding adults training session that Luke attended to update his knowledge of how to recognise signs of abuse, the participants also considered and discussed the different visible and non-visible changes there may be in individuals they work with that may alert them to abuse occurring. Luke did not realise that there were so many different signs and/or symptoms of abuse and found it useful to listen to these, as he had not heard of some of these before. Luke also learnt at the training session how the most important way of recognising signs and/or symptoms of abuse is to spend time getting to know each individual you work with so that you notice any unusual changes that may occur.

Evidencing AC1.2 to your assessor:

For AC1.2 you must evidence your knowledge of the signs and/or symptoms associated with the following types of abuse: physical abuse, sexual abuse, emotional/psychological abuse, financial abuse, institutional abuse, self-neglect, and neglect by others.

Assessment Methods:

Oral or **Written** Questioning or **Discussion** or a **Spidergram**

- You can **tell** your assessor about the signs and/or symptoms of the types of abuse.
  Or
- You can **talk** to your assessor about the signs and/or symptoms of the types of abuse.
  Or
- You can complete a **spidergram** of the signs and/or symptoms of the types of abuse.

REMEMBER TO:

- Provide **the signs and/or symptoms** associated with each of the seven types of abuse.
- Include a **list** of the signs and/or symptoms that **each type of abuse involves**.
- Provide details that relate specifically to each type of abuse.
- Think about **different types of abuse** that you have received training on in **your work setting** and the signs and/or symptoms associated with each of these.

Learning Outcome 1: Know how to recognise signs of abuse

Assessment Criterion 1.3: Describe factors that may contribute to an individual being more vulnerable to abuse

What does AC1.3 mean?

- The lead word **describe** means that you must provide an **account** that **details** the factors that may contribute to an individual being more vulnerable to abuse.
- Your **account** must detail different factors that may contribute to an individual being more vulnerable to abuse. These may include the setting, a situation, or an individual.
- For the key word **vulnerable** you can think about how and why some individuals may be at a higher risk of being abused, such as factors relating to a work setting, a situation, or the individual.
- For the key word **abuse** you can think about the danger and/or harm an individual may be at risk of having inflicted.

Read the following **Real Work Setting** scenario and think about how it relates to your work setting and role:

Real Work Setting

Name: Luke

Job Role: Support Worker to people who have diverse needs living independently
(See page 42 for a description of the role)

Factors that may contribute to an individual being more vulnerable to abuse: In the final part of the safeguarding adults training session Luke attended to update his knowledge of how to recognise signs of abuse, the trainer shared with them different pieces of research that had been undertaken into why some individuals may be at higher risk of abuse. Luke found that the factors were related to how the health or social care setting itself is managed, the needs of individuals and the background of the abuser including their history, personality, circumstances and awareness of abuse. It was evident from the research undertaken that when any of these factors are present the likelihood of individuals being abused rises substantially.

Evidencing AC1.3 to your assessor:

For AC1.3 you must evidence your knowledge of the factors that may contribute to an individual being more vulnerable to abuse.

Assessment Methods:

Oral or **Written** Questioning or **Discussion** or a **Personal Statement** or **Reflection**

- You can **tell** your assessor the factors that may contribute to an individual being more vulnerable to abuse.
  Or
- You can **talk** to your assessor about the factors that may contribute to an individual being more vulnerable to abuse.
  Or
- You can write a **personal statement** or **reflection** about your experience of the factors that may contribute to an individual being more vulnerable to abuse.

REMEMBER TO:

- Provide a detailed **account**.
- Include **different factors** to take into consideration.
- Think about **examples** of factors that may contribute to an individual in **your work setting** being more vulnerable to abuse.

Learning Outcome 2: Know how to respond to suspected or alleged abuse

Assessment Criterion 2.1: Explain the actions to take if there are suspicions that an individual is being abused

What does AC2.1 mean?

- The lead word **explain** means that you must **make clear** the actions to take if you or others have suspicions that an individual is being abused.
- Your **account** must make clear the **different** actions to take, as well as the reasons why.
- For the key words **actions to take** you can think about your responsibilities for responding to allegations or suspicions of abuse when suspicions implicate a colleague, someone in the individual's personal network, you, your line manager, others.
- For the key word **suspicions** you can think about the reasons that may lead you or others to believe that an individual is being abused.

Read the following **Real Work Setting** scenario and think about how it relates to your work setting and role:

Real Work Setting

Name: Loise
Job Role: Personal Assistant for people who have learning disabilities
Loise has been working as a Personal Assistant for five months. Her responsibilities include supporting individuals with day-to-day activities such as swimming and shopping, attending health appointments with individuals, and supporting individuals to plan and go on holiday once a year.
Suspected abuse: Loise has noticed some unusual reddish marks on the back of one of the individuals she supports and thinks that this may be why she required a lot of persuasion from her this morning to have a shower. Loise thought it was unusual for this individual to not want a shower, as she knows how much she enjoys them. Loise did not say anything to the individual but did document her concerns immediately and recorded clearly what she observed and when. In confidence, she then shared these with the Safeguarding Officer.

Evidencing AC2.1 to your assessor:

For AC2.1 you must evidence your knowledge of the actions to take if there are suspicions that an individual is being abused.

Assessment Methods:

Oral or **Written** Questioning or **Discussion** or a **Personal Statement** or **Reflection**

- You can **tell** your assessor the different actions to take, as well as the reasons why.
  Or
- You can **talk** to your assessor about the different actions to take, as well as the reasons why.
  Or
- You can write a **personal statement** or **reflection** about your experience of the different actions to take, as well as the reasons why, if there are suspicions an individual in your work setting is being abused.

REMEMBER TO:

- Provide an **account** and explain why.
- Include **varied** reasons.
- Think about **your own work setting** and why you must take action if there are suspicions an individual is being abused.

Learning Outcome 2: Know how to respond to suspected or alleged abuse

Assessment Criterion 2.2: Explain the actions to take if an individual alleges that they are being abused

What does AC2.2 mean?

- The lead word **explain** means that you must **make clear** the actions to take if an individual alleges that they are being abused.
- Your **account** must make clear the **different** actions to take, as well as the reasons why.
- For the key words **actions to take** you can think about your responsibilities for responding to allegations of abuse when allegations implicate a colleague, someone in the individual's personal network, you, your line manager, others.
- For the key word **alleges** you can think about the different ways an individual may disclose that they are being abused.

Read the following **Real Work Setting** scenario and think about how it relates to your work setting and role:

Real Work Setting

Name: Loise

Job Role: Personal Assistant for people who have learning disabilities
(See page 45 for a description of the role)

Alleged abuse: At the end of Loise's shift the individual she was supporting today asks whether she can speak to her alone. The individual begins by saying that she does not want Loise to share what she is about to tell her with anyone else. Loise listened to the individual and then explained to her that, depending on what she tells her, she may need to report this in confidence to another named person as part of her job role and responsibilities. The individual rolls up her sleeve and shows Loise a bite mark that she says was caused by her boyfriend when they were having an argument. Loise reassures the individual over what she has shared with her, does not question her any further and explains that she will need to document what she has told her and the bite mark she has observed on her arm and report this in confidence to the Safeguarding Officer.

Evidencing AC2.2 to your assessor:

For AC2.2 you must evidence your knowledge of the actions to take if an individual alleges that they are being abused.

Assessment Methods:

Oral or **Written** Questioning or **Discussion** or a **Personal Statement** or **Reflection**

- You can **tell** your assessor the different actions to take, as well as the reasons why.
  Or
- You can **talk** to your assessor about the different actions to take, as well as the reasons why.
  Or
- You can write a **personal statement** or **reflection** about your experience of the different actions to take, as well as the reasons why, if an individual alleges they are being abused.

REMEMBER TO:

- Provide an **account** and explain **why**.
- Include **varied** reasons.
- Think about **your own work setting** and the actions you must take, and why, if an individual alleges they are being abused.

Learning Outcome 2: Know how to respond to suspected or alleged abuse

Assessment Criterion 2.3: Identify ways to ensure that evidence of abuse is preserved

What does AC2.3 mean?

- The lead word **identify** means that you must **make clear** the different methods to ensure that evidence of abuse is preserved.
- Your **list** must make clear the **different** ways to ensure that evidence of abuse is preserved.
- For the key word **evidence** you can think about the individual and their environment.
- For the key word **abuse** you can think about the danger and/or harm an individual may have had inflicted upon them.
- For the key word **preserve** you can think about the actions to take and not take when protecting evidence of abuse.

Read the following **Real Work Setting** scenario and think about how it relates to your work setting and role:

Real Work Setting

Name: Loise

Job Role: Personal Assistant for people who have learning disabilities
(See page 45 for a description of the role)

Preserving evidence of abuse: Loise asks the individual who has disclosed to her that her boyfriend bit her arm during an argument whether her boyfriend will be visiting her tonight. The individual explains that her boyfriend is away and her parents tend to come round in the evenings so that she is not alone in the flat. Loise explains to the individual that she should not change her clothes or tidy up her room where the argument happened, as this will all be evidence of what she has told her. Loise adds that she has documented what she has told her and that this is also evidence. Loise agrees to stay with the individual until she has received some further advice and guidance from the Safeguarding Officer on what to do next.

Evidencing AC2.3 to your assessor:

For AC2.3 you must evidence your knowledge of the different ways to ensure that evidence of abuse is preserved.

Assessment Methods:

Oral or **Written** Questioning or **Discussion** or a **Spidergram**

- You can **tell** your assessor about the different ways to ensure that evidence of abuse is preserved.
  Or
- You can **talk** to your assessor about the different ways to ensure that evidence of abuse is preserved.
  Or
- You can complete a **spidergram** of the different ways to ensure that evidence of abuse is preserved.

REMEMBER TO:

- Provide the **different ways** to ensure that evidence of abuse is preserved.
- Provide ways that relate to different types of abuse.
- Think about the different ways to ensure that evidence of abuse is preserved in **your work setting**.

Learning Outcome 3: Understand the national and local context of safeguarding and protection from abuse

Assessment Criterion 3.1: Identify national policies and local systems that relate to safeguarding and protection from abuse

What does AC3.1 mean?

- The lead word **identify** means that you must **make clear** the different national policies and local systems that are in place and relate to safeguarding and protection from abuse.
- Your **list** must make clear **both** national policies and local systems that are in place.
- For the key words **national policies** you can think about the policies the government has in place in relation to safeguarding and protection of adults from abuse.
- For the key words **local systems** you can think about the systems that local authorities and organisations have in place in relation to safeguarding and protection of adults from abuse, such as employer and organisational policies and procedures, and multi-agency adult protection arrangements for a local area.
- For the key word **abuse** you can think about the danger and/or harm an individual may have had inflicted upon them.

Read the following **Real Work Setting** scenario and think about how it relates to your work setting and role:

Real Work Setting

Name: Terrence

Job Role: Support Worker to young adults who have learning disabilities

Terrence works as a Support Worker and his duties include assisting with general tasks in the home, supporting individuals to maintain their personal hygiene, access community facilities and try new and different facilities available both within and outside their local communities.

National policies and local systems: Terrence has recently attended a safeguarding training update facilitated by his manager, where the key legislation and policies that have been introduced in the UK to safeguard and protect adults from abuse were reviewed with the team, as well as all the relevant policies, procedures and professionals that are relevant to his work role and the local authority where he works.

Evidencing AC3.1 to your assessor:

For AC3.1 you must evidence your understanding of the different national policies and local systems that relate to safeguarding and protecting adults from abuse.

Assessment Methods:

Oral or **Written** Questioning or **Discussion** or a **Spidergram**

- You can **tell** your assessor about the different national policies and local systems that relate to safeguarding and protecting adults from abuse.

  Or
- You can **talk** to your assessor about the different national policies and local systems that relate to safeguarding and protecting adults from abuse.

  Or
- You can complete a **spidergram** of the different national policies and local systems that relate to safeguarding and protecting adults from abuse.

REMEMBER TO:

- Provide examples of **different** national policies and local systems.
- Ensure that the **examples** you provide relate to safeguarding and protecting adults from abuse.
- Think about the different policies, procedures and systems available in **your work setting** and in the local authority in which you work.

Learning Outcome 3: Understand the national and local context of safeguarding and protection from abuse

Assessment Criterion 3.2: Explain the roles of different agencies in safeguarding and protecting individuals from abuse

What does AC3.2 mean?

- The lead word **explain** means that you must **make clear** what the roles of different agencies are in safeguarding and protecting individuals from abuse.
- Your **account** must make clear the roles of **different** agencies, as well as the reasons why.
- For the key word **agencies** you can think about the different organisations who work with the individual and/or are involved in their lives.

Read the following **Real Work Setting** scenario and think about how it relates to your work setting and role:

Real Work Setting

Name: Terrence

Job Role: Support Worker to young adults who have learning disabilities
(See page 48 for a description of the role)

Roles of different agencies in safeguarding and protecting individuals from abuse: Terrence also spent some time reading through again his work setting's procedures for safeguarding and protecting individuals from abuse and has learnt a lot more about the different agencies that are involved, including how they are involved, why and when. Terrence found it useful to learn more about their different roles and responsibilities, as well as how they worked jointly together for the protection of individuals from abuse.

Evidencing AC3.2 to your assessor:

For AC3.2 you must evidence your understanding of the roles of different agencies in safeguarding and protecting individuals from abuse.

Assessment Methods:

Oral or **Written** Questioning or **Discussion** or a **Personal Statement**

- You can **tell** your assessor the different roles of different agencies in safeguarding and protecting individuals from abuse, as well as the reasons why.

  Or
- You can **talk** to your assessor about the different roles of different agencies in safeguarding and protecting individuals from abuse, as well as the reasons why.

  Or
- You can write a **personal statement** about the different roles of different agencies in safeguarding and protecting individuals from abuse, as well as the reasons why.

REMEMBER TO:

- Provide an **account** and **explain why**.
- Include **varied** reasons.
- Think about **your own work setting** and the different agencies that are involved in safeguarding and protecting individuals, including the reasons why.

Learning Outcome 3: Understand the national and local context of safeguarding and protection from abuse

Assessment Criterion 3.3: Identify reports into serious failures to protect individuals from abuse

What does AC3.3 mean?

- The lead word **identify** means that you must **make clear** the different reports into serious failures to protect individuals from abuse.
- Your **list** must make clear the **different** reports that relate to serious failures to protect adults from abuse.
- For the key word **reports** you can think about incidents of serious abuse that have been revealed and resulted in investigations and serious case reviews.

Read the following **Real Work Setting** scenario and think about how it relates to your work setting and role:

Real Work Setting

Name: Terrence

Job Role: Support Worker to young adults who have learning disabilities
(See page 48 for a description of the role)

Reports into serious failures to protect individuals from abuse: Another useful way for Terrence to update his knowledge and practices around safeguarding adults from abuse is by taking note of any inquiries and reports into serious failures to protect adults from abuse that have arisen both locally and nationally. Terrence has found it very useful to research and reflect on these in more detail, as this has provided him with the opportunity to gain a valuable insight into why the serious failures occurred, as well as the lessons that can be learnt for the future. Having this knowledge helps Terrence to also reflect on how effective his own and his colleagues' working practices are in terms of safeguarding adults from abuse, as well as raise his awareness of what constitutes abuse and the range of factors that can lead to abuse occurring and continuing.

Evidencing AC3.3 to your assessor:

For AC3.3 you must evidence your understanding of different reports into serious failures to protect individuals from abuse.

Assessment Methods:

Oral or **Written** Questioning or **Discussion** or a **Spidergram**

- You can **tell** your assessor about the different reports into serious failures to protect adults from abuse.
  Or
- You can **talk** to your assessor about the different reports into serious failures to protect adults from abuse.
  Or
- You can complete a **spidergram** of the different reports into serious failures to protect adults from abuse.

REMEMBER TO:

- Provide examples of **different** reports into serious failures.
- Ensure that the **examples** you provide relate to protecting adults from abuse.
- Think about the different reports into serious failures to protect adults from abuse that you may have discussed with others in **your work setting** and/or read or heard about in the media.

Learning Outcome 3: Understand the national and local context of safeguarding and protection from abuse

Assessment Criterion 3.4: Identify sources of information and advice about your role in safeguarding and protecting individuals from abuse

What does AC3.4 mean?

- The lead word **identify** means that you must **make clear** the different sources of both information and advice that are available.
- Your **list** must make clear the **different** sources that relate to your role in safeguarding and protecting individuals from abuse.
- For the key word **sources** you can think about the places and people within your workplace and outside your workplace from which information and advice can be obtained.

Read the following **Real Work Setting** scenario and think about how it relates to your work setting and role:

Real Work Setting

Name: Terrence

Job Role: Support Worker to young adults who have learning disabilities
(See page 48 for a description of the role)

Sources of information and advice: Terrence has a range of sources of information and advice available to him in relation to his own role in safeguarding and protecting individuals from abuse. Information is made available to Terrence both from within his workplace and from external sources. Terrence was made aware of these sources of information and advice available at his induction and these are also reinforced when he attends safeguarding training updates and meets with the Senior Support Worker for supervision. It is important for Terrence to know about what each source can provide in terms of information and advice so that he can access the correct source when he requires it, depending on the nature of what he needs information and/or advice about.

Evidencing AC3.4 to your assessor:

For AC3.4 you must evidence your understanding of different sources of information and advice about your role in safeguarding and protecting individuals from abuse.

Assessment Methods:

Oral or **Written** Questioning or **Discussion** or **Spidergrams**

- You can **tell** your assessor about the different sources of information and advice about your role in safeguarding and protecting individuals from abuse.
  Or
- You can **talk** to your assessor about the different sources of information and advice about your role in safeguarding and protecting individuals from abuse.
  Or
- You can complete two **spidergrams**: one of the different sources of information and another of the different sources of advice about your role in safeguarding and protecting individuals from abuse.

REMEMBER TO:

- Provide examples of **different** sources of both information and advice.
- Ensure that the **examples** you provide relate to safeguarding and protecting adults from abuse.
- Think about the different sources of information and advice about your role in safeguarding and protecting individuals from abuse that are available in **your work setting**.

Learning Outcome 4: Understand ways to reduce the likelihood of abuse

Assessment Criterion 4.1: Explain how the likelihood of abuse may be reduced by working with person-centred values, encouraging active participation and promoting choice and rights

What does AC4.1 mean?

- The lead word **explain** means that you must **make clear** how working practices that use person-centred values, encourage active participation and promote choice and rights can reduce the likelihood of abuse.
- Your **account** must make clear the **different** ways each of these working practices can help reduce the likelihood of abuse, as well as the reasons why.
- For the key words **person-centred values** you can think about how you support the uniqueness of individuals and their rights to choice, privacy, independence, dignity, respect and partnership.
- For the key words **active participation** you can think about how you can support individuals to be fully involved in all aspects of their lives.

Read the following **Real Work Setting** scenario and think about how it relates to your work setting and role:

Real Work Setting

Name: Eva
Job Role: Personal Assistant to adults who have physical disabilities
Eva has been working as a Personal Assistant for two years. Her responsibilities include providing assistance with housework, cleaning and gardening, preparing meals, driving and accompanying individuals to do food shopping, as well as attend doctor and hospital appointments.
Working with person-centred values: Eva recognises that each individual is unique and that the support she provides will vary from one individual to another. Ensuring she respects each individual's rights is essential.
Encouraging active participation: Eva encourages each individual to take the lead in the support she provides to ensure they remain an active partner.
Promoting choice and rights: Eva's working relationship with each individual is based on promoting choice and their rights at all times.

Evidencing AC4.1 to your assessor:

For AC4.1 you must evidence your understanding of how the likelihood of abuse may be reduced by working with person-centred values, encouraging active participation and promoting choice and rights.

Assessment Methods:

Oral or **Written** Questioning or **Discussion** or a **Personal Statement** or **Reflection**

- You can **tell** your assessor how the likelihood of abuse may be reduced.
  Or
- You can **talk** to your assessor about how the likelihood of abuse may be reduced.
  Or
- You can write a **personal statement** or **reflection** about your experience of how the likelihood of abuse may be reduced.

REMEMBER TO:

- Provide an **account** and **explain how**.
- Include **varied** reasons.
- Include details about each one of the three working approaches.
- Think about **your own work setting** and how different approaches to working with individuals can reduce the likelihood of abuse.

Learning Outcome 4: Understand ways to reduce the likelihood of abuse

Assessment Criterion 4.2: Explain the importance of an accessible complaints procedure for reducing the likelihood of abuse

What does AC4.2 mean?

- The lead word **explain** means that you must **make clear** how an accessible complaints procedure can reduce the likelihood of abuse.
- Your **account** must make clear the **different** ways an accessible complaints procedure can help reduce the likelihood of abuse, as well as the reasons why.
- For the key word **accessible** you can think about how to ensure that a complaints procedure is open, made available to all, gives people the right to be heard, is easy to access, understand and use.

Read the following **Real Work Setting** scenario and think about how it relates to your work setting and role:

Real Work Setting

Name: Eva

Job Role: Personal Assistant to adults with physical disabilities
(See page 52 for a description of the role)

An accessible complaints procedure: Eva finds it very important to ensure that all individuals she supports are aware of the purpose of the complaints procedure and where it is located. Ensuring that individuals understand the reasons why they may need to use the complaints procedure and how to use it is central, Eva believes, to making certain that all individuals and others involved in their lives can express their views and create an environment in which the likelihood of abuse occurring is minimised.

Evidencing AC4.2 to your assessor:

For AC4.2 you must evidence your understanding of the importance of an accessible complaints procedure for reducing the likelihood of abuse.

Assessment Methods:

Oral or **Written** Questioning or **Discussion** or a **Personal Statement** or **Reflection**

- You can **tell** your assessor the reasons why an accessible complaints procedure is important for reducing the likelihood of abuse.
  Or
- You can **talk** to your assessor about the reasons why an accessible complaints procedure is important for reducing the likelihood of abuse.
  Or
- You can write a **personal statement** or **reflection** about the reasons why an accessible complaints procedure is important for reducing the likelihood of abuse.

REMEMBER TO:

- Provide an **account** and **explain why**.
- Include **varied** reasons.
- Include details about how the likelihood of abuse can be reduced.
- Think about **your own work setting** and the importance of an accessible complaints procedure for reducing the likelihood of abuse.

Learning Outcome 5: Know how to recognise and report unsafe practices

Assessment Criterion 5.1: Describe unsafe practices that may affect the well-being of individuals

What does AC5.1 mean?

- The lead word **describe** means that you must provide an **account** that **details** the unsafe practices that may affect the well-being of individuals.
- Your **account** must detail **different** factors that may affect the well-being of individuals.
- For the key words **unsafe practices** you can think about how this may include poor working practices, shortage of equipment and staff, or poor management of the service.
- For the key word **well-being** you can think about an individual's physical, emotional and mental health.

Read the following **Real Work Setting** scenario and think about how it relates to your work setting and role:

Real Work Setting

Name: Harry
Job Role: Care Assistant to older people
Harry has been working as a Care Assistant for ten years. Harry's responsibilities include: providing care and support to individuals as specified in their care plans, supporting individuals with activities such as moving and positioning, personal hygiene and grooming, and reporting to senior staff any changes in individuals.
Unsafe practices: Harry reflects on the care he has provided to individuals in his role as a Care Assistant and how maintaining these high standards is essential to the comfort, well-being and safety of individuals and all others involved in their lives. For Harry, recognising and then reporting any unsafe practices he notices are a responsibility that he takes very seriously. Unsafe practices may relate to poor working practices such as poor personal hygiene, unsafe moving and handling, not having sufficient experienced and competent staff on duty, or poor leadership and supervision of staff.

Evidencing AC5.1 to your assessor:

For AC5.1 you must evidence your knowledge of different unsafe practices that may affect the well-being of individuals.

Assessment Methods:

Oral or **Written** Questioning or **Discussion** or a **Personal Statement** or **Reflection**

- You can **tell** your assessor about the different unsafe practices that may affect the well-being of individuals.
  Or
- You can **talk** to your assessor about the different unsafe practices that may affect the well-being of individuals.
  Or
- You can write a **personal statement** or **reflection** about your experience of the different unsafe practices that may affect the well-being of individuals in your work setting.

REMEMBER TO:

- Provide a detailed **account**.
- Include examples of **different** unsafe practices.
- Include how these examples can affect the **well-being** of individuals.
- Think about examples of **unsafe practices** that, if they occurred, may affect the well-being of individuals in **your work setting**.

Learning Outcome 5: Know how to recognise and report unsafe practices

Assessment Criterion 5.2: Explain the actions to take if unsafe practices have been identified

What does AC5.2 mean?

- The lead word **explain** means that you must **make clear** the actions to take, as well as the reasons why, if unsafe practices have been identified.
- Your **account** must make clear the **different** actions to take, as well as the reasons why, if unsafe practices have been identified.
- For the key words **unsafe practices** you can think about how this may include poor working practices, shortage of equipment and staff, or poor management of the service.
- For the key word **actions** you can think about the process you must follow if unsafe practices have been identified.

Read the following **Real Work Setting** scenario and think about how it relates to your work setting and role:

Real Work Setting

Name: Harry

Job Role: Care Assistant to older people
(See page 54 for a description of the role)

Actions taken: Today, Harry is working with a less experienced colleague who has asked him what he would do if he saw any unsafe practices taking place. Harry explains to his colleague that it is really important to not ignore any unsafe practices observed and to always report these immediately to senior staff, who will then be able to advise on the next actions to be taken. Harry also shows his colleague the policy in place that details what unsafe practices may include, as well as a step-by-step approach of the actions to take as a Care Assistant if unsafe practices have been identified.

Evidencing AC5.2 to your assessor:

For AC5.2 you must evidence your understanding of the actions to take if unsafe practices have been identified.

Assessment Methods:

Oral or **Written** Questioning or **Discussion** or a **Personal Statement** or **Reflection**

- You can **tell** your assessor the actions to take, as well as the reasons why, if unsafe practices have been identified.
  Or
- You can **talk** to your assessor about the actions to take, as well as the reasons why, if unsafe practices have been identified.
  Or
- You can write a **personal statement** or **reflection** about your experience of the actions to take, as well as the reasons why, if unsafe practices have been identified.

REMEMBER TO:

- Provide an **account** and **explain why**.
- Include **varied** reasons.
- Include details about the process that must be followed when unsafe practices have been identified.
- Think about **your own work setting** and the actions to take if unsafe practices have been identified.

Learning Outcome 5: Know how to recognise and report unsafe practices

Assessment Criterion 5.3: Describe the actions to take if suspected abuse or unsafe practices have been reported but nothing has been done in response

What does AC5.3 mean?

- The lead word **describe** means that you must provide an **account** that **details** the actions to take, as well as the reasons why, if suspected abuse or unsafe practices have been reported but nothing has been done in response.
- Your **account** must detail the **different** actions to take, as well as the reasons why.
- For the key words **unsafe practices** you can think about how this may include poor working practices such as failure to comply with policies and procedures, resource difficulties such as shortage of equipment and staff, or operational difficulties such as poor management of the service.
- For the key word **actions** you can think about the process you must follow if unsafe practices have been identified.

Read the following **Real Work Setting** scenario and think about how it relates to your work setting and role:

Real Work Setting

Name: Harry
Job Role: Care Assistant to older people (See page 54 for a description of the role)
Further actions if nothing has been done in response: After carefully reading through the home's procedure for the actions to take if suspected abuse or unsafe practices have been reported but nothing has been done in response, Harry's colleague explains that he would not feel comfortable about going above his Senior, as this may be viewed as undermining him. Harry explains to him that as a professional, and to safeguard the individuals he works with, he must feel able to use the work setting's whistleblowing procedure and suggests he talks to his Senior about how he feels.

Evidencing AC5.3 to your assessor:

For AC5.3 you must evidence your knowledge of the actions to take if suspected abuse or unsafe practices have been reported but nothing has been done in response.

Assessment Methods:

Oral or **Written** Questioning or **Discussion** or a **Personal Statement** or **Reflection**

- You can **tell** your assessor about the actions to take if suspected abuse or unsafe practices have been reported but nothing has been done in response.
  Or
- You can **talk** to your assessor about the actions to take if suspected abuse or unsafe practices have been reported but nothing has been done in response.
  Or
- You can write a **personal statement** or **reflection** about your experience of the actions to take if suspected abuse or unsafe practices have been reported but nothing has been done in response.

REMEMBER TO:

- Provide an **account** and detail **how** and **why**.
- Include **varied** reasons.
- Include details about the process that must be followed if suspected abuse or unsafe practices have been reported but nothing has been done in response.
- Think about **your own work setting** and the actions to take if suspected abuse or unsafe practices have been reported but nothing has been done in response.

HSC025 The role of the health and social care worker

Learning Outcome 1: Understand working relationships in health and social care

Assessment Criterion 1.1: Explain how a working relationship is different from a personal relationship

What does AC1.1 mean?

- The lead word **explain** means that you must **make clear** the differences that exist between working and personal relationships.
- Your **account** must make clear how working and personal relationships are **different**.
- For the key words **working relationships** you can think about the different people you have contact with as part of your work role.
- For the key words **personal relationships** you can think about the different people you have contact with outside work.

Read the following **Real Work Setting** scenario and think about how it relates to your work setting and role:

Real Work Setting

Name: Alecia

Job Role: Personal Assistant

Alecia has been working as a Personal Assistant for eight months and provides support to adults with disabilities so that they can maintain their independence and live in their homes. At present Alecia is working with one individual who requires assistance with all aspects of personal and intimate care. Alecia also supports this individual with all daily routines, including shopping, cooking and housework, as well as a range of activities in the community and at home.

Working and personal relationships: As part of Alecia's initial training, when she worked alongside a more experienced Personal Assistant both discussed the importance of developing a good working relationship with this individual and with each other. They both considered when assisting this individual, in particular when socialising with friends and family, how to ensure that they worked within the boundaries of their job roles as Personal Assistants at all times.

Evidencing AC1.1 to your assessor:

For AC1.1 you must evidence your understanding of the differences between a working and a personal relationship.

Assessment Methods:

Oral or **Written** Questioning or **Discussion** or a **Personal Statement**

- You can **tell** your assessor about the differences between a working and a personal relationship.
  Or
- You can **talk** to your assessor about the differences between a working and a personal relationship.
  Or
- You can write a **personal statement** about the differences between a working and a personal relationship.

REMEMBER TO:

- Provide an **account** and **explain** the differences.
- Include varied differences.
- Include details about what is meant by working and personal relationships.
- Think about your **own work setting** and the working relationships you have.

Learning Outcome 1: Understand working relationships in health and social care

Assessment Criterion 1.2: Describe different working relationships in health and social care settings

What does AC1.2 mean?

- The lead word **describe** means that you must provide **an account** that **details** the different working relationships in health and social care settings.
- Your **account** must detail different working relationships that exist in health and social care settings.
- For the key words **working relationships** you can think about the different people you have contact with as part of your work role.

Read the following **Real Work Setting** scenario and think about how it relates to your work setting and role:

Real Work Setting

Name: Alecia

Job Role: Personal Assistant
(See page 57 for a description of the role)

Working relationships: Over the eight months that she has been employed as a Personal Assistant, Alecia's job role has involved working alongside not only other team members, but also others involved in the individual's life such as friends, family and other health and social care professionals. Supporting this individual to go swimming regularly and take part in a drawing class has meant that Alicia has also formed working relationships with the staff who work at the local swimming pool and with the tutor that holds the weekly drawing class. Each of these relationships has developed differently over time, depending on the people involved and how much contact Alecia has with them. Developing good working relationships has been central to Alecia's job role of being able to support this individual to live her life as she wishes and take part in the activities she likes.

Evidencing AC1.2 to your assessor:

For AC1.2 you must evidence your understanding of different working relationships in health and social care settings.

Assessment Methods:

Oral or **Written** Questioning or **Discussion** or a **Personal Statement** or **Reflection**

- You can **tell** your assessor about different working relationships in health and social care settings.
  Or
- You can **talk** to your assessor about different working relationships in health and social care settings.
  Or
- You can write a **personal statement** or **reflection** about your experience of the different working relationships in **your work setting**.

REMEMBER TO:

- Provide a detailed **account.**
- Include examples of **different working relationships.**
- Think about examples of **working relationships** in your **work setting.**

Learning Outcome 2: Be able to work in ways that are agreed with the employer

Assessment Criterion 2.1: Describe why it is important to adhere to the agreed scope of the job role

What does AC2.1 mean?

- The lead word **describe** means that you must provide **an account** that **details** the reasons why it is important to carry out your job role, duties and responsibilities as set out in your job description.
- Your **account** must detail different reasons for why it is important to adhere to the agreed scope of the job role.
- For the key words **scope of the job role** you can think about the duties and responsibilities you are required to carry out as part of your job role.

Read the following **Real Work Setting** scenario and think about how it relates to your work setting and role:

Real Work Setting

Name: David

Job Role: Care Assistant for older people

David has been working as a care assistant for six years. His duties include respecting the individuals' rights of choice, privacy, independence and dignity in line with their needs, working together with the team on implementing individualised care plan activities, as well as maintaining relationships with individuals and others involved in their lives.

Adhering to the scope of the job role: David has built up good working relationships with the individuals he supports and is a very caring, committed and enthusiastic member of the team, always willing to help as much as he can. One of the Senior Care Assistants has requested to meet with David, as he is concerned that David may be spending too much of his own time outside work supporting individuals with tasks such as posting letters for them, collecting prescriptions, shopping for items and making telephone calls.

Evidencing AC2.1 to your assessor:

For AC2.1 you must evidence your knowledge of why it is important to adhere to the agreed scope of the job role.

Assessment Methods:

Oral or **Written** Questioning or **Discussion** or a **Personal Statement** or **Reflection**

- You can **tell** your assessor about the different reasons why it is important to adhere to the agreed scope of the job role.
  Or
- You can **talk** to your assessor about the different reasons why it is important to adhere to the agreed scope of the job role.
  Or
- You can write a **personal statement** or **reflection** about the different reasons why it is important to adhere to the agreed scope of the job role.

REMEMBER TO:

- Provide a detailed **account.**
- Include examples of **different reasons** for why it is important.
- Think about the consequences of not adhering to the scope of the job role.
- Think about the importance of adhering to the scope of job roles in your **work setting.**

Learning Outcome 2: Be able to work in ways that are agreed with the employer

Assessment Criterion 2.2: Access full and up-to-date details of agreed ways of working

What does AC2.2 mean?

- The lead word **access** means that you must **be able to show through your work practices** how to demonstrate that you can obtain full and up-to-date details of agreed ways of working.
- Your **observations of your work practices** must include you obtaining full and up-to-date details of agreed ways of working.
- For the key word **access** you can think about the different documents and records you obtain, read and complete as part of your job role.
- For the key words **agreed ways of working** you can think about your work setting's policies and procedures, as well as the specific guidelines that are in place for the individuals that you provide care and support to.

Read the following **Real Work Setting** scenario and think about how it relates to your work setting and role:

Real Work Setting

Name: David
Job Role: Care Assistant for older people (See page 59 for a description of the role)
Accessing full and up-to-date details of agreed ways of working: During David's meeting with the Senior, David begins to realise that his enthusiasm to support individuals the best he can has taken him outside the remit of his job role and that this is a risk not only for himself, but also for the individuals he supports. David and the Senior talk through the work setting's policies and procedures that detail the areas of responsibilities that David has, including how these must be undertaken within the hours agreed with his employer. David thanks the Senior for the meeting and agrees to no longer work outside his contracted hours and discusses with him what he can say to individuals when they ask him to carry out tasks for them when he is not at work.

Evidencing AC2.2 to your assessor:

For AC2.2 you must evidence your skills of how to access full and up-to-date details of agreed ways of working.

Assessment Method:

Direct Observation of your work practices

- You can **show** your assessor how to access full and up-to-date details of agreed ways of working.
- You can also use as a **supporting piece of work product evidence** records that you have completed as part of your day-to-day activities in your current job role.

REMEMBER TO:

- Make arrangements for **observation** of **your work practices.**
- Include evidence of your work practices in accessing agreed ways of working.
- Include evidence of how any documents and records you access are complete and up to date.
- Think about how you access agreed ways of working in **your work setting.**
- Think about **different documents and records that are available to you** in your **work setting.**

Learning Outcome 2: Be able to work in ways that are agreed with the employer

Assessment Criterion 2.3: Implement agreed ways of working

What does AC2.3 mean?

- The lead word **implement** means that you must **be able to show through your work practices** how to put into practice agreed ways of working.
- Your **observations of your work practices** must include you putting into practice in your work setting agreed ways of working.
- For the key word **implement** you can think about how you put into practice agreed ways of working.
- For the key words **agreed ways of working** you can think about your work setting's policies and procedures, as well as the specific guidelines that are in place for the individuals that you provide care and support to.

Read the following **Real Work Setting** scenario and think about how it relates to your work setting and role:

Real Work Setting

Name: David

Job Role: Care Assistant for older people
(See page 59 for a description of the role)

Implementing agreed ways of working: Over the next few weeks David's working practices are monitored to ensure he is putting into practice agreed ways of working. David shows that he has the ability to change the way he has been working by ensuring he supports individuals only within his contracted hours. David has also shown a lot of initiative in supporting residents to remain as active and independent as possible when completing daily activities. David has also taken it upon himself to read through again all of his work setting's policies and procedures that detail how he must carry out his job role and duties and has also considered the guidelines that are in place to meet different individuals' needs.

Evidencing AC2.3 to your assessor:

For AC2.3 you must evidence your skills of how to implement agreed ways of working.

Assessment Method:

Direct Observation of your work practices

- You can **show** your assessor how you put into practice agreed ways of working.
- You can also use as a **supporting piece of work product evidence** records that you have completed as part of your day-to-day activities in your current job role.

REMEMBER TO:

- Make arrangements for **observation** of **your work practices.**
- Include evidence of how your work practices put agreed ways of working into practice.
- Include evidence of how any documents and records you access are complete and up to date.
- Think about how you put into practice agreed ways of working in **your work setting.**
- Think about **different documents and records** that you complete in your **work setting** as part of your job role.

Learning Outcome 3: Be able to work in partnership with others

Assessment Criterion 3.1: Explain why it is important to work in partnership with others

What does AC3.1 mean?

- The lead word **explain** means that you must **make clear** the reasons why it is important to work in partnership with others.
- Your **account** must make clear the **importance** of working in partnership with others.
- For the key words **working in partnership** you can think about how and why you work together with other people to carry out your job role effectively.
- For the key word **others** you can think about the people you work with both within and outside your work setting such as individuals who require care or support, families, friends, advocates or others who are important to individuals, team members, colleagues and other professionals.

Read the following **Real Work Setting** scenario and think about how it relates to your work setting and role:

Real Work Setting

Name: Julie

Job Role: Support Worker

Julie has been working as a Support Worker for five years, supporting people with alcohol-related difficulties to live independently in their own homes. Julie's responsibilities include: building supportive working relationships with individuals, supporting individuals to set goals as part of their support plans, providing support to individuals with daily activities such as budgeting and cooking, and working closely with partner organisations to provide a high-quality service.

Working in partnership with others: As part of Julie's day-to-day Support Worker activities she works in partnership with individuals so that they are able to live their lives as they choose and maintain a healthy environment to do so. Julie also ensures she works in partnership with her colleagues and that she adheres to the work setting's policies and procedures, especially when visiting individuals on her own. Working closely with other partner organisations, Julie has found, has value in terms of improving the quality of the service and support.

Evidencing AC3.1 to your assessor:

For AC3.1 you must evidence your understanding of the reasons why it is important to work in partnership with others.

Assessment Methods:

Oral or **Written** Questioning or **Discussion** or a **Personal Statement** or **Reflection**

- You can **tell** your assessor about the reasons why it is important to work in partnership with others.
  Or
- You can **talk** to your assessor about the reasons why it is important to work in partnership with others.
  Or
- You can write a **personal statement** or **reflection** about your experience of the reasons why it is important to work in partnership with others.

REMEMBER TO:

- Provide an **account** and **explain** the reasons why it is important to work in partnership with others.
- Include **varied** differences.
- Include details about the importance of working in partnership with others.
- Think about your **own work setting** and the working relationships you have.

Learning Outcome 3: Be able to work in partnership with others

Assessment Criterion 3.2: Demonstrate ways of working that can help improve partnership working

What does AC3.2 mean?

- The lead word **demonstrate** means that you must **be able to show through your work practices** ways of working that can help improve working in partnership with others.
- Your **observations of your work practices** must include you putting into practice different ways of working to improve partnership working.
- For the key words **working in partnership** you can think about how and why you work together with other people to carry out your job role effectively.
- For the key word **others** you can think about the people you work with both within and outside your work setting such as individuals who require care or support, families, friends, advocates or others who are important to individuals, team members, colleagues and other professionals.

Read the following **Real Work Setting** scenario and think about how it relates to your work setting and role:

Real Work Setting

Name: Julie

Job Role: Support Worker
(See page 62 for a description of the role)

Improving partnership working: Julie and one of the Senior Support Workers have been invited to attend a meeting, at which the organisation will be reviewing with its partner agents how effectively they are working together, as the manager of the service thinks that it will be important to have Julie and the Senior's opinions taken into account too. It is the first time Julie has been invited to attend one of these meetings so she has prepared for it by writing down the areas where working in partnership works well and the areas and individuals where this does not work as well, including, where possible, reasons why she thinks this may be the case and how this could be improved. Julie finds that meeting together to openly discuss different ways of how to improve partnership working is important in terms of ensuring they are providing the best possible service and support to all individuals.

Evidencing AC3.2 to your assessor:

For AC3.2 you must evidence your skills of how to work in ways that help improve partnership working.

Assessment Method:

Direct Observation of your work practices

- You can **show** your assessor or an expert witness how you work in ways that help improve partnership working.

REMEMBER TO:

- Make arrangements for **observation** of **your work practices.**
- Include evidence of how your work practices can help improve partnership working.
- Include evidence of different ways of working that can help to improve partnership working with others.
- Think about how ways of working that you use in **your work setting** can improve partnership working.

Learning Outcome 3: Be able to work in partnership with others

Assessment Criterion 3.3: Identify skills and approaches for resolving conflicts

What does AC3.3 mean?

- The lead word **identify** means that you must **list** the skills and approaches needed for resolving conflicts.
- Your list must include **different** examples of skills and approaches.
- For the key word **skills** you can think about what you need to know and be able to do to resolve conflicts.
- For the key word **approaches** you can think about different ways of working that can be used to resolve conflicts.

Read the following **Real Work Setting** scenario and think about how it relates to your work setting and role:

Real Work Setting

Name: Julie

Job Role: Support Worker
(See page 62 for a description of the role)

Identifying skills and approaches for resolving conflicts: During the meeting with the partner organisations a conflict arises over whether to continue providing support to one individual using the service, as he is not maintaining his appointments with all team members and not making sufficient progress to achieving goals set out in his support plan. Those present consider this individual's past history, as well as other reasons why he may be reluctant to keep some of his appointments; they all agree that all appointments that relate to his use of alcohol and to his children, in particular, he seems to avoid, as all other appointments relating to his flat and his support with his daily activities he attends and are very productive. Those present agree that it would not be in this individual's interest to withdraw the support being provided, particularly as he is progressing well in some areas of his support plan, and that a further meeting will need to be arranged with him and his alcohol worker to talk through the areas of his support plan that he is not meeting.

Evidencing AC3.3 to your assessor:

For AC3.3 you must evidence your knowledge of skills and approaches that are needed for resolving conflicts.

Assessment Methods:

Oral or **Written** Questioning or **Discussion** or a **Spidergram**

- You can **tell** your assessor about the different skills and approaches that are needed for resolving conflicts.
  Or
- You can **talk** to your assessor about the different skills and approaches that are needed for resolving conflicts.
  Or
- You can complete a **spidergram** of the different skills and approaches that are needed for resolving conflicts.

REMEMBER TO:

- **List** both skills and approaches.
- Include **different** examples of both in your list.
- Ensure they relate to resolving conflicts.
- Think about the skills and approaches that have been used in your **work setting** for resolving conflicts.

Learning Outcome 3: Be able to work in partnership with others

Assessment Criterion 3.4: Demonstrate how and when to access support and advice about partnership working and resolving conflicts

What does AC3.4 mean?

- The lead word **demonstrate** means that you must **be able to show through your work practices** how and when to access support and advice about partnership working and resolving conflicts.
- Your **observations of your work practices** must include you putting into practice accessing support and advice about partnership working and resolving conflicts.
- For the key words **partnership working** you can think about the different working relationships you have with others.
- For the key word **conflicts** you can think about the disagreements that may arise in your work setting.

Read the following **Real Work Setting** scenario and think about how it relates to your work setting and role:

Real Work Setting

Name: Julie

Job Role: Support Worker
(See page 62 for a description of the role)

Accessing support and advice: The meeting with the partner organisations provided Julie with an opportunity to learn more about each partner organisation's role, as well as how and when to access support and advice about partnership working and resolving conflicts. Listening to others' experiences and questions made Julie realise the range of sources of support and advice that are available both from her own organisation, the partner organisations and from other specialist services and agencies that exist. Julie has also discussed this with the Senior Support Worker that attended the meeting with her and both agree how Julie can read through again her work setting's policies and procedures for accessing support and advice about both partnership working and resolving conflicts and then meet with him afterwards to confirm her understanding of these and answer any further questions she may have about the process to go through.

Evidencing AC3.4 to your assessor:

For AC3.4 you must evidence your skills of how and when to access support and advice about partnership working and resolving conflicts.

Assessment Method:

Direct Observation of your work practices

- You can **show** your assessor or an expert witness how and when to access support and advice about partnership working and resolving conflicts.

REMEMBER TO:

- Make arrangements for **observation of your work practices.**
- Include evidence of how you have accessed support and advice.
- Include evidence of when you have accessed support and advice.
- Think about sources of support and advice available to you in and outside **your work setting.**

HSC026 Implement person-centred approaches in health and social care

Learning Outcome 1: Understand person-centred approaches for care and support

Assessment Criterion 1.1: Define person-centred values

What does AC1.1 mean?

- The lead word **define** means that you must **make clear** the meaning of person-centred values.
- Your **definition** must make clear what is meant by **person-centred values**.
- For the key words **person-centred values** you can think about how to carry out your job role in a way that enables the individuals you work with to lead their lives as they wish, through promoting their individuality, rights, choice, privacy, independence, dignity, respect and by working in partnership with them.

Read the following **Real Work Setting** scenario and think about how it relates to your work setting and role:

Real Work Setting

Name: Roxette

Job Role: Care Assistant for older people

Roxette's responsibilities include assisting individuals with daily living activities such as eating, drinking, washing and dressing, enabling individuals to maintain and, where possible, improve their independence and mobility, working closely with individuals' families and friends, where appropriate, and ensuring a safe and comfortable living environment that promotes well-being.

Person-centred values: Roxette met with her assessor for her Level 2 Diploma in Health and Social Care last week. At this meeting she agreed to look closely at Learning Outcome 1 of Unit HSC026 and start thinking about the evidence she could generate for the four assessment criteria included within the first learning outcome of this unit. Roxette begins by thinking about what person-centred values are and how these relate to her job as a Care Assistant and the care and support she provides to individuals. Roxette soon realises that person-centred values underpin all her work activities and writes down all the person-centred values she uses in her daily work activities when supporting individuals, including what each of these values mean.

Evidencing AC1.1 to your assessor:

For AC1.1 you must evidence your understanding of the meaning of person-centred values.

Assessment Methods:

Oral or **Written** Questioning or **Discussion** or a **Spidergram**

- You can **tell** your assessor about the meaning of person-centred values.

  Or
- You can talk to your assessor about the meaning of person-centred values.

  Or
- You can complete a **spidergram** of the meaning of person-centred values.

REMEMBER TO:

- Provide the **meaning** of the term **person-centred values**.
- Include details about what person-centred values involve.
- Provide details that **relate** specifically to person-centred values that are relevant in your job role and work setting.
- Think about your **work setting** and the meaning of person-centred values.

Learning Outcome 1: Understand person-centred approaches for care and support

Assessment Criterion 1.2: Explain why it is important to work in a way that embeds person-centred values

What does AC1.2 mean?

- The lead word **explain** means that you must **make clear** the reasons why it is important to work in a way that embeds person-centred values.
- Your **account** must make clear the **different** reasons why it is important.
- For the key word **embeds** you can think about how to carry out your job role in a way that is underpinned by person-centred values.
- For the key words **person-centred values** you can think about how to carry out your job role in a way that respects the individuals you work with and supports them to lead their lives as they wish, through promoting their individuality, rights, choice, privacy, independence, dignity, respect and by working in partnership with them.

Read the following **Real Work Setting** scenario and think about how it relates to your work setting and role:

Real Work Setting

Name: Roxette

Job Role: Care Assistant for older people
(See page 66 for a description of the role)

Person-centred values: Roxette then moves on to think about the importance of working in a way that embeds person-centred values, including what working in this way involves, how this affects the individuals she works with, her colleagues and the overall service being provided. Roxette also spends some time considering the consequences of not working in this way, how this would impact on her working practices, the care and support she provides to individuals, the team she is part of and the overall service being delivered.

Evidencing AC1.2 to your assessor:

For AC1.2 you must evidence your understanding of why it is important to work in a way that embeds person-centred values.

Assessment Methods:

Oral or **Written** Questioning or **Discussion** or a **Personal Statement**

- You can **tell** your assessor about why it is important to work in a way that embeds person-centred values.
  Or
- You can **talk** to your assessor about why it is important to work in a way that embeds person-centred values.
  Or
- You can write a **personal statement** about why it is important to work in a way that embeds person-centred values.

REMEMBER TO:

- Provide an **account** and **explain** why it is important.
- Include **varied** examples of the reasons why.
- Include details about working in a way that **embeds person-centred values**.
- Think about your **work setting** and why it is important to work in a way that embeds person-centred values.

Learning Outcome 1: Understand person-centred approaches for care and support

Assessment Criterion 1.3: Explain why risk-taking can be part of a person-centred approach

What does AC1.3 mean?

- The lead word **explain** means that you must **make clear** the reasons why risk-taking can be part of a person-centred approach.
- Your **account** must make clear the **different** reasons why it is important.
- For the key word **risk-taking** you can think about how taking risks can benefit individuals.
- For the key words **person-centred approach** you can think about how taking risks can be part of a way of working that respects the individuals you work with and supports them to lead their lives as they wish.

Read the following **Real Work Setting** scenario and think about how it relates to your work setting and role:

Real Work Setting

Name: Roxette

Job Role: Care Assistant for older people
(See page 66 for a description of the role)

Risk-taking: To generate evidence for AC1.3, Roxette's assessor has advised her to reflect on her experience of supporting one of the individuals she works with to take risks. Roxette reflects on the occasion when she supported Ruby to take part in activities outside the work setting, which Ruby did find difficult initially, as she is very prone to anxiety attacks and very rarely accesses facilities in the community. Roxette reflects on how supporting Ruby to do this enabled Ruby to meet other people, discover that she really enjoyed crafts and increased her independence, in terms of making her own choices about other community facilities she wishes to access in the local area where she lives: so much so that she is now one of the individuals who frequently choose to go out and about in the local community. The team, as well as Ruby's family and friends and others who know her, have all noted that Ruby seems a lot more content in herself, has become a lot more sociable and constantly talks about her plans and goals for the future.

Evidencing AC1.3 to your assessor:

For AC1.3 you must evidence your understanding of person-centred approaches for care and support.

Assessment Methods:

Oral or **Written** Questioning or **Discussion** or a **Personal Statement**.

- You can **tell** your assessor about why risk-taking can be part of a person-centred approach.
  Or
- You can **talk** to your assessor about why risk-taking can be part of a person-centred approach.
  Or
- You can write a **personal statement** about why risk-taking can be part of a person-centred approach.

REMEMBER TO:

- Provide an **account** and **explain** why it is important.
- Include **varied** examples of the reasons why.
- Include details about why risk-taking can be part of a person-centred approach.
- Think about your **work setting** and why risk-taking can be part of a person-centred approach.

Learning Outcome 1: Understand person-centred approaches for care and support

Assessment Criterion 1.4: Explain how using an individual's care plan contributes to working in a person-centred way

What does AC1.4 mean?

- The lead word **explain** means that you must **make clear** how using an individual's care plan contributes to working in a person-centred way.
- Your **account** must make clear **how**.
- For the key words **care plan** you can think about how individuals' day-to-day care and support requirements, needs and preferences are detailed. A care plan may be known by other names such as a support plan, individual plan, person-centred plan.
- For the key words **working in a person-centred way** you can think about how to work in a way that respects the individuals you work with and supports them to lead their lives as they wish.

Read the following **Real Work Setting** scenario and think about how it relates to your work setting and role:

Real Work Setting

Name: Roxette

Job Role: Care Assistant for older people
(See page 66 for a description of the role)

Using an individual's care plan: To generate evidence for AC1.4, Roxette again reflects on the care and support she has provided to Ruby and how her care plan also contributed to enabling Roxette and her colleagues to work in a person-centred way. Roxette and the team involved Ruby fully from the beginning when setting up a plan of how best to support her with her day-to-day needs and preferences. Part of this process involved talking with Ruby's family and friends so that the team built up a good profile of who Ruby is as an individual, her likes, dislikes, interests, qualities, strengths, needs, goals and wishes for now and the future. This information was very useful in helping the team to ensure they worked together in partnership with Ruby and others involved in her life to enable her to live her life as she wishes.

Evidencing AC1.4 to your assessor:

For AC1.4 you must evidence your understanding of how using an individual's care plan contributes to working in a person-centred way.

Assessment Methods:

Oral or **Written** Questioning or **Discussion** or a **Personal Statement** or **Reflection**

- You can **tell** your assessor about how using an individual's care plan contributes to working in a person-centred way.
  Or
- You can **talk** to your assessor about how using an individual's care plan contributes to working in a person-centred way.
  Or
- You can write a **personal statement** or **reflection** about your experience of about how using an individual's care plan contributes to working in a person-centred way.

REMEMBER TO:

- Provide an **account** and **explain** how.
- Include **varied** examples of how using an individual's care plan **contributes to working in a person-centred way**.
- Include details about **using an individual's care plan**.
- Think about your **work setting** and how using an individual's care plan contributes to working in a person-centred way.

Learning Outcome 2: Be able to work in a person-centred way

Assessment Criterion 2.1: Find out the history, preferences, wishes and needs of an individual

What does AC2.1 mean?

- The lead words **find out** mean that you must **be able to show through your work practices** how you can identify and discover more about an individual's history, preferences, wishes and needs.
- Your **observations of your work practices** must include you finding out the history, preferences, wishes and needs of an individual.
- For the key word **history** you can think about how to find out about an individual's background and upbringing.
- For the key word **preferences** you can think about how to find out about the day-to-day choices an individual makes.

Read the following **Real Work Setting** scenario and think about how it relates to your work setting and role:

Real Work Setting

Name: Alan
Job Role: Home Carer
Alan has been working as a Home Carer for five years. His responsibilities include supporting older people and people with disabilities in their own homes with day-to-day activities, assisting with personal care tasks, preparing meals and cleaning, as well as supporting individuals to access their local communities.
Finding out an individual's history, preferences, wishes and needs: When supporting individuals, Alan always ensures he first finds out as much information as he can about an individual's background, upbringing, preferences, wishes and needs so that he can ensure he adapts his working approaches to meet each individual's unique needs. Alan has developed a range of different ways to find out about an individual's background and upbringing such as talking to the individual, talking through photographs the individual has, if willing to do so, talking to family and friends and others who know the individual including advocates, carers and professionals. Reading through the referral information can provide, Alan has found, a useful insight into an individual's preferences, wishes and needs, but as these may have changed over time Alan finds it is still important to clarify these with the individual and others involved in their life.

Evidencing AC2.1 to your assessor:

For AC2.1 you must evidence your skills of how to find out an individual's history, preferences, wishes and needs.

Assessment Method:

Direct Observation of your work practices

- You can show your assessor or an expert witness how to find out about an individual's history, preferences, wishes and needs.
- You can use as a **supporting piece of work product evidence** the information you have found out about an individual and you have documented in the care plan.

REMEMBER TO:

- Make arrangements for **observation** of your **work practices**.
- Include evidence of what you have found out about an individual's history, preferences, wishes and needs and **how** you have found this out.
- Think about sources of information available to you in and outside **your work setting** to find out about the history, preferences, wishes and needs of an individual.

Learning Outcome 2: Be able to work in a person-centred way

Assessment Criterion 2.2: Apply person-centred values in day-to-day work, taking into account the history, preferences, wishes and needs of an individual

What does AC2.2 mean?

- The lead word **apply** means that you must **be able to show through your work practices** how to put person-centred values into practice in day-to-day work, taking into account the history, preferences, wishes and needs of an individual.
- Your **observations of your work practices** must include you showing different ways of putting person-centred values into practice.
- For the key words **person-centred values** you can think about how to carry out your job role in a way that respects the individuals you work with and supports them to lead their lives as they wish, through promoting their individuality, rights, choice, privacy, independence, dignity, respect and by working in partnership with them.
- For the key word **history** you can think about how to take into account an individual's background and upbringing in day-to-day work.
- For the key word **preferences** you can think about how to take into account the choices an individual makes in day-to-day work.

Read the following **Real Work Setting** scenario and think about how it relates to your work setting and role:

Real Work Setting

Name: Alan

Job Role: Home Carer
(See page 70 for a description of the role)

Putting person-centred values into practice: Today, Alan is meeting with Alfredo who has told him that he is very proud of his West Indian background and likes the idea of doing more cooking at home and trying different recipes but doesn't really have the confidence to do so. Alan is spending some time with Alfredo to talk through with him what he would like to cook and what recipes he would like to find or use. Alan listens carefully as Alfredo tells him that he would like to learn to cook new recipes he has never tried before, such as those involving Italian and Chinese food.

Evidencing AC2.2 to your assessor:

For AC2.2 you must evidence your skills of applying person-centred values in day-to-day work, taking into account the history, preferences, wishes and needs of an individual.

Assessment Method:

Direct Observation of your work practices

- You can show your assessor how to apply person-centred values in day-to-day work, taking into account the history, preferences, wishes and needs of an individual.

REMEMBER TO:

- Make arrangements for **observation of your work practices**.
- Include evidence of applying person-centred values in day-to-day work.
- Include evidence of how you take into account the history, preferences, wishes and needs of an individual.
- Think about **your work setting** and how you apply person-centred values in day-to-day work and take into account the history, preferences, wishes and needs of an individual.

Derby Teaching Hospitals
NHS Foundation Trust
Library and Knowledge Centre

Learning Outcome 3: Be able to establish consent when providing care or support

Assessment Criterion 3.1: Explain the importance of establishing consent when providing care or support

What does AC3.1 mean?

- The lead word **explain** means that you must **make clear** the importance of establishing consent when providing care or support.
- Your **account** must make clear the importance of establishing consent when providing care or support.
- For the key word **consent** you can think about the ability of different individuals to show their agreement to carry out an activity or make a decision. The process of establishing an individual's informed agreement to an action or decision will vary according to an individual's assessed capacity to consent.

Read the following **Real Work Setting** scenario and think about how it relates to your work setting and role:

Real Work Setting

Name: Fartun

Job Role: Volunteer in a self-advocacy group for adults who have physical and learning disabilities

Fartun has worked as a Volunteer for one year. Her responsibilities include assisting individuals to speak up for themselves, have their voices heard and access the support and information they need.

The importance of establishing consent: Fartun is meeting with the self-advocacy group today to agree on what they would like to work on together first, as they developed a long list of different areas at their last meeting. Prior to the meeting starting, Fartun checks with each member what issues or questions they have, how they plan to present these to the other members of the group, what support, if any, is required and how they would like Fartun to provide this support. Some of the members decide to share their ideas with the group themselves and do not require Fartun to support them; other members ask Fartun to help them with speaking up and with showing photographs and drawings of the issues that are important to them.

Evidencing AC3.1 to your assessor:

For AC3.1 you must evidence your knowledge of the importance of establishing consent when providing care or support.

Assessment Methods:

Oral or **Written** Questioning or **Discussion** or a **Personal Statement** or **Reflection**

- You can **tell** your assessor about the importance of establishing consent when providing care or support.
  Or
- You can **talk** to your assessor about the importance of establishing consent when providing care or support.
  Or
- You can write a **personal statement** or **reflection** about your experience of the importance of establishing consent when providing care or support.

REMEMBER TO:

- Provide an **account** and **explain** the importance.
- Include **varied** examples of the reasons why it is important to establish consent when providing care or support.
- Include details about the importance of establishing consent.
- Think about your **work setting** and the importance of establishing consent when providing care or support.

Learning Outcome 3: Be able to establish consent when providing care or support

Assessment Criterion 3.2: Establish consent for an activity or action

What does AC3.2 mean?

- The lead word **establish** means that you must **be able to show through your work practices** how to agree consent with an individual for an activity or action.
- Your **observations of your work practices** must include you showing how you can seek an individual's permission to complete an activity or action.
- For the key word **consent** you can think about the ways different individuals agree to an activity or action. The process of establishing an individual's informed agreement to an action or decision will vary according to an individual's assessed capacity to consent.

Read the following **Real Work Setting** scenario and think about how it relates to your work setting and role:

Real Work Setting

Name: Fartun

Job Role: Volunteer in a self-advocacy group for adults who have physical and learning disabilities (See page 72 for a description of the role)

Establishing consent: Fartun's support to each member of the group varies, as each individual's requirements are different and Fartun therefore finds that each individual will have their own way of agreeing to an activity or action. For example, Maryse asked Fartun to write down what she was going to support her saying to the group before she agreed to this. When supporting Philip, Fartun checked with a thumbs up or down whether she had his agreement to go ahead and share his drawings with the rest of the members. Fartun asked Gladis's advocate to find out from her whether she was happy to continue attending the group and participating in the meetings in the way she had been doing over the last few weeks. Syreeta's brother was very helpful when interpreting what his sister was trying to tell Fartun in relation to the most important issues for her to work on.

Evidencing AC3.2 to your assessor:

For AC3.2 you must evidence your skills of how you establish consent for an activity or action.

Assessment Method:

Direct Observation of your work practices

- You can show your assessor how you establish consent for an activity or action.

REMEMBER TO:

- Make arrangements for **observation of your work practices**.
- Include evidence of how you establish consent.
- Include evidence of why you establish consent in this way.
- Think about individuals in **your work setting** and how and why you establish consent in different ways when providing care or support.

Learning Outcome 3: Be able to establish consent when providing care or support

Assessment Criterion 3.3: Explain what steps to take if consent cannot be readily established

What does AC3.3 mean?

- The lead word **explain** means that you must **make clear** the steps that must be taken if consent cannot be readily established.
- Your **account** must make clear the process to follow if consent cannot be readily established.
- For the key word **consent** you can think about the action to take if an individual is not able to show their agreement for an activity or action and you are not able to establish the individual's informed agreement to an action or decision.

Read the following **Real Work Setting** scenario and think about how it relates to your work setting and role:

Real Work Setting

Name: Fartun

Job Role: Volunteer in a self-advocacy group for adults who have physical and learning disabilities (See page 72 for a description of the role)

When consent cannot be established: Gladis's advocate informs Fartun that Gladis does not appear to want to express today how she is feeling on attending the group and has also shown her wish to not share with the group today the issues she thinks the group should work on. Fartun asks Gladis's advocate whether she would like more time to make a decision and suggests that perhaps she may like to discuss this away from the group and then let her know her decision. A little while later, Gladis's advocate confirms with Fartun that she has spoken with Gladis and that she has decided she would like more time to discuss this away from the group and will let her know her decision by the end of next week.

Evidencing AC3.3 to your assessor:

For AC3.3 you must evidence your knowledge of the steps to take if consent cannot be readily established.

Assessment Methods:

Oral or **Written** Questioning or **Discussion** or a **Personal Statement** or **Reflection**

- You can **tell** your assessor about the steps to take if consent cannot be readily established, as well as the reasons why.
  Or
- You can **talk** to your assessor about the steps to take if consent cannot be readily established, as well as the reasons why.
  Or
- You can write a **personal statement** or **reflection** about your experience of the steps to take if consent cannot be readily established, as well as the reasons why.

REMEMBER TO:

- Provide an **account** and **explain** the steps to take.
- Include **details** about the **process to follow**.
- Include **varied** examples of the reasons why.
- Think about **your own work setting** and the steps to take if consent cannot be readily established, as well as the reasons why.

Learning Outcome 4: Be able to encourage active participation

Assessment Criterion 4.1: Describe how active participation benefits an individual

What does AC4.1 mean?

- The lead word **describe** means that you must provide an **account** that **details** how active participation benefits an individual.
- Your **account** must detail **different ways** of how active participation benefits an individual.
- For the key words **active participation** you can think about how you can ensure that you support individuals to live their lives as they wish.

Read the following **Real Work Setting** scenario and think about how it relates to your work setting and role:

Real Work Setting

Name: Stojan

Job Role: Personal Assistant to young adults who have autism

Stojan has worked as a Personal Assistant for one year. His responsibilities include: supporting individuals with daily activities such as washing, bathing, dressing, shaving and grooming; assisting with household tasks such as cleaning, cooking, laundry and shopping; and enabling individuals to go out and socialise.

Applying active participation: Stojan has been Michael's personal assistant for the last six months and has seen the many positive changes that Michael has made to the way he lives his life. Since Michael has been working with Stojan, Michael has developed his independent living skills and depends far less on Stojan and the other Personal Assistants in the team when it comes to deciding what activities he would like to complete each day and the support he requires to achieve each of these to his satisfaction. Michael's confidence in himself and others has also grown and this has encouraged him to form new relationships outside his immediate circle of family and friends who have known him for most of his life.

Evidencing AC4.1 to your assessor:

For AC4.1 you must evidence your knowledge of how active participation benefits an individual.

Assessment Methods:

Oral or **Written** Questioning or **Discussion** or a **Personal Statement** or **Reflection**

- You can **tell** your assessor about how active participation benefits an individual.

  Or
- You can **talk** to your assessor about how active participation benefits an individual.

  Or
- You can write a **personal statement** or **reflection** about your experience of how active participation benefits an individual.

REMEMBER TO:

- Provide a detailed **account** and detail **how.**
- Include **different benefits** of active participation.
- Think about examples of how **active participation** benefits an individual.
- Think about **your work setting** and how active participation benefits an individual.

Learning Outcome 4: Be able to encourage active participation

Assessment Criterion 4.2: Identify possible barriers to active participation

What does AC4.2 mean?

- The lead word **identify** means that you must **make clear** the possible barriers to active participation.
- Your **list** must make clear the **different** possible barriers.
- For the key word **barriers** you can think about the physical, emotional, social and financial reasons that may prevent active participation.
- For the key words **active participation** you can think about what may prevent you from ensuring that you support individuals to live their lives as they wish.

Read the following **Real Work Setting** scenario and think about how it relates to your work setting and role:

Real Work Setting

Name: Stojan

Job Role: Personal Assistant to young adults who have autism
(See page 75 for a description of the role)

Barriers to active participation: Stojan is meeting with the Senior Personal Assistant today to review how effective he has been in working with individuals in a way that recognises and supports them to live their lives as they wish. Stojan explains to the Senior that at times he has found it difficult to encourage active participation with every individual he works with and with all activities they participate in. Stojan reflects on the reasons why this may have happened and he decides that this has been at times due to the individual and their self-esteem, at other times due to the nature of the activity the individual is being supported to actively participate in, and at times due to others involved in individuals' lives and the role they play in supporting individuals to live their lives as they wish. Stojan's Senior asks him whether there are any other possible barriers that he can think about and, after a little while, Stojan recognises that at times his approach to different individuals and tasks they require support with may have also acted as possible barriers to enable those individuals to be active participants.

Evidencing AC4.2 to your assessor:

For AC4.2 you must evidence your knowledge of the possible barriers to active participation.

Assessment Methods:

Oral or **Written** Questioning or **Discussion** or a **Spidergram**

- You can **tell** your assessor about the possible barriers to active participation.
  Or
- You can **talk** to your assessor about the possible barriers to active participation.
  Or
- You can complete a **spidergram** about the possible barriers to active participation.

REMEMBER TO:

- Provide **examples** of different barriers.
- Include **varied** barriers to active participation.
- Think about **your work setting** and the possible barriers to active participation.

Learning Outcome 4: Be able to encourage active participation

Assessment Criterion 4.3: Demonstrate ways to reduce the barriers and encourage active participation

What does AC4.3 mean?

- The lead word **demonstrate** means that you must **be able to show through your work practices** how to reduce the barriers and encourage active participation.
- Your **observation of your work practices** must include you showing how to reduce the barriers and encourage active participation.
- For the key word **barriers** you can think about how to minimise the physical, emotional, social and financial reasons that may prevent active participation.
- For the key words **active participation** you can think about how to encourage individuals to live their lives as they wish.

Read the following **Real Work Setting** scenario and think about how it relates to your work setting and role:

Real Work Setting

Name: Stojan

Job Role: Personal Assistant to young adults who have autism
(See page 75 for a description of the role)

Reducing the barriers and encouraging active participation: Stojan then talks through with his Senior the different ways that he has used to reduce the barriers he has encountered to active participation for each individual he provides support to and how he has actively encouraged all individuals he works with to participate in activities and relationships with others as independently as possible. Stojan's Senior confirms that he does recall observing Stojan work in this way and remembers thinking how well he knew each individual and ensured at all times that he was able to adapt his support and the techniques he used to encourage them to complete all activities as independently as possible. Stojan's Senior shares with him how he has developed his skills in doing so very well over the last few months and wants him to consider getting involved in mentoring other new Personal Assistants who will soon be joining the team so that they too can encourage active participation and learn about different ways of reducing barriers that may exist to doing so.

Evidencing AC4.3 to your assessor:

For AC4.3 you must evidence your skills of how to demonstrate ways to reduce the barriers and encourage active participation.

Assessment Method:

Direct Observation of your work practices

- You can show your assessor or an expert witness how to demonstrate ways to reduce the barriers and encourage active participation.

REMEMBER TO:

- Make arrangements for **observation of your work practices**.
- Include evidence of **different ways to reduce** the barriers to active participation.
- Include evidence of **different ways to encourage** active participation.
- Think about **your work setting** and ways to reduce the barriers and encourage active participation.

Learning Outcome 5: Be able to support the individual's right to make choices

Assessment Criterion 5.1: Support an individual to make informed choices

What does AC5.1 mean?

- The lead word **support** means that you must **be able to show through your work practices** how to assist an individual to make informed choices.
- Your **observations of your work practices** must include you providing support to an individual to make informed choices.
- For the key words **informed choices** you can think about how to support individuals to access and understand all available information before making choices in their lives.

Read the following **Real Work Setting** scenario and think about how it relates to your work setting and role:

Real Work Setting

Name: Jody

Job Role: Personal Assistant to adults who have physical disabilities

Jody has worked as a Personal Assistant for three years. Her responsibilities include supporting individuals with all aspects of personal care to enable them to get up in the morning and ready for bed at night, assisting with a range of domestic duties, enabling individuals to go shopping, accessing activities they wish to participate in both inside and outside their home and feeling comfortable working alongside individuals who have friendly and well-behaved pets.

Making informed choices: For Jody to be able to provide high-quality care and support, she feels that it is essential as a Personal Assistant to be able to assist individuals to make their own choices. To do so effectively, it is important that Jody keeps herself up to date with the latest information and opportunities that may be relevant for different individuals she works with and to be able to communicate this information to individuals in a way that enables their understanding of all available information, including the different options to choose from. Supporting individuals in this way not only supports their rights to make informed choices, but also enables individuals' lives to be improved in many different ways.

Evidencing AC5.1 to your assessor:

For AC5.1 you must evidence your skills to support an individual to make informed choices.

Assessment Method:

Direct Observation of your work practices

- You can show your assessor how to support an individual to make informed choices.

REMEMBER TO:

- Make arrangements for **observation** of **your work practices**.
- Include evidence of **providing support** to an individual.
- Include evidence of **how** you supported an individual **to make informed choices**.
- Think about how you support an individual in **your work setting** to make informed choices.

Learning Outcome 5: Be able to support the individual's right to make choices

Assessment Criterion 5.2: Use agreed risk-assessment processes to support the right to make choices

What does AC5.2 mean?

- The lead word **use** means that you must **be able to show through your work practices** how to work with agreed risk-assessment processes to support the right to make choices.
- Your **observations of your work practices** must include you using agreed risk-assessment processes.
- For the key words **agreed risk-assessment processes** you can think about the potential that exists for danger or harm to support individuals' rights to make choices, as well as your work setting's policies and procedures that you are required to use to identify, control and reduce risks while maintaining individuals' rights to make choices.

Read the following **Real Work Setting** scenario and think about how it relates to your work setting and role:

Real Work Setting

Name: Jody
Job Role: Personal Assistant to adults who have physical disabilities (See page 78 for a description of the role)
Using agreed risk-assessment processes: Jody is supporting Lorna to decide whether she wants to continue going swimming every week, as the epileptic seizures she has have become a lot more frequent and irregular over the last month. In order to assist Lorna to make her own decision about this, Jody agrees to complete a risk assessment with her and begins by talking through with her what she enjoys about swimming and how she feels this activity benefits her, as well as how she would feel if she no longer went swimming every week and whether there are any other activities that she would like to do instead. Jody and Lorna then discuss what the risks are of going swimming while her epileptic seizures are a lot more frequent and irregular. Having considered both the benefits and the disadvantages of going swimming every week, Jody and Lorna then discuss how these risks could be controlled and managed and what additional support could be put in place for Lorna temporarily. Lorna explains that having the additional support from three, instead of two, Personal Assistants would enable her to feel more comfortable about going swimming. Both agree to review the plan of support they have put in place on a weekly basis.

Evidencing AC5.2 to your assessor:

For AC5.2 you must evidence your skills in using agreed risk-assessment processes to support the right to make choices.

Assessment Method:

Direct Observation of your work practices

- You can show your assessor how to use agreed risk-assessment processes to support the right to make choices.

REMEMBER TO:

- Make arrangements for **observation** of **your work practices**.
- Include evidence of **how to use** agreed risk-assessment processes.
- Include evidence of **how you support** the individual's right **to make choices**.
- Think about how to use agreed risk-assessment processes to support the right to make choices in **your work setting**.

Learning Outcome 5: Be able to support the individual's right to make choices

Assessment Criterion 5.3: Explain why a worker's personal views should not influence an individual's choices

What does AC5.3 mean?

- The lead word **explain** means that you must **make clear** why a worker's personal views should not influence an individual's choices.
- Your **account** must make clear **the reasons why**.
- For the key words **personal views**, you can think about the reasons why it is important that your personal thoughts and beliefs do not influence an individual's choices.
- For the key word **influence** you can think about how your role and the way you carry out your role can have an effect on the choices an individual makes.

Read the following **Real Work Setting** scenario and think about how it relates to your work setting and role:

Real Work Setting

Name: Jody

Job Role: Personal Assistant to adults who have physical disabilities
(See page 78 for a description of the role)

Why a worker's personal views should not influence an individual's choices: Jody has developed very good working relationships with all of the individuals she works with and feels that the reason why she has developed both trusting and meaningful relationships with every individual is because she has a genuine interest in their well-being and in providing them with the best possible support to make their own choices in life. In doing so, Jody remembers how she was taught in her training how it is very important for her personal views to not influence in any way an individual's choices, as her role as a Personal Assistant is to enable individuals to make their own choices.

Evidencing AC5.3 to your assessor:

For AC5.3 you must evidence your knowledge of why a worker's personal views should not influence an individual's choices.

Assessment Methods:

Oral or **Written** Questioning or **Discussion** or a **Personal Statement** or **Reflection**

- You can **tell** your assessor about why a worker's personal views should not influence an individual's choices.
  Or
- You can **talk** to your assessor about why a worker's personal views should not influence an individual's choices.
  Or
- You can write a **personal statement** or **reflection** about your experience of why a worker's personal views should not influence an individual's choices.

REMEMBER TO:

- Provide an **account** and **explain** the reasons why.
- Include **varied** examples of the reasons why.
- Think about **your work setting** and why a worker's personal views should not influence an individual's choices.

Learning Outcome 5: Be able to support the individual's right to make choices

Assessment Criterion 5.4: Describe how to support an individual to question or challenge decisions concerning them that are made by others

What does AC5.4 mean?

- The lead word **describe** means that you must provide **an account** that **details** how to support an individual to question or challenge decisions concerning them that are made by others.
- Your **account** must detail the support provided and be based on decisions concerning individuals that are made by others.
- For the key word **others** you can think about different people that are involved in individuals' lives such as their families, friends, advocates, your colleagues and other professionals.

Read the following **Real Work Setting** scenario and think about how it relates to your work setting and role:

Real Work Setting

Name: Jody

Job Role: Personal Assistant to adults who have physical disabilities
(See page 78 for a description of the role)

How to support an individual to question or challenge decisions concerning them that are made by others: During her time working as a Personal Assistant Jody has supported different individuals, when required, to question and challenge decisions about them and their lives that have been made by other professionals and family members. Jody has found that this process has varied quite significantly between different individuals, depending on their needs, requirements and the nature of their questions or decisions that have been made about them by others.

Evidencing AC5.4 to your assessor:

For AC5.4 you must evidence your knowledge of how to support an individual to question or challenge decisions concerning them that are made by others.

Assessment Methods:

Oral or **Written** Questioning or **Discussion** or a **Personal Statement** or **Reflection**

- You can **tell** your assessor about how to support an individual to question or challenge decisions concerning them that are made by others.
  Or
- You can **talk** to your assessor about how to support an individual to question or challenge decisions concerning them that are made by others.
  Or
- You can write a **personal statement** or **reflection** about your experience of how to support an individual to question or challenge decisions concerning them that are made by others.

REMEMBER TO:

- Provide a detailed **account**.
- Include **different ways** of supporting an individual.
- Think about examples of when an individual may **question or challenge decisions concerning them**.
- Include evidence of **who** made **the decisions concerning them**.
- Think about how to support an individual you work with in **your work setting** to challenge decisions concerning them that are made by others.

Learning Outcome 6: Be able to promote individuals' well-being

Assessment Criterion 6.1: Explain how individual identity and self-esteem are linked with well-being

What does AC6.1 mean?

- The lead word **explain** means that you must **make clear** the links between individual identity, self-esteem and well-being.
- Your **account** must make clear what each of these terms mean and how each one, in turn, is related to the others.
- For the key words **individual identity** you can think about what the different characteristics are that make each individual unique and how this links to an individual's well-being.
- For the key word **self-esteem** you can think about how individuals value themselves and how others can contribute to this and how this links to an individual's well-being.
- For the key word **well-being** you can think about how this is related to spiritual, emotional, cultural, religious, social and political aspects of individuals' lives.

Read the following **Real Work Setting** scenario and think about how it relates to your work setting and role:

Real Work Setting

Name: Rakhel
Job Role: Carer in a day service for older people
Rakhel has been working as a Carer for three years. Her responsibilities include supporting individuals to take part in a range of activities including arts and crafts, croquet, gardening, sewing and quizzes, as well as enabling individuals to socialise with others over a meal and a cup of tea.
Individual identity, self-esteem and well-being: Rakhel discusses with one of her colleagues how individual identity and self-esteem can affect an individual's emotional, physical, cultural, religious, spiritual, political and social well-being. Rakhel considers the meanings of the concepts of individual identity and self-esteem, as well as how and why they may impact on an individual's well-being; this makes Rakhel think about how important it is for her to fully understand how these are linked if she is to be effective in promoting individuals' well-being.

Evidencing AC6.1 to your assessor:

For AC6.1 you must evidence your understanding of how individual identity and self-esteem are linked with well-being.

Assessment Methods:

Oral or **Written** Questioning or **Discussion** or a **Personal Statement**

- You can **tell** your assessor about how individual identity and self-esteem are linked with well-being.

  Or
- You can **talk** to your assessor about how individual identity and self-esteem are linked with well-being.

  Or
- You can write a **personal statement** about how individual identity and self-esteem are linked with well-being.

REMEMBER TO:

- Provide an **account** and **explain** what each term means, as well as the reasons why each concept is related to the others
- Include **varied** examples of how each concept has an impact on the others.
- Include details about the links that exist between individual identity and self-esteem and how these relate to an individual's well-being.
- Think about **your work setting** and how individual identity and self-esteem are linked with well-being.

Learning Outcome 6: Be able to promote individuals' well-being

Assessment Criterion 6.2: Describe attitudes and approaches that are likely to promote an individual's well-being

What does AC6.2 mean?

- The lead word **describe** means that you must provide **an account** that **details** the attitudes and approaches that are likely to promote an individual's well-being.
- Your **account** must detail **different** attitudes and approaches.
- For the key word **attitudes** you can think about how different ways of thinking are likely to promote an individual's well-being.
- For the key word **approaches** you can think about how different ways of working are likely to promote an individual's well-being.
- For the key word **well-being** you can think about the attitudes and approaches that are likely to promote the spiritual, emotional, cultural, religious, social and political aspects of individuals' lives.

Read the following **Real Work Setting** scenario and think about how it relates to your work setting and role:

Real Work Setting

Name: Rakhel

Job Role: Carer in a day service for older people
(See page 82 for a description of the role)

Attitudes and approaches for promoting an individual's well-being: Rakhel talks through with her colleague the top five attitudes and approaches that she feels are more likely to promote an individual's well-being, including examples of what each of these is, how they can be used to promote an individual's well-being and the reasons why she thinks they are effective in doing so across different individuals. Rakhel and her colleague then consider how to ensure that different carers use these consistently when working with individuals, while still being able to adapt them to suit individuals' unique situations and requirements.

Evidencing AC6.2 to your assessor:

For AC6.2 you must evidence your knowledge of attitudes and approaches that are likely to promote an individual's well-being.

Assessment Methods:

Oral or **Written** Questioning or **Discussion** or a **Personal Statement** or **Reflection**

- You can **tell** your assessor about attitudes and approaches that are likely to promote an individual's well-being.
  Or
- You can **talk** to your assessor about attitudes and approaches that are likely to promote an individual's well-being.
  Or
- You can write a **personal statement** or **reflection** about your experience of attitudes and approaches that are likely to promote an individual's well-being.

REMEMBER TO:

- Provide a detailed **account**.
- Include **different examples** of **attitudes** and **approaches**.
- Think about how these are likely to promote an individual's well-being.
- Think about **your work setting** and the attitudes and approaches that are likely to promote an individual's well-being.

Learning Outcome 6: Be able to promote individuals' well-being

Assessment Criterion 6.3: Support an individual in a way that promotes a sense of identity and self-esteem

What does AC6.3 mean?

- The lead word **support** means that you must **be able to show through your work practices** how to support an individual in a way that promotes a sense of identity and self-esteem.
- Your observations of your work practices must include you providing support to an individual.
- For the key word **identity** you can think about how you can take into account the different characteristics that make each individual unique when providing support.
- For the key word **self-esteem** you can think about how individuals value themselves and how you and others can contribute to this when providing support.

Read the following **Real Work Setting** scenario and think about how it relates to your work setting and role:

Real Work Setting

Name: Rakhel

Job Role: Carer in a day service for older people
(See page 82 for a description of the role)

Supporting an individual in a way that promotes a sense of identity and self-esteem: Today, Rakhel has been asked by her manager to support Helen to take part in the gardening session this afternoon, as although Helen has a genuine interest in gardening she does not feel that she has anything to contribute to this activity and therefore remains indoors and watches others individuals participate instead. Rakhel begins by suggesting to Helen that they should both go and sit outside on the bench in the garden, as it is very pleasant outside; Helen agrees to go and sit outside providing that Rakhel stays with her. Rakhel agrees to do so and soon Helen starts observing what each member of the gardening group is doing and providing them with advice on different ways of doing the activities they are taking part in and why it is important for them to do so in that way. One of the members of the group explains to Helen that she does not know how to tie the broad beans, so Helen promptly gets up and shows her and then with a big smile says to her, 'Now that's how you do it.'

Evidencing AC6.3 to your assessor:

For AC6.3 you must evidence your skills to support an individual in a way that promotes a sense of identity and self-esteem.

Assessment Method:

Direct Observation of your work practices

- You can show your assessor how to support an individual in a way that promotes a sense of identity and self-esteem.

REMEMBER TO:

- Make arrangements for **observation of your work practices**.
- Include evidence of providing support to an individual.
- Include evidence of how you promoted an individual's sense of identity and self-esteem.
- Think about **your work setting** and how you support an individual in a way that promotes a sense of identity and self-esteem.

Learning Outcome 6: Be able to promote individuals' well-being

Assessment Criterion 6.4: Demonstrate ways to contribute to an environment that promotes well-being

What does AC6.4 mean?

- The lead word **demonstrate** means that you must **be able to show through your work practices** different ways to contribute to an environment that promotes well-being.
- Your **observations of your work practices** must include you showing different ways to contribute to an environment that promotes well-being.
- For the key word **environment** you can think about an individual's safety and physical surroundings, as well as the atmosphere and feel of an individual's environment.
- For the key word **well-being** you can think about how this involves individuals' emotional, physical, cultural, religious, spiritual, political and social aspects of their lives and environment.

Read the following **Real Work Setting** scenario and think about how it relates to your work setting and role:

Real Work Setting

Name: Rakhel

Job Role: Carer in a day service for older people
(See page 82 for a description of the role)

Contributing to an environment that promotes well-being: After the gardening group activity had finished, Rakhel and the team reflected on how the session had gone today. All feel it worked very well and that Helen, with Rakhel's support, made a big contribution to the atmosphere in the group; the team noticed how motivated and interested everyone was regarding the new skills and knowledge that Helen shared with all the group members by taking an active part in the session. Rakhel's manager explained that she also observed how Rakhel's discreet visual prompting and reassurance enabled Helen to feel more confident in her abilities and genuinely enjoy a hobby that used to be a great part of her life many years ago. Rakhel added that she felt Helen's self-esteem was also affected when group members thanked her for helping them and praised her personally on her in-depth knowledge of gardening.

Evidencing AC6.4 to your assessor:

For AC6.4 you must evidence your skills to demonstrate ways to contribute to an environment that promotes well-being.

Assessment Method:

Direct Observation of your work practices

- You can show your assessor different ways to contribute to an environment that promotes well-being.

REMEMBER TO:

- Make arrangements for **observation of your work practices**.
- Include evidence of different ways.
- Include evidence and examples of how you contribute to an environment that promotes well-being.
- Think about ways to contribute to an environment that promotes well-being in **your work setting**.

HSC027 Contribute to health and safety in health and social care

Learning Outcome 1: Understand your responsibilities and the responsibilities of others relating to health and safety in the work setting

Assessment Criterion 1.1: Identify legislation relating to general health and safety in a health or social care work setting

What does AC1.1 mean?

- The lead word **identify** means that you must **list** health and safety legislation.
- Your list must include **different** examples of health and safety legislation.
- For the key word **legislation** you can think about the laws that are in place relating to health and safety in health and social care work settings.
- For the key words **work setting** you can think about the laws that are in place relating to health and safety in health and social care work settings. This may include one specific location where you work, or in a range of locations, depending on your job role.

Read the following **Real Work Setting** scenario and think about how it relates to your work setting and role:

Real Work Setting

Name: Claudia

Job Role: Support Worker to people who have mental health needs

Claudia has been working as a Support Worker for eight years. Her responsibilities include supporting individuals who are recovering from mental illness to live independently again, supporting individuals to meet their goals and targets, as agreed in their support plans, and developing their skills and confidence through daily activities to promote their independence.

Health and safety legislation: Claudia is attending a health and safety training update today. The session begins with considering all the health and safety legislation that exists and that is relevant to maintaining health and safety in a health or social care work setting. The trainer explains that it is important for all those who work, live and are involved in health and social care settings to be aware of what these are, as health and safety are everyone's responsibility.

Evidencing AC1.1 to your assessor:

For AC1.1 you must evidence your understanding of legislation relating to health and safety in a health or social care work setting.

Assessment Methods:

Oral or **Written** Questioning or **Discussion** or a **Spidergram**

- You can **tell** your assessor about the different health and safety legislation that exists.

  Or
- You can **talk** to your assessor about the different health and safety legislation that exists.

  Or
- You can complete a **spidergram** of the different health and safety legislation that exists.

REMEMBER TO:

- **List** health and safety legislation.
- Include **different** examples of health and safety legislation.
- Ensure they relate to health and safety in a health or social care work setting.
- Think about the health and safety legislation in place in your **work setting.**

Learning Outcome 1: Understand your responsibilities and the responsibilities of others relating to health and safety in the work setting

Assessment Criterion 1.2: Describe the main points of health and safety policies and procedures agreed with the employer

What does AC1.2 mean?

- The lead word **describe** means that you must provide an **account** that **details** the main points of health and safety policies and procedures that have been agreed with your employer.
- Your **account** must **detail** the main points of health and safety policies and procedures.
- For the key words **policies and procedures** you can think about how the setting where you work operates on a day-to-day basis in terms of health and safety, both formally and in line with other agreed ways of working.

Read the following **Real Work Setting** scenario and think about how it relates to your work setting and role:

Real Work Setting

Name: Claudia

Job Role: Support Worker to people who have mental health needs
(See page 86 for a description of the role)

Health and safety policies and procedures: After identifying the key pieces of health and safety legislation that exist, the training session then moves on to consider how employers and organisations ensure health and social care work settings are safe and how working practices meet health and safety requirements. The trainer asks each participant to share with the rest of the group three health and safety policies and procedures that they have in place in their work setting and provide details of the main points included in each one.

Evidencing AC1.2 to your assessor:

For AC1.2 you must evidence your understanding of the main points of health and safety policies and procedures agreed with your employer.

Assessment Methods:

Oral or **Written** Questioning or **Discussion** or a **Personal Statement**

- You can **tell** your assessor about the main points of health and safety policies and procedures agreed with the employer.
  Or
- You can **talk** to your assessor about the main points of health and safety policies and procedures agreed with the employer.
  Or
- You can write a **personal statement** about the main points of health and safety policies and procedures agreed with the employer.

REMEMBER TO:

- Provide a detailed **account.**
- Include evidence of **different** health and safety policies and procedures that have been agreed with your employer.
- Include **details** of their **main points** in terms of how they relate to health and safety in your work setting.
- Think about your **work setting** and the main points of health and safety policies and procedures agreed with your employer.

AC 1.3

Learning Outcome 1: Understand your responsibilities and the responsibilities of others relating to health and safety in the work setting

Assessment Criterion 1.3: Outline the main health and safety responsibilities for yourself, the employer or manager and others in the work setting

What does AC1.3 mean?

- The lead word **outline** means that you must provide an **account** that **details briefly** the different health and safety responsibilities for yourself, the employer or manager and others in the work setting.
- Your **account** must provide brief details of **different** health and safety responsibilities for yourself, the employer or manager and others in the work setting.
- For the key word **responsibilities** you can think about how and why health and safety tasks are carried out in the work setting.
- For the key word **others** you can think about how this may include team members, other colleagues, those who use or commission their own health or social care services, families, carers or advocates.

Read the following **Real Work Setting** scenario and think about how it relates to your work setting and role:

Real Work Setting

Name: Claudia

Job Role: Support Worker to people who have mental health needs
(See page 86 for a description of the role)

Health and safety responsibilities: The next activity Claudia participates in during the training session involves researching and then discussing the main health and safety responsibilities for her, her employer and manager and others in her work setting, such as other members of the team and visitors. The trainer also discusses with the group the importance of ensuring that everyone is aware of not only their own but also each other's health and safety responsibilities.

Evidencing AC1.3 to your assessor:

For AC1.3 you must evidence your understanding of the main health and safety responsibilities for yourself, the employer or manager and others in the work setting.

Assessment Methods:

Oral or **Written** Questioning or **Discussion** or a **Personal Statement** or **Reflection**

- You can **tell** your assessor about the main health and safety responsibilities for yourself, the employer or manager and others in the work setting.

  Or
- You can **talk** to your assessor about the main health and safety responsibilities for yourself, the employer or manager and others in the work setting.

  Or
- You can write a **personal statement** or **reflection** about your experience of the main health and safety responsibilities for yourself, the employer or manager and others **in your work setting.**

REMEMBER TO:

- Provide an **account and brief details** of different health and safety responsibilities.
- Include details about what each **responsibility is, who it is for and why.**
- Include **varied** examples of health and safety responsibilities.
- Think about the health and safety responsibilities for yourself, the employer or manager and others in **your work setting.**

Learning Outcome 1: Understand your responsibilities and the responsibilities of others relating to health and safety in the work setting

Assessment Criterion 1.4: Identify tasks relating to health and safety that should not be carried out without special training

What does AC1.4 mean?

- The lead word **identify** means that you must **list** specific tasks that should not be carried out without special training in the work setting.
- Your list must include **different** examples of tasks.
- For the key word **tasks** you can think about the day-to-day work activities you carry out that should not be carried out without special training. This may include tasks relating to use of equipment, first aid, medication, healthcare procedures, food handling and preparation.

Read the following **Real Work Setting** scenario and think about how it relates to your work setting and role:

Real Work Setting

Name: Claudia

Job Role: Support Worker to people who have mental health needs
(See page 86 for a description of the role)

Tasks that require special training: While the group discuss each other's health and safety responsibilities, Claudia shares with the participants how it is important that all staff read the health and safety guidelines in place for individuals, including any agreed ways of working that must be adhered to and that all staff attend all training updates provided by the work setting. Claudia shares with the group how she finds the training updates very useful and necessary for her to maintain her knowledge up to date, in particular around how to carry out the tasks that she is required to undertake as part of her role that must not be carried out without special training.

Evidencing AC1.4 to your assessor:

For AC1.4 you must evidence your understanding of tasks in the work setting that should not be carried out without special training.

Assessment Methods:

Oral or **Written** Questioning or **Discussion** or a **Spidergram**

- You can **tell** your assessor about the tasks that should not be carried out in the work setting without special training.
  Or
- You can **talk** to your assessor about the tasks that should not be carried out in the work setting without special training.
  Or
- You can complete a **spidergram** of the specific tasks that should not be carried out in the work setting without special training.

REMEMBER TO:

- **List** specific tasks.
- Include **different** examples of tasks.
- Ensure they relate to the work setting.
- Think about the tasks that should not be carried out in your **work setting** without special training.

Learning Outcome 1: Understand your responsibilities and the responsibilities of others relating to health and safety in the work setting

Assessment Criterion 1.5: Explain how to access additional support and information relating to health and safety

What does AC1.5 mean?

- The lead word **explain** means that you must **make clear** how to access additional support and information relating to health and safety.
- Your **account** must make clear how.
- For the key words **additional support** you can think about the people to approach, both within and outside your work setting for support relating to health and safety, such as your manager or the health and safety representative in your work setting.
- For the key word **information** you can think about health and safety policies, procedures and guidelines available within your work setting and useful websites and notices available from external organisations, such as the Health and Safety Executive.

Read the following **Real Work Setting** scenario and think about how it relates to your work setting and role:

Real Work Setting

Name: Claudia

Job Role: Support Worker to people who have mental health needs
(See page 86 for a description of the role)

Additional support and information: In the final part of the training session, Claudia finds it interesting to listen to the other participants' experiences of different occasions when they have had to access additional support and information in relation to health and safety. Claudia considers the range of sources available and reflects on the procedure in her work setting that she used when she required additional support and information about how to maintain her safety and the safety of others when going out with an individual who was very prone to aggressive outbursts.

Evidencing AC1.5 to your assessor:

For AC1.5 you must evidence your understanding of how to access additional support and information relating to health and safety.

Assessment Methods:

Oral or **Written** Questioning or **Discussion** or a **Personal Statement** or **Reflection**

- You can **tell** your assessor about how to access additional support and information relating to health and safety.
  Or
- You can **talk** to your assessor about how to access additional support and information relating to health and safety.
  Or
- You can write a **personal statement** or **reflection** about how to access additional support and information relating to health and safety.

REMEMBER TO:

- Provide an **account** and **explain.**
- Include **details of the process** to follow.
- Ensure your evidence relates to **accessing additional support and information** relating to **health and safety.**
- Think about your **work setting** and how to access additional support and information relating to health and safety.

Learning Outcome 2: Understand the use of risk assessments in relation to health and safety

Assessment Criterion 2.1: Explain why it is important to assess health and safety hazards posed by the work setting or by particular activities

What does AC2.1 mean?

- The lead word **explain** means that you must **make clear** why it is important to assess health and safety hazards posed by the work setting or by particular activities.
- Your **account** must make clear the reasons why.
- For the key word **assess** you can think about why it is important to identify and then measure the dangers posed by the health and safety hazards in the work setting or by particular activities.
- For the key words **health and safety hazards** you can think about the actual dangers that can exist for harm to take place at work, such as faulty equipment, poorly maintained fixtures, not knowing, or finding out, how to support individuals.
- For the key words **particular activities** you can think about the tasks you carry out as part of your day-to-day work that may pose a danger to others, such as supporting individuals with daily activities or using equipment.

Read the following **Real Work Setting** scenario and think about how it relates to your work setting and role:

Real Work Setting

Name: James

Job Role: Support Worker for people who have learning disabilities

James has been working as a support worker for eight years. His responsibilities include supporting individuals with their daily activities including accessing the facilities available in their local communities.

Assessing health and safety hazards: James is meeting with the Senior Support Worker today for his supervision and, following an incident earlier on this week, both discuss the importance of assessing health and safety hazards that may arise.

Evidencing AC2.1 to your assessor:

For AC2.1 you must evidence your understanding of why it is important to assess health and safety hazards posed by the work setting or by particular activities.

Assessment Methods:

Oral or **Written** Questioning or **Discussion** or a **Personal Statement** or **Reflection**

- You can **tell** your assessor about why it is important to assess health and safety hazards posed by the work setting or by particular activities.
  Or
- You can **talk** to your assessor about why it is important to assess health and safety hazards posed by the work setting or by particular activities.
  Or
- You can write a **personal statement** or **reflection** about why it is important to assess health and safety hazards posed by the work setting or by particular activities.

REMEMBER TO:

- Provide an **account** and **explain.**
- Include **details** of the reasons **why.**
- Ensure your evidence relates to **assessing health and safety hazards** posed by the work setting or by particular activities.
- Think about your **work setting** and why it is important to assess health and safety hazards posed by the work setting or by particular activities.

Learning Outcome 2: Understand the use of risk assessments in relation to health and safety

Assessment Criterion 2.2: Explain how and when to report potential health and safety risks that have been identified

What does AC2.2 mean?

- The lead word **explain** means that you must **make clear** how and when to report potential health and safety risks that have been identified.
- Your **account** must make clear both **how** and **when**.
- For the key word **assess** you can think about why it is important to identify and then measure the dangers posed by the health and safety hazards in the work setting or by particular activities.
- For the key word **report** you can think about the procedure in your work setting that you must follow as well as the actions you must take when you identify potential health and safety risks.
- For the key words **health and safety risks** you can think about the potential that exists for danger or harm to take place in health or social care work settings.

Read the following **Real Work Setting** scenario and think about how it relates to your work setting and role:

Real Work Setting

Name: James

Job Role: Support Worker for people who have learning disabilities
(See page 91 for a description of the role)

Reporting potential health and safety risks: James's Senior discusses with him why he did not report the potential health and safety risks of one of the individual's neighbours who used the individual's garden to store garden items. James explains that he thought this individual didn't use his garden and as he was friendly with his neighbour did not see any harm in allowing him to do so; upon reflection, James realises that he should have reported this to his Senior immediately, as this may have avoided this individual having a fall when he walked out into his garden. Both agree that all risks, including potential ones, must be reported and not ignored.

Evidencing AC2.2 to your assessor:

For AC2.2 you must evidence your understanding of how and when to report potential health and safety risks that have been identified.

Assessment Methods:

Oral or **Written** Questioning or **Discussion** or a **Personal Statement** or **Reflection**

- You can **tell** your assessor about how and when to report potential health and safety risks that have been identified.
  Or
- You can **talk** to your assessor about how and when to report potential health and safety risks that have been identified.
  Or
- You can write a **personal statement** or **reflection** about how and when to report potential health and safety risks that have been identified.

REMEMBER TO:

- Provide an **account** and **explain.**
- Include **details of the process to follow** for **reporting** potential health and safety risks.
- Ensure your evidence provides details of both **how** and **when.**
- Think about your **work setting** and how and when to report potential health and safety risks that have been identified.

Learning Outcome 2: Understand the use of risk assessments in relation to health and safety

Assessment Criterion 2.3: Explain how risk assessment can help address dilemmas between rights and health and safety concerns

What does AC2.3 mean?

- The lead word **explain** means that you must **make clear** how risk assessment can help to address dilemmas between rights and health and safety concerns.
- Your **account** must make clear how risk assessment can help to address dilemmas.
- For the key words **risk assessment** you can think about how ensuring identified risks are minimised and controlled can help to address dilemmas between rights and health and safety concerns.
- For the key word **dilemmas** you can think about how risk assessment can help to manage conflicts that may arise between supporting an individual's rights and health and safety concerns.

Read the following **Real Work Setting** scenario and think about how it relates to your work setting and role:

Real Work Setting

Name: James

Job Role: Support Worker for people who have learning disabilities
(See page 91 for a description of the role)

Risk assessment: James's Senior then asked him about what actions he would have taken if he had pointed out to this individual the dangers of his neighbour using his garden to store items and the individual told him that it's his home and therefore his right to let his neighbour store items in his garden. James says that he would have contacted the Senior on duty for advice. James's Senior agrees that this is the correct action to take and that he would also expect James to explain to the individual how they could work together at finding a resolution to the situation by completing a risk assessment so that this individual did not place himself or others at risk of any danger or harm.

Evidencing AC2.3 to your assessor:

For AC2.3 you must evidence your understanding of how risk assessment can help address dilemmas between rights and health and safety concerns.

Assessment Methods:

Oral or **Written** Questioning or **Discussion** or a **Personal Statement** or **Reflection**

- You can **tell** your assessor about how risk assessment can help to address dilemmas between rights and health and safety concerns.
  Or
- You can **talk** to your assessor about how risk assessment can help to address dilemmas between rights and health and safety concerns.
  Or
- You can write a **personal statement** or **reflection** about how risk assessment can help to address dilemmas between rights and health and safety concerns.

REMEMBER TO:

- Provide an **account** and **explain.**
- Include **details of how risk assessment** can help to address dilemmas.
- Ensure your evidence includes examples of dilemmas between rights and health and safety concerns that may arise.
- Think about your **work setting** and how risk assessment can help to address dilemmas between rights and health and safety concerns.

Learning Outcome 3: Understand procedures for responding to accidents and sudden illness

Assessment Criterion 3.1: Describe different types of accidents and sudden illness that may occur in your work setting

What does AC3.1 mean?

- The lead word **describe** means that you must provide **an account** that **details** the different types of accidents and sudden illness that may occur in your work setting.
- Your **account** must detail types of both accidents and sudden illness that may occur in your work setting.
- For the key word **accidents** you can think about the different hazards that exist in your work setting that may cause injury or harm to others.
- For the key words **sudden illness** you can think about the different types of unexpected medical conditions that may occur in individuals or others in your work setting, such as in your colleagues, other professionals or visitors.

Read the following **Real Work Setting** scenario and think about how it relates to your work setting and role:

Real Work Setting

Name: Rose Marie

Job Role: Residential Carer to older people

Rose Marie works as a Residential Carer. Rose Marie's responsibilities include assisting with the care of individuals and attending to all aspects of their physical, emotional and spiritual care needs.

Accidents and sudden illness: Rose Marie is completing a first aid course and, during her break, discusses with her colleagues that she is finding the course very informative and full of facts she did not know, in particular around the very many types of accidents and sudden illness that may arise while at work and that may involve individuals, their visitors and/or other staff. Rose Marie, like her colleagues, feels that the course is making her feel more confident about dealing with accidents or sudden illness that may arise in her work setting.

Evidencing AC3.1 to your assessor:

For AC3.1 you must evidence your understanding of the different types of accidents and sudden illness that may occur in your work setting.

Assessment Methods:

Oral or **Written** Questioning or **Discussion** or a **Personal Statement** or **Reflection**

- You can **tell** your assessor about the different types of accidents and sudden illness that may occur in your work setting.
  Or
- You can **talk** to your assessor about the different types of accidents and sudden illness that may occur in your work setting.
  Or
- You can write a **personal statement** or **reflection** about your experience of the different types of accidents and sudden illness that may occur in your work setting.

REMEMBER TO:

- Provide a detailed **account.**
- Include details of **different types of accidents and sudden illness** that include how they may occur.
- Think about examples of both accidents and sudden illness that may occur.
- Think about accidents and sudden illness that have occurred in your **work setting.**

Learning Outcome 3: Understand procedures for responding to accidents and sudden illness

Assessment Criterion 3.2: Outline the procedures to be followed if an accident or sudden illness should occur

What does AC3.2 mean?

- The lead word **outline** means that you must provide **an account** that includes **brief details** of the procedures to be followed if an accident or sudden illness should occur.
- Your **account** must make clear the process to be followed for either an accident or a sudden illness.
- For the key word **procedures** you can think about the steps you must take when an accident or sudden illness occurs.

Read the following **Real Work Setting** scenario and think about how it relates to your work setting and role:

Real Work Setting

Name: Rose Marie

Job Role: Residential Carer to older people
(See page 94 for a description of the role)

Procedures for an accident or sudden illness: During the remaining part of the first aid course the trainer reviews with the participants the actions that must be taken, including the Dos and Don'ts for different accidents and sudden illness you may come across such as: when and why not to move someone who has had a fall, why an individual who has swallowed a hazardous substance should not be encouraged to make themselves vomit, and why the environment must be made safe for an individual who has had an epileptic seizure. Rose Marie is also fully aware that although it is very important for her to know about the correct actions to take for different types of accidents and sudden illnesses, it is also very important for her to know what her work setting's procedure says about the actions she is required to take in her day-to-day work role as a residential carer.

Evidencing AC3.2 to your assessor:

For AC3.2 you must evidence your understanding of the procedures to be followed if an accident or sudden illness should occur.

Assessment Methods:

Oral or **Written** Questioning or **Discussion** or a **Personal Statement** or **Reflection**

- You can **tell** your assessor about the procedures to be followed if an accident or sudden illness should occur.
  Or
- You can **talk** to your assessor about the procedures to be followed if an accident or sudden illness should occur.
  Or
- You can write a **personal statement** or **reflection** about your experience of the procedures to be followed if an accident or sudden illness should occur.

REMEMBER TO:

- Provide an **account** and **outline** the procedures to be followed.
- Include **brief details** about the **procedures to be followed** for either **an accident** or **a sudden illness.**
- Think about your **work setting** and the procedures you must follow when an accident or sudden illness occurs.

Learning Outcome 4: Be able to reduce the spread of infection

Assessment Criterion 4.1: Demonstrate the recommended method for hand washing

What does AC4.1 mean?

- The lead word **demonstrate** means that you must **be able to show through your work practices** how to use the recommended method for hand washing.
- Your **observations of your work practices** must include you using the recommended method for hand washing.
- For the key words **recommended method** you can think about the approved guidelines in place for washing your hands.

Read the following **Real Work Setting** scenario and think about how it relates to your work setting and role:

Real Work Setting

Name: Emmanuel

Job Role: Support Worker in a mental health unit

Emmanuel has been working as a Support Worker for seven years. His responsibilities include supporting individuals with daily living activities using a person-centred approach, promoting individuals' personal independence and contributing to a homely and stimulating environment.

Recommended method for hand washing: Emmanuel always refers to the World Health Organization's diagrams for the correct hand-washing techniques to use that are available in his work setting. The diagrams outline the following steps that must be followed to wash hands thoroughly: 1) Wet hands with warm water 2) Apply soap 3) Rub hands together, palm to palm 4) Rub the right palm and then the left palm over the other hand with interlaced fingers 5) Rub hands together, palm to palm with fingers interlaced 6) Rub backs of palms together with fingers interlocked 7) Rotationally rub left thumb clasped in right palm and then right thumb in left palm 8) Rotational rub, backwards and forwards with clasped fingers of right hand in left palm and left hand in right palm 9) Rinse hands with water and 10) Dry thoroughly with paper towels.

Evidencing AC4.1 to your assessor:

For AC4.1 you must evidence your skills in demonstrating the recommended method for hand washing.

Assessment Method:

Direct Observation of your work practices

- You can **show** your assessor how you wash your hands using the recommended method for hand washing.

REMEMBER TO:

- Make arrangements for **observation of your work practices.**
- Include evidence of you washing your hands.
- Ensure the evidence you provide is in line with **the recommended method** for hand washing.
- Think about the recommended method for hand washing you follow in **your work setting.**

Learning Outcome 4: Be able to reduce the spread of infection

Assessment Criterion 4.2: Demonstrate ways to ensure that your health and hygiene do not pose a risk to others at work

What does AC4.2 mean?

- The lead word **demonstrate** means that you must **be able to show through your work practices** how to ensure that your health and hygiene do not pose a risk to others at work.
- Your **observations of your work practices** must include you using different ways.
- For the key word **health** you can think about how your physical ill-being can impact on others.
- For the key word **hygiene** you can think about how levels of cleanliness and health can impact on others.
- For the key word **risk** you can think about the dangers or harm that may be caused by ill-health or poor hygiene.
- For the key word **others** you can think about how to ensure that your health and hygiene do not pose a risk to your colleagues, other professionals and visitors to the work setting.

Read the following **Real Work Setting** scenario and think about how it relates to your work setting and role:

Real Work Setting

Name: Emmanuel

Job Role: Support Worker in a mental health unit
(See page 96 for a description of the role)

Health and hygiene: As well as using the recommended method for hand washing, Emmanuel is also aware that his work setting has other procedures in place to reduce the spread of infection. Emmanuel takes responsibility for ensuring that he does not attend work if he is physically unwell and always reports to his Senior any symptoms that he experiences in relation to how he is feeling emotionally, such as if he is stressed or anxious so that he keeps himself and all others in the work setting safe. Emmanuel ensures that the uniform he wears to work is clean and tidy and that he does not wear this outside the work setting; again, doing so, Emmanuel is aware, will reduce the spread of infection. Finally, Emmanuel ensures he follows the correct procedures when handling items such as bed linen and individuals' clothes that may contain bodily fluids.

Evidencing AC4.2 to your assessor:

For AC4.2 you must evidence your skills in demonstrating ways to ensure that your health and hygiene do not pose a risk to others at work.

Assessment Method:

Direct Observation of your work practices

- You can **show** your assessor or an expert witness different ways to ensure that your health and hygiene do not pose a risk to others at work.

REMEMBER TO:

- Make arrangements for **observation** of **your work practices.**
- Include evidence of you using **different ways.**
- Ensure the evidence you provide is related to **both your health and hygiene.**
- Think about the different ways to ensure that your health and hygiene do not pose a risk to others in **your work setting.**

Learning Outcome 5: Be able to move and handle equipment and other objects safely

Assessment Criterion 5.1: Identify legislation that relates to moving and handling

What does AC5.1 mean?

- The lead word **identify** means that you must **list** moving and handling legislation.
- Your list must include **different** examples of moving and handling legislation.
- For the key word **legislation** you can think about the laws that are in place relating to moving and handling in health and social care work settings.

Read the following **Real Work Setting** scenario and think about how it relates to your work setting and role:

Real Work Setting

Name: Jonathan

Job Role: Care Assistant for older people living in a residential care home

Jonathan works as a Care Assistant. His duties include supporting individuals' needs, assisting individuals who wish to take part in social activities, both within and outside the home, and working closely with the rest of the team including individuals' families and friends to promote dignity and independence at all times.

Moving and handling legislation: Jonathan and his colleagues have been asked to read through the home's newly revised procedure for moving and handling equipment and other objects safely. Jonathan begins by reading about all the moving and handling legislation that is relevant to his role as a Care Assistant. Jonathan asks his colleagues about where he could find out more details about each of these pieces of legislation; they suggest that he has a look on the Health and Safety Executive's website for more information about these and then read through the fact sheets that are available, as they explain well and simply the relevance of each piece of moving and handling legislation.

Evidencing AC5.1 to your assessor:

For AC5.1 you must evidence your understanding of moving and handling legislation.

Assessment Methods:

Oral or **Written** Questioning or **Discussion** or a **Spidergram**

- You can **tell** your assessor about the different moving and handling legislation that exists.

  Or
- You can **talk** to your assessor about the different moving and handling legislation that exists.

  Or
- You can complete a **spidergram** about the different moving and handling legislation that exists.

REMEMBER TO:

- **List** moving and handling legislation.
- Include **different** examples of **moving and handling** legislation.
- Ensure they relate to moving and handling in a health or social care work setting.
- Think about the moving and handling legislation in place in your **work setting.**

Learning Outcome 5: Be able to move and handle equipment and other objects safely

Assessment Criterion 5.2: Explain principles for moving and handling equipment and other objects safely

What does AC5.2 mean?

- The lead word **explain** means that you must **make clear** the principles for safe moving and handling of equipment and other objects.
- Your **account** must make clear the principles for safe moving and handling.
- For the key word **principles** you can think about the different ways to make moving and handling safe.

Read the following **Real Work Setting** scenario and think about how it relates to your work setting and role:

Real Work Setting

Name: Jonathan

Job Role: Care Assistant for older people living in a residential care home
(See page 98 for a description of the role)

Safe moving and handling principles: Jonathan then continues to read through the home's newly revised procedure for moving and handling equipment and other objects safely and discusses with his colleagues the main points that underpin all of these processes that form part of the acronym TILEO: in relation to the manual handling Task, the Individual, the Load, the Environment and Other factors in relation to the equipment and techniques being used. Jonathan and his colleagues discuss the principles that are relevant and underpin different types of moving and handling tasks, working with individuals who have differing levels of well-being, the ease with which the load can be moved, the different conditions and types of environment where moving and handling are taking place, as well as the quality of equipment and safety of techniques being used.

Evidencing AC5.2 to your assessor:

For AC5.2 you must evidence your knowledge of the principles for safe moving and handling.

Assessment Methods:

Oral or **Written** Questioning or **Discussion** or a **Personal Statement**

- You can **tell** your assessor about the principles for safe moving and handling.
  Or
- You can **talk** to your assessor about the principles for safe moving and handling.
  Or
- You can write a **personal statement** about the principles for safe moving and handling.

REMEMBER TO:

- Provide an **account** and **explain** the principles for safe moving and handling.
- Include **details** about the principles to follow for safe moving and handling.
- Include **examples** of different principles to follow for **both** moving and handling **equipment** and **other objects** safely.
- Think about the principles for safe moving and handling of both equipment and objects that are in place in **your work setting.**

Learning Outcome 5: Be able to move and handle equipment and other objects safely

Assessment Criterion 5.3: Move and handle equipment or other objects safely

What does AC5.3 mean?

- The lead words **move and handle** mean that you must **be able to show through your work practices** how to use equipment safely and follow procedures for moving and handling equipment or objects.
- Your **observations of your work practices** must include you moving and handling equipment or other objects safely.
- For the key words **move and handle** you can think about the procedures you follow in your work setting for the correct use of equipment and the safe moving of objects.
- For the key word **equipment** you can think about the equipment you use in your work setting for moving and handling, such as hoists.
- For the key word **objects** you can think about other items and loads you move in your work setting.

Read the following **Real Work Setting** scenario and think about how it relates to your work setting and role:

Real Work Setting

Name: Jonathan

Job Role: Care Assistant for older people living in a residential care home
(See page 98 for a description of the role)

Safe moving and handling: As a follow-up to the home revising the procedure for moving and handling equipment and other objects safely, all the team will be observed over the next few weeks in putting this into practice to ensure their working practices are up to date, are in line with agreed ways of working and that each team member fully understands the practices they must follow to move and handle both equipment and other objects safely. Jonathan plans to familiarise himself with the new adapted bath that is being installed this week in the downstairs bathroom and also with the ceiling hoist that another individual has recently had fitted in his room.

Evidencing AC5.3 to your assessor:

For AC5.3 you must evidence your skills in moving and handling equipment or other objects safely.

Assessment Method:
Direct Observation of your work practices

- You can **show** your assessor how you move and handle equipment or other objects safely.

REMEMBER TO:

- Make arrangements for **observation** of **your work practices.**
- Include evidence of you using moving and handling equipment or moving other objects safely.
- Ensure the evidence you provide is related to moving and handling equipment or objects.
- Ensure the evidence you provide is within the remit of your job role.
- Think about how you use moving and handling equipment or move other objects safely in **your work setting.**

Learning Outcome 6: Know how to handle hazardous substances and materials

Assessment Criterion 6.1: Identify hazardous substances and materials that may be found in the work setting

What does AC6.1 mean?

- The lead word **identify** means that you must **list** hazardous substances and materials that may be found in the work setting.
- Your **list** must include different examples of hazardous substances and materials.
- For the key words **hazardous substances** you can think about the different forms that a substance may take and why a substance may be classed as hazardous, such as whether it is corrosive, toxic, irritant or flammable.
- For the key words **hazardous materials** you can think about the different materials that are present in your work setting and why a material may be classed as hazardous, such as whether it is infectious, dangerous or harmful.

Read the following **Real Work Setting** scenario and think about how it relates to your work setting and role:

Real Work Setting

Name: Debra

Job Role: Support Worker for adults with mental health needs

Debra has been working as a Support Worker for two years. Her responsibilities include supporting individuals with preparing and cooking meals, maintaining their personal hygiene, following individuals' support plans and risk assessments, completing visual health and safety checks and accompanying individuals in the community for appointments, shopping and socialising.

Hazardous substances: As part of Debra's annual health and safety training update she has been asked, along with her colleagues, to see how many hazardous substances and materials they think there are in the work setting and to list these on a piece of flip chart paper. Debra offers to write these on the flip chart paper as she and the group share their ideas of what these are.

Evidencing AC6.1 to your assessor:

For AC6.1 you must evidence your knowledge of the different hazardous substances and materials that may be found in the work setting.

Assessment Methods:

Oral or **Written** Questioning or **Discussion** or a **Spidergram**

- You can **tell** your assessor about the different hazardous substances and materials that exist in **your work setting.**

  Or
- You can **talk** to your assessor about the different hazardous substances and materials that exist in **your work setting.**

  Or
- You can complete a **spidergram** about the different types of hazardous substances and materials that exist in **your work setting**.

REMEMBER TO:

- **List** hazardous substances and materials.
- Include **different** examples of **both** hazardous substances and materials.
- Ensure they are examples of hazardous substances and materials that can be found in **your work setting.**
- Think about your **work setting** and the hazardous substances and materials that may be found there.

Learning Outcome 6: Know how to handle hazardous substances and materials

Assessment Criterion 6.2: Describe safe practices for storing hazardous substances, using hazardous substances and disposing of hazardous substances and materials

What does AC6.2 mean?

- The lead word **describe** means that you must provide **an account** that **details** safe practices for storing hazardous substances, using hazardous substances and disposing of hazardous substances and materials.
- Your **account** must detail safe practices for storing, using and disposing of both hazardous substances and materials.
- For the key word **storing** you can think about the procedures to follow in your work setting for ensuring hazardous substances and materials are kept secure.
- For the key word **using** you can think about the procedures to follow in your work setting for ensuring the safe application of hazardous substances and materials.
- For the key word **disposing** you can think about the procedures to follow in your work setting for ensuring the safe removal of hazardous substances and materials.
- For the key word **hazardous** you can think about the different substances and materials that are found in your work setting and can cause ill health, danger or harm to others.

Read the following **Real Work Setting** scenario and think about how it relates to your work setting and role:

Real Work Setting

Name: Debra
Job Role: Support Worker for adults with mental health needs (See page 101 for a description of the role)
Following safe practices: Debra and her colleagues are then asked to refresh their knowledge of how to safely store, use and dispose of a variety of hazardous substances and materials as part of their day-to-day work activities and share their working practices with each other.

Evidencing AC6.2 to your assessor:

For AC6.2 you must evidence your knowledge of safe practices for storing, using and disposing of hazardous substances and materials.

Assessment Methods:

Oral or **Written** Questioning or **Discussion** or a **Personal Statement** or **Reflection**

- You can **tell** your assessor about safe practices for storing hazardous substances, using hazardous substances and disposing of hazardous substances and materials.

  Or
- You can **talk** to your assessor about safe practices for storing hazardous substances, using hazardous substances and disposing of hazardous substances and materials.

  Or
- You can write a **personal statement** or **reflection** about your experience of safe practices for storing hazardous substances, using hazardous substances and disposing of hazardous substances and materials in your work setting.

REMEMBER TO:

- Provide a **detailed account.**
- Include details of safe practices for storing, using and disposing of different hazardous substances and materials.
- Ensure the evidence you provide is related to both hazardous substances and materials.
- Think about how you store, use and dispose of hazardous substances and materials safely in **your work setting.**

Learning Outcome 7: Understand how to promote fire safety in the work setting

Assessment Criterion 7.1: Describe practices that prevent fires from starting and spreading

What does AC7.1 mean?

- The lead word **describe** means that you must provide **an account** that **details** the different ways of preventing fires from starting and spreading.
- Your **account** must detail the different ways of preventing fires from starting and spreading.
- For the key word **practices** you can think about your work setting's fire safety procedures.

Read the following **Real Work Setting** scenario and think about how it relates to your work setting and role:

Real Work Setting

Name: Pierre

Job Role: Support Worker

Pierre has been working as a Support Worker for one year. His responsibilities include providing support to individuals living in their own homes in a way that is responsive to their needs, to assist individuals to meet their care needs and develop independent living skills as specified in their care plans, to support individuals in identifying and participating in social, leisure and educational activities and maintain records for individuals.

Fire safety work practices: Pierre's role as a Support Worker involves him in assisting individuals to ensure they live in a safe environment; this is especially important as he and his colleagues work in individuals' homes. As part of promoting fire safety, Pierre always completes the required fire safety checks each time he visits an individual; these checks are in line with agreed ways of working. Pierre also ensures he is aware of the practices that can prevent fires from starting and spreading and ensures he communicates this information to the individuals he works with.

Evidencing AC7.1 to your assessor:

For AC7.1 you must evidence your understanding of the practices that prevent fires from starting and spreading.

Assessment Methods:

Oral or **Written** Questioning or **Discussion** or a **Personal Statement**

- You can **tell** your assessor about the different ways to prevent fires from starting and spreading in **your work setting.**

  Or
- You can **talk** to your assessor about the different ways to prevent fires from starting and spreading in **your work setting.**

  Or
- You can write a **personal statement** about the different ways to prevent fires from starting and spreading in **your work setting.**

REMEMBER TO:

- Provide a detailed **account.**
- Include details of **different work practices** you use to prevent fires from starting and spreading.
- Include examples of different ways to prevent fires from both starting and spreading.
- Think about different ways of working to prevent fires from both starting and spreading that exist in your **work setting.**

Learning Outcome 7: Understand how to promote fire safety in the work setting

Assessment Criterion 7.2: Outline emergency procedures to be followed in the event of a fire in the work setting

What does AC7.2 mean?

- The lead word **outline** means that you must provide **an account** that includes **brief details** about the emergency procedures to be followed in the event of a fire in your work setting.
- Your **account** must detail briefly **the emergency procedures to be followed**.
- For the key words **emergency procedures** you can think about the actions that must be taken in line with agreed ways of working in the event of a fire in your work setting.

Read the following **Real Work Setting** scenario and think about how it relates to your work setting and role:

Real Work Setting

Name: Pierre

Job Role: Support Worker
(See page 103 for a description of the role)

Fire emergency procedures: To fully understand how to promote fire safety at work, Pierre has also familiarised himself with the emergency procedures to follow in the event of a fire. When Pierre started carrying out his job role he soon realised that emergency procedures to follow in the event of a fire varied depending on where he was working such as whether he was in the office, or in different individuals' homes, as each location had different emergency procedures to be followed in the event of a fire; for example, fire exit routes and assembly points all varied. It was therefore really important that Pierre took the time to read through and understand the emergency procedures.

Evidencing AC7.2 to your assessor:

For AC7.2 you must evidence your understanding of the emergency procedures to follow in the event of a fire in your work setting.

Assessment Methods:

Oral or **Written** Questioning or **Discussion** or a **Personal Statement**

- You can **tell** your assessor about the emergency procedures to follow in the event of a fire in your work setting.
  Or
- You can **talk** to your assessor about the emergency procedures to follow in the event of a fire in your work setting.
  Or
- You can write a **personal statement** about the emergency procedures to follow in the event of a fire in your work setting.

REMEMBER TO:

- Provide an **account** and include **brief details.**
- Include details about **the emergency procedures to follow** in the event of a fire in your work setting.
- Include **details** about the actions that must be taken.
- Think about the emergency procedures that are in place in **your work setting** and that must be followed in the event of a fire.

Learning Outcome 7: Understand how to promote fire safety in the work setting

Assessment Criterion 7.3: Explain the importance of maintaining clear evacuation routes at all times

What does AC7.3 mean?

- The lead word **explain** means that you must **make clear** the importance of maintaining clear evacuation routes at all times.
- Your **account** must make clear the reasons why it is important to maintain clear evacuation routes at all times.
- For the key words **evacuation routes** you can think about the fire escape routes that exist in your work setting and how these are kept clear at all times.

Read the following **Real Work Setting** scenario and think about how it relates to your work setting and role:

Real Work Setting

Name: Pierre

Job Role: Support Worker
(See page 103 for a description of the role)

Maintaining clear evacuation routes: Pierre is being shadowed today by a less experienced colleague to show him how the fire safety checks that have to be completed in different individuals' homes work in practice. Before doing so, Pierre talks through with his colleague the reasons why it is important to ensure that the evacuation routes are kept clear at all times, as well as the consequences of not doing so. Pierre and his colleague also read through together the evacuation procedures available within each individual's home and contained within their files.

Evidencing AC7.3 to your assessor:

For AC7.3 you must evidence your understanding of the importance of maintaining clear evacuation routes at all times.

Assessment Methods:

Oral or **Written** Questioning or **Discussion** or a **Personal Statement**

- You can **tell** your assessor about the importance of maintaining clear evacuation routes at all times.
  Or
- You can **talk** to your assessor about the importance of maintaining clear evacuation routes at all times.
  Or
- You can write a **personal statement** about the importance of maintaining clear evacuation routes at all times.

REMEMBER TO:

- Provide an **account** and **explain** the importance.
- Include **details** about **the reasons why** it is important to maintain clear fire evacuation routes at all times.
- Include **details** about **the consequences** of not doing so.
- Ensure the evidence you provide is related to fire safety.
- Think about the procedures in place in **your work setting** to ensure that clear fire evacuation routes are maintained at all times.

Learning Outcome 8: Be able to implement security measures in the work setting

Assessment Criterion 8.1: Use agreed ways of working for checking the identity of anyone requesting access to the premises and information

What does AC8.1 mean?

- The lead word **use** means that you must **be able to show through your work practices** how to follow the correct procedure for checking the identity of anyone requesting access to the premises and to information.
- Your **observations of your work practices** must include you checking the identity of people requesting access to the premises and to information.
- For the key words **agreed ways of working** you can think about your work setting's procedures for checking a person's identity when requesting access to the building and access to information.

Read the following **Real Work Setting** scenario and think about how it relates to your work setting and role:

Real Work Setting

Name: Venus

Job Role: Residential Care Worker for adults who have complex needs

Venus has been working as a Residential Care Worker for three years. Her responsibilities include supporting adults with daily living activities, household tasks and budgeting, maintaining relationships with family and friends and implementing person-centred plans.

Checking visitors' identity: Following a number of security incidents in the local area, Venus is attending a team meeting being held at lunchtime to discuss the work setting's agreed ways of working for checking the identity of anyone wishing to enter the building and/or requesting information about an individual or the setting. The team discuss the work setting's procedures that must be followed and this proves to be a useful activity for raising everyone's awareness of what these involve. Venus shares with the group how she had to call for assistance from the manager earlier on in the week when she noted a man walking round the back of the building who, when approached, insisted that his mother was living at the service and wanted to know which room she was living in; Venus thought this was odd, as this individual had not lived at this service for over a year and Venus did not recall her ever being visited by her son.

Evidencing AC8.1 to your assessor:

For AC8.1 you must evidence your skills in following your work setting's procedures for checking the identity of anyone requesting access to the premises and information.

Assessment Method:

Direct Observation of your work practices

- You can **show** your assessor or an expert witness how you use your work setting's procedures for checking the identity of anyone requesting access to the premises and to information.

REMEMBER TO:

- Make arrangements for **observation** of **your work practices.**
- Include evidence of you checking a person's identity.
- Ensure the evidence you provide is related to both access to the premises and a request for information.
- Think about the procedures in place in **your work setting** for checking the identity of anyone requesting access to the premises and to information.

Learning Outcome 8: Be able to implement security measures in the work setting

Assessment Criterion 8.2: Implement measures to protect your security and the security of others in the work setting

What does AC8.2 mean?

- The lead word **implement** means that you must **be able to show through your work practices** how to put measures into place to protect your security and those of others.
- Your **observations of your work practices** must include you working in ways that protect your security and the security of others at work.
- For the key word **procedures** you can think about your work setting's procedures for protecting your security and the security of others.

Read the following **Real Work Setting** scenario and think about how it relates to your work setting and role:

Real Work Setting

Name: Venus

Job Role: Residential Care Worker for adults who have complex needs
(See page 106 for a description of the role)

Security procedures: During the meeting, the team also discuss the measures that are currently in place to protect the security of everyone. Venus raises the issue of how she does not feel safe when she has to leave the building at night at the end of an evening shift, as she has to walk round the back of the building to her car. The manager suggests that Venus and other staff should move their cars round to the front of the building during the afternoon and also shares with the team how she has installed brighter lights in both car parks and has checked that the sensor lights are working effectively for added protection. The manager also reminds everyone how it is very important to know each other's whereabouts at all times while on shift and to sign in and out when entering and leaving the building, even if this is only for a short while.

Evidencing AC8.2 to your assessor:

For AC8.2 you must evidence your skills in following your work setting's procedures for putting into practice measures to protect your security and the security of others.

Assessment Method:

Direct Observation of your work practices

- You can **show** your assessor how you implement measures for protecting your security and the security of others.

REMEMBER TO:

- Make arrangements for **observation** of **your work practices.**
- Include evidence of you implementing measures for protecting your security and the security of others.
- Ensure the evidence you provide is related to security in the work setting.
- Think about the procedures in place in **your work setting** for protecting both your security and the security of others.

Learning Outcome 8: Be able to implement security measures in the work setting

Assessment Criterion 8.3: Explain the importance of ensuring that others are aware of your whereabouts

What does AC8.3 mean?

- The lead word **explain** means that you must **make clear** the reasons why it is important to ensure that others are aware of your whereabouts when you are working.
- Your **account** must make clear why it is important to ensure that others are aware of your whereabouts when you are working.
- For the key word **whereabouts** you can think about why it is important to let others know where you are working, with whom and the times you arrive and leave the work setting.

Read the following **Real Work Setting** scenario and think about how it relates to your work setting and role:

Real Work Setting

Name: Venus

Job Role: Residential Care Worker for adults who have complex needs
(See page 106 for a description of the role)

Security procedures: When the manager raises the issue of signing in and out when leaving the building, Venus adds that she has also noted on several occasions that even when this is completed it is not always entered clearly in the records where the staff member can be found and the time the staff member left or returned to the building. Venus shares with the team that this happened the other evening when she was on duty and it caused a number of difficulties for those staff left in the building and also affected the activities that could be carried out that evening with individuals.

Evidencing AC8.3 to your assessor:

For AC8.3 you must evidence your knowledge of the importance of ensuring that others are aware of your whereabouts.

Assessment Methods:

Oral or **Written** Questioning or **Discussion** or a **Personal Statement**

- You can **tell** your assessor about the reasons why it is important to ensure that others are aware of your whereabouts when you are working.
  Or
- You can **talk** to your assessor about the reasons why it is important to ensure that others are aware of your whereabouts when you are working.
  Or
- You can write a **personal statement** about the reasons why it is important to ensure that others are aware of your whereabouts when you are working.

REMEMBER TO:

- Provide an **account** and **explain** the importance of ensuring that others are aware of your whereabouts when you are working.
- Include **details** about the reasons why.
- Include **examples** of the consequences of not doing so.
- Think about the importance of ensuring that others are aware of your whereabouts in **your work setting.**

Learning Outcome 9: Know how to manage your stress

Assessment Criterion 9.1: Identify common signs and indicators of stress

What does AC9.1 mean?

- The lead word **identify** means that you must **list** the common signs and indicators of stress.
- Your **list** must include different examples of common signs and indicators of stress.
- For the key word **signs** you can think about the visible changes that may be seen and/or noticed in you when you are stressed.
- For the key word **indicators** you can think about how you feel when you are stressed and how this may be expressed in a variety of ways.
- For the key word **stress** you can think about the common signs and symptoms that show that you are under mental or emotional strain or tension.

Read the following **Real Work Setting** scenario and think about how it relates to your work setting and role:

Real Work Setting

Name: Esther
Job Role: Carer in a dementia care service
Esther has been working as a Carer for five years. Her responsibilities include providing support and information to individuals who have dementia and their families or friends, enabling individuals to maintain links with their families and friends, and make referrals for other services or support that may be required.
Signs and indicators of stress: Esther is meeting with Margaret and her husband today who are visiting the service for the first time, as Margaret has recently been diagnosed with Alzheimer's disease. It is clear from her meeting with both that they are finding it difficult to understand and deal with Margaret's diagnosis and their fears for the future appear to be their main focus. This has resulted in both looking and feeling stressed and their children becoming increasingly worried over their health and well-being.

Evidencing AC9.1 to your assessor:

For AC9.1 you must evidence your knowledge of the common signs and indicators of stress.

Assessment Methods:

Oral or **Written** Questioning or **Discussion** or a **Spidergram**.

- You can **tell** your assessor about the common signs and indicators of stress.
  Or
- You can **talk** to your assessor about the common signs and indicators of stress.
  Or
- You can complete a **spidergram** about the common signs and indicators of stress.

REMEMBER TO:

- **List** common signs and indicators of stress.
- Include **different** examples of **both** signs and indicators of stress.
- Think about different signs and indicators of stress that you've experienced or identified in others in your **work setting.**

AC 9.2

Learning Outcome 9: Know how to manage your stress

Assessment Criterion 9.2: Identify circumstances that tend to trigger your stress

What does AC9.2 mean?

- The lead word **identify** means that you must list the circumstances that tend to trigger your stress.
- Your **list** must include different examples of circumstances that trigger your stress.
- For the key word **circumstances** you can think about the factors that tend to trigger your stress such as those related to work, family, friends, health or finances.
- For the key word **trigger** you can think about the reasons that cause you to get stressed.
- For the key word **stress** you can think about the negative circumstances that may place a mental or emotional strain or tension on you.

Read the following **Real Work Setting** scenario and think about how it relates to your work setting and role:

Real Work Setting

Name: Esther

Job Role: Carer in a dementia care service
(See page 109 for a description of the role)

Circumstances that trigger your stress: Esther meets with her manager for supervision and shares with her some personal difficulties she is having both at home and at work at the moment. Esther explains how she thinks that all these difficulties are affecting how she feels when she is at work and although she believes she is not letting this show to individuals she works with and to her colleagues, she is increasingly anxious about being able to do her job properly and is not sleeping very well at nights. Esther agrees with her manager to take some time away from work so that she can try to address the difficulties she is experiencing at home and that while she is away Esther's manager will look into the difficulties she has experienced in accessing additional support and information from other dementia care services. Esther and her manager agree to review the situation again in two weeks and book in another meeting date.

Evidencing AC9.2 to your assessor:

For AC9.2 you must evidence your knowledge of the circumstances that tend to trigger your stress.

Assessment Methods:

Oral or **Written** Questioning or **Discussion** or a **Spidergram**

- You can **tell** your assessor about the circumstances that tend to trigger your stress.
  Or
- You can **talk** to your assessor about the circumstances that tend to trigger your stress.
  Or
- You can complete a **spidergram** about the circumstances that tend to trigger your stress.

REMEMBER TO:

- **List** the circumstances that tend to trigger your stress.
- Include **different** examples of **circumstances.**
- Think about your **work setting** and the circumstances that tend to trigger your stress.

Learning Outcome 9: Know how to manage your stress

Assessment Criterion 9.3: Describe ways to manage your stress

What does AC9.3 mean?

- The lead word **describe** means that you must provide **an account** that **details** how to manage your stress.
- Your **account** must provide **details** of different ways for managing stress.
- For the key word **manage** you can think about the different ways for dealing with your stress.
- For the key word **stress** you can think about the different ways of managing the negative circumstances that may place a mental or emotional strain or tension on you.

Read the following **Real Work Setting** scenario and think about how it relates to your work setting and role:

Real Work Setting

Name: Esther

Job Role: Carer in a dementia care service
(See page 109 for a description of the role)

Managing stress: Two weeks later Esther meets with her manager, as agreed, and is not only looking, but also feeling a lot better. Esther explains to her manager how having two weeks off from work has really helped her to focus on the personal difficulties she was experiencing with her son at school and spend time with her son talking through his feelings and how they were going to resolve the recent difficulties he had been experiencing. Esther's manager then shares how she has identified why she stopped receiving responses to her requests for additional support and information about specialist dementia care services and explains that this was due to another system being introduced that meant there was a lack of information being provided in this transition period to not only her but all carers in dementia care services. Esther's manager then proceeds to show her the new system and talk through the benefits of this new way of working. Esther explains to her manager that she feels ready to return to work and to resume her day-to-day work activities as usual.

Evidencing AC9.3 to your assessor:

For AC9.3 you must evidence your knowledge of ways to manage your stress.

Assessment Methods:

Oral or **Written** Questioning or **Discussion** or a **Personal Statement or Reflection**

- You can **tell** your assessor about the ways you manage your stress.
  Or
- You can **talk** to your assessor about the ways you manage your stress.
  Or
- You can write a **personal statement** or **reflection** about your experience of the ways you manage your stress.

REMEMBER TO:

- Provide a detailed **account.**
- Include **details** of how you **manage your stress.**
- Include **examples** of **different ways** that you use to manage your stress.
- Think about different ways that you use to manage your stress in your **work setting.**

HSC028 Handle information in health and social care settings

Learning Outcome 1: Understand the need for secure handling of information in health and social care settings

Assessment Criterion 1.1: Identify the legislation that relates to the recording, storage and sharing of information in health and social care

What does AC1.1 mean?

- The lead word **identify** means that you must **list** legislation relating to the recording, storage and sharing of information in health and social care.
- Your list must include **different** examples of legislation.
- For the key word **legislation** you can think about the laws that are in place relating to recording, storing and sharing of information in health and social care.
- For the key word **recording** you can think about the legislation relevant to documenting information in writing and electronically in health and social care.
- For the key word **storage** you can think about the legislation relevant to securing safely written and electronic information in health and social care.
- For the key word **sharing** you can think about the legislation relevant to securing safely verbal, written and electronic information shared with others in health and social care.

Read the following **Real Work Setting** scenario and think about how it relates to your work setting and role:

Real Work Setting

Name: Danielle

Job Role: Support Worker for adults with mental health needs

Danielle has been working as a Support Worker for two years. Her responsibilities include developing individuals' independent living skills and working towards the goals agreed in individuals' support plans.

Legislation and the secure handling of information: Danielle has been asked by her Senior to read through the work setting's procedure for the recording, storing and sharing of information and think about how this meets the requirements of the legislation in place.

Evidencing AC1.1 to your assessor:

For AC1.1 you must evidence your understanding of the legislation that relates to the recording, storage and sharing of information in health and social care.

Assessment Methods:

Oral or **Written** Questioning or **Discussion** or a **Spidergram**

- You can **tell** your assessor about the legislation that relates to the recording, storage and sharing of information in health and social care.
  Or
- You can **talk** to your assessor about the legislation that relates to the recording, storage and sharing of information in health and social care.
  Or
- You can complete a **spidergram** of the legislation that relates to the recording, storage and sharing of information in health and social care.

REMEMBER TO:

- **List** legislation relating to the recording, storage and sharing of information.
- Include **different** examples of legislation.
- Ensure your evidence relates to recording, storing and sharing of information in a health or social care work setting.
- Think about **your work setting** and the legislation relating to the recording, storage and sharing of information.

Learning Outcome 1: Understand the need for secure handling of information in health and social care settings

Assessment Criterion 1.2: Explain why it is important to have secure systems for recording and storing information in a health and social care setting

What does AC1.2 mean?

- The lead word **explain** means that you must **make clear** the reasons why it is important to have secure systems for recording and storing information in a health and social care setting.
- Your **account** must make clear the reasons why it is important.
- For the key words **secure systems** you can think about why it is important to ensure that recorded and stored information is kept secure.
- For the key word **recording** you can think about why it is important to ensure that all documented information in writing and electronically is kept secure.
- For the key word **storing** you can think about why it is important to ensure that all written and electronic information is stored securely.

Read the following **Real Work Setting** scenario and think about how it relates to your work setting and role:

Real Work Setting

Name: Danielle
Job Role: Support Worker for adults with mental health needs (See page 112 for a description of the role)
Secure systems: While reading her work setting's procedure Danielle also refreshes her knowledge of the recording and storing procedures that she must follow when completing her daily reports and recording updates or changes relating to different individuals she supports. Danielle also familiarises herself with the process to follow when she returns individuals' files to the office and closes down documents she has accessed electronically on the computer in the office.

Evidencing AC1.2 to your assessor:

For AC1.2 you must evidence your understanding of why it is important to have secure systems for recording and storing information in a health and social care setting.

Assessment Methods:

Oral or **Written** Questioning or **Discussion** or a **Personal Statement**

- You can **tell** your assessor about the reasons why it is important to have secure systems for recording and storing information in a health and social care setting.
  Or
- You can **talk** to your assessor about the reasons why it is important to have secure systems for recording and storing information in a health and social care setting.
  Or
- You can write a **personal statement** about the reasons why it is important to have secure systems for recording and storing information in a health and social care setting.

REMEMBER TO:

- Provide an **account** and **explain** the importance of having secure systems in place.
- Include **details** about the reasons why.
- Include **examples** of the consequences of not doing so.
- Think about the importance of having secure systems for recording and storing information in your work setting.

Learning Outcome 2: Know how to access support for handling information

Assessment Criterion 2.1: Describe how to access guidance, information and advice about handling information

What does AC2.1 mean?

- The lead word **describe** means that you must provide **an account** that **details** how to access guidance, information and advice about handling information.
- Your **account** must detail the process to follow.
- For the key word **guidance** you can think about the situations when you may require advice from another team member, such as when you experience difficulties with handling information.
- For the key word **information** you can think about additional details you may require about handling information, such as how to make a record, or who to go to with a question you may have about handling information.
- For the key word **advice** you can think about the situations when you may require suggestions for the best way of handling information from another team member, such as when you handle information in a different format.

Read the following **Real Work Setting** scenario and think about how it relates to your work setting and role:

Real Work Setting

Name: Guy

Job Role: Waking Night Support Worker

Guy has been working as a Waking Night Support Worker for six months. His responsibilities include supporting individuals with personal care, promoting individuals' rights to rest and physical comfort and ensuring that all individuals' dignity and independence are respected at all times.

Accessing guidance, information and advice: At the beginning of his shift, Guy meets with his manager as he would like to go through with him the new electronic system in place for sharing information about individuals' conditions with the rest of the team. He would also like to ask his manager about the details he has documented in individuals' paper-based records, as he is not sure whether these are sufficient and meet the requirements of his role.

Evidencing AC2.1 to your assessor:

For AC2.1 you must evidence your knowledge of how to access guidance, information and advice about handling information.

Assessment Methods:

Oral or **Written** Questioning or **Discussion** or a **Personal Statement**

- You can **tell** your assessor about how to access guidance, information and advice about handling information.
  Or
- You can **talk** to your assessor about how to access guidance, information and advice about handling information.
  Or
- You can write a **personal statement** about how to access guidance, information and advice about handling information.

REMEMBER TO:

- Provide a detailed **account** of the **process to follow**.
- Include **details of how** to access guidance, information and advice about handling information.
- Include **examples** of **guidance, information** and **advice** that can be accessed.
- Ensure your evidence relates to **handling information**.
- Think about **your work setting** and how to how to access guidance, information and advice about handling information.

Learning Outcome 2: Know how to access support for handling information

Assessment Criterion 2.2: Explain what actions to take when there are concerns over the recording, storing or sharing of information

What does AC2.2 mean?

- The lead word **explain** means that you must **make clear** the actions to take when there are concerns over the recording, storing or sharing of information.
- Your **account** must make clear the actions to take as well as the reasons why.
- For the key word **concerns** you can think about what actions you must take when you are anxious or worried about the recording, storing or sharing of information, such as when you are unsure you understand how to do this, or when you have noted that others are not following the correct procedures.
- For the key word **recording** you can think about what actions you must take when you have concerns relating to how written and electronic information is documented.
- For the key word **storing** you can think about what actions you must take when you have concerns relating to how written and electronic information is stored.
- For the key word **sharing** you can think about what actions you must take when you have concerns relating to how verbal, written and electronic information is shared with others.

Read the following **Real Work Setting** scenario and think about how it relates to your work setting and role:

Real Work Setting

Name: Guy

Job Role: Waking Night Support Worker
(See page 114 for a description of the role)

Concerns and actions to take: While meeting with his manager, Guy also raises his concerns over how information about individuals is shared amongst the team, kept secure and then recorded afterwards. Guy explains that sometimes he is unable to fully understand the information discussed at team meetings if he has not attended them, and cannot always find the relevant records on the computer in the office that have been referred to in the minutes of the team meetings.

Evidencing AC2.2 to your assessor:

For AC2.2 you must evidence your knowledge of what actions to take when there are concerns over the recording, storing or sharing of information.

Assessment Methods:

Oral or **Written** Questioning or **Discussion** or a **Personal Statement** or **Reflection**

- You can **tell** your assessor about what actions to take when there are concerns over the recording, storing or sharing of information.
  Or
- You can **talk** to your assessor about what actions to take when there are concerns over the recording, storing or sharing of information.
  Or
- You can write a **personal statement** or **reflection** about your experience of what actions to take when there are concerns over the recording, storing or sharing of information.

REMEMBER TO:

- Provide an **account** and **explain** what actions to take.
- Include **details** about the actions as well as the reasons why.
- Include **examples** of the consequences of not doing so.
- Think about **your work setting** and the actions to take when there are concerns over the recording, storing or sharing of information.

Learning Outcome 3: Be able to handle information in accordance with agreed ways of working

Assessment Criterion 3.1: Keep records that are up to date, complete, accurate and legible

What does AC3.1 mean?

- The lead word **keep** means that you must **be able to show through your work practices** how to ensure records maintained are up to date, complete, accurate and legible.
- Your **observations of your work practices** must include you maintaining records that are up to date, complete, accurate and legible.
- For the key word **records** you can think about your work setting's procedures for how you and others must ensure that manual and electronic records are up to date, complete, accurate and legible.

Read the following **Real Work Setting** scenario and think about how it relates to your work setting and role:

Real Work Setting

Name: Lorna

Job Role: Support Worker for adults who have physical disabilities

Lorna has been working as a Support Worker for nine years. Her senior responsibilities include following individuals' care plans, promoting independence with day-to-day activities and living, and maintaining accurate and complete records.

Maintaining records: Lorna is a very experienced Support Worker and one of her strengths is being able to maintain records to a high standard and in line with her work setting's policies and procedures. Lorna always completes her records as soon as she can after she has supported individuals with their daily activities and ensures that she makes sufficient time to record all information required in full. By documenting the details using factual information only and in a way that can be easily understood and read by those who need to access them, Lorna ensures that her records are also accurate and legible.

Evidencing AC3.1 to your assessor:

For AC3.1 you must evidence your skills in following your work setting's procedures for maintaining records that are up to date, complete, accurate and legible.

Assessment Method:

Direct Observation of your work practices

- You can **show** your assessor how you follow your work setting's procedures for ensuring that you maintain records that are up to date, complete, accurate and legible.

REMEMBER TO:

- Make arrangements for **observation** of **your work practices**.
- Include evidence of you maintaining records.
- Ensure the evidence you provide is related to maintaining records that are up to date, complete, accurate and legible.
- Think about the procedures in place in **your work setting** for maintaining records.

Learning Outcome 3: Be able to handle information in accordance with agreed ways of working

Assessment Criterion 3.2: Follow agreed ways of working for recording, storing and sharing information

What does AC3.2 mean?

- The lead word **follow** means that you must **be able to show through your work practices** how to record, store and share information in line with agreed ways of working.
- Your **observations of your work practices** must include you following your work setting's policies and procedures for recording, storing and sharing information.
- For key word **recording** you can think about your work setting's procedures for how you and others must document written and electronic information.
- For the key word **storing** you can think about your work setting's procedures for how you and others must store written and electronic information.
- For the key word **sharing** you can think about your work setting's procedures for how you and others must share verbal, written and electronic information.
- **Agreed ways of working** will include policies and procedures where they exist in your work setting.

Read the following **Real Work Setting** scenario and think about how it relates to your work setting and role:

Real Work Setting

Name: Lorna

Job Role: Support Worker for adults who have physical disabilities
(See page 116 for a description of the role)

Agreed ways of working: Lorna has acted as a role model and mentor to many new and less experienced Support Workers over the years, in particular in relation to showing them how to record, store and share information in line with her work setting's agreed ways of working. Information recording practices to be followed involve not only knowing what to document, but also how to document, when and why. Good practice to be followed for storing information involves being aware of why information needs to be kept secure, where and for how long. In terms of sharing information, Lorna's working practices reflect how to share verbal, written and electronic information, including how to do this in a way that respects individuals' privacy and dignity at all times.

Evidencing AC3.2 to your assessor:

For AC3.2 you must evidence your skills in following your work setting's procedures for recording, storing and sharing information.

Assessment Method:

Direct Observation of your work practices

- You can show your assessor how you follow your work setting's procedures for recording, storing and sharing information.

REMEMBER TO:

- Make arrangements for **observation** of **your work practices**.
- Include evidence of you recording, storing and sharing information.
- Ensure the evidence you provide is about you following agreed ways of working.
- Think about the procedures in place in **your work setting** for recording, storing and sharing information.

CMH301 Understand mental well-being and mental health promotion

Learning Outcome 1: Understand the different views on the nature of mental well-being and mental health and the factors that may influence both across the lifespan

Assessment Criterion 1.1: Evaluate two different views on the nature of mental well-being and mental health

What does AC1.1 mean?

- The lead word **evaluate** means that you must **assess** two different views on the nature of mental well-being and mental health.
- Your **account** must include how you assess the strengths and weaknesses of two different views.
- For the key words **mental well-being** you can think about how this involves feeling good about yourself, enjoying how you live your life, being able to manage the different stresses of life and being an active part of your family, friends and community.
- For the key words **mental health** you can think about how this involves your psychological and emotional well-being and how these can change throughout your lifespan.

Read the following **Real Work Setting** scenario and think about how it relates to your work setting and role:

Real Work Setting

Name: Sadie
Job Role: Support Worker for adults who have mental health needs
Sadie has been working as a Support Worker for six years. Her responsibilities: include: supporting individuals with daily living skills, assisting individuals to engage in community facilities and participate in individual groups in organised therapeutic activity in the wider community.
Different views on the nature of mental well-being and mental health: Sadie is working with her colleague Angela today who has worked in the mental health field for over 20 years. During their morning break they both discuss in the staff office the essential features of mental well-being and mental health. Sadie finds it interesting to hear Angela's views on what these are, as they are based on her personal and professional experiences of the mental health field over many years.

Evidencing AC1.1 to your assessor:

For AC1.1 you must evidence your evaluation of two different views on the nature of mental well-being and mental health.

Assessment Methods:

Oral or **Written** Questioning or **Discussion** or a **Personal Statement**

- You can **tell** your assessor about your evaluation of two different views on the nature of mental well-being and mental health.

  Or
- You can **talk** to your assessor about your evaluation of two different views on the nature of mental well-being and mental health.

  Or
- You can write a **personal statement** about your evaluation of two different views on the nature of mental well-being and mental health.

REMEMBER TO:

- Provide an account and evaluate.
- Include details with examples about two different views.
- Ensure your evidence includes both the nature of mental well-being and mental health.
- Think about **your work setting** and two different views on the nature of mental well-being and mental health.

Learning Outcome 1: Understand the different views on the nature of mental well-being and mental health and the factors that may influence both across the lifespan

Assessment Criterion 1.2: Explain the range of factors that may influence mental well-being and mental health problems across the lifespan, including: biological factors, social factors and psychological factors

What does AC1.2 mean?

- The lead word **explain** means that you must **make clear** the range of factors that may influence mental well-being and mental health problems across the lifespan, including: biological factors, social factors and psychological factors.
- Your **account** must **detail** the range of factors.
- For the key words **mental health problems** you can think about how this involves experiencing difficulties with how you think, feel and behave and how these can occur throughout your lifespan.
- For the key word **lifespan** you can think about how factors arising from individuals' early lives may influence their well-being as adults and potentially impact on levels of well-being in adulthood and in later life.
- For the key words **biological factors** you can think about how genetics can influence mental well-being and mental health problems as in mental illnesses such as depression, bipolar disorder and schizophrenia.
- For the key words **social factors** you can think about how factors such as lifestyle, religion, education and wealth can influence individuals' mental well-being and mental health problems across the lifespan, in terms of their personality and attitude.
- For the key words **psychological factors** you can think about how factors such as attitude, personality and traits can influence individuals' mental well-being and mental health problems across the lifespan.

Read the following **Real Work Setting** scenario and think about how it relates to your work setting and role:

Real Work Setting

Name: Sadie

Job Role: Support Worker for adults who have mental health needs
(See page 118 for a description of the role)

The range of factors that may influence mental well-being and mental health problems across the lifespan: Sadie and Angela then debate how biological, social and psychological factors influence individuals' mental well-being and mental health problems.

Evidencing AC1.2 to your assessor:

For AC1.2 you must evidence your understanding of the range of factors that may influence mental well-being and mental health problems across the lifespan, including: biological factors, social factors and psychological factors.

Assessment Methods:

Oral or **Written** Questioning or **Discussion** or a **Personal Statement** or **Reflection**

- You can **tell** your assessor about the range of factors.
  Or
- You can **talk** to your assessor about the range of factors.
  Or
- You can write a **personal statement** or **reflection** about your experience of the range of factors.

REMEMBER TO:

- Provide an account and explain.
- Include examples of different factors.
- Think about **your work setting** and the range of factors that may influence mental well-being and mental health problems across the lifespan, including: biological factors, social factors and psychological factors.

Derby Teaching Hospitals
NHS Foundation Trust
Library and Knowledge Centre

Learning Outcome 1: Understand the different views on the nature of mental well-being and mental health and the factors that may influence both across the lifespan

Assessment Criterion 1.3: Explain how the following types of risk factors and protective factors influence levels of resilience in individuals and groups in relation to mental well-being and mental health: risk factors including inequalities, poor-quality social relationships; protective factors including socially valued roles, social support and contact

What does AC1.3 mean?

- The lead word **explain** means that you must **make clear** how the following types of risk factors and protective factors influence levels of resilience in individuals and groups in relation to mental well-being and mental health: risk factors including inequalities, poor-quality social relationships; and protective factors including socially valued roles, social support and contact.
- Your **account** must detail how.
- For the key word **inequalities** you can think about how differences such as in lifestyle, religion, education and wealth can influence individuals' and groups' recovery in relation to mental well-being and mental health.
- For the key words **poor-quality social relationships** you can think about how poor-quality interactions with others, such as negative contact, can influence individuals' and groups' recovery in relation to mental well-being and mental health.
- For the key words **socially valued roles** you can think about how an individual's perception of themselves and how they are perceived by others can influence individuals' and groups' recovery in relation to mental well-being and mental health.
- For the key words **social support and contact** you can think about how individuals' involvement with others such as family, friends and other people can influence individuals' and groups' recovery in relation to mental well-being and mental health.

Read the following **Real Work Setting** scenario and think about how it relates to your work setting and role:

Real Work Setting

Name: Sadie

Job Role: Support Worker for adults who have mental health needs
(See page 118 for a description of the role)

Influences on levels of resilience: Sadie and Angela share with each other how different risk and protective factors can impact on individuals' and groups' mental well-being and mental health recovery.

Evidencing AC1.3 to your assessor:

For AC1.3 you must evidence your understanding of how the following types of risk factors and protective factors influence levels of resilience in individuals and groups in relation to mental well-being and mental health: risk factors including inequalities, poor-quality social relationships; and protective factors including socially valued roles, social support and contact.

Assessment Methods:

Oral or **Written** Questioning or **Discussion** or a **Personal Statement** or **Reflection**

- You can **tell** your assessor about the risk factors and protective factors.
  Or
- You can **talk** to your assessor about the risk factors and protective factors.
  Or
- You can write a **personal statement** or **reflection** about your experience of the risk factors and protective factors.

REMEMBER TO:

- Provide an account and explain.
- Include examples of different risk factors and protective factors.
- Think about **your work setting** and how the following types of risk factors and protective factors influence levels of resilience in individuals and groups in relation to mental well-being and mental health: risk factors including inequalities, poor-quality social relationships; and protective factors including socially valued roles, social support and contact.

Learning Outcome 2: Know how to implement an effective strategy for promoting mental well-being and mental health with individuals and groups

Assessment Criterion 2.1: Explain the steps that an individual may take to promote their mental well-being and mental health

What does AC2.1 mean?

- The lead word **explain** means that you must **make clear** the steps that an individual may take to promote their mental well-being and mental health.
- Your **account** must **detail** the steps that an individual may take.
- For the key word **steps** you can think about how this includes five key steps: connect with others, be active, keep learning skills, give to others, and take notice of yourself and others around you.
- For the key words **mental well-being** you can think about how this involves feeling good about yourself, enjoying how you live your life, being able to manage the different stresses of life and being an active part of your family, friends and community.
- For the key words **mental health** you can think about how this involves your psychological and emotional well-being and how these can change throughout your lifespan.

Read the following **Real Work Setting** scenario and think about how it relates to your work setting and role:

Real Work Setting

Name: Guilherme

Job Role: Mental Health Support Worker in a mental health project

Guilherme has worked as a Mental Health Support Worker for four years. His responsibilities include: providing individual, family and group counselling and support services to individuals and families experiencing mental health issues and requiring referrals to treatment.

The five steps to mental well-being: Guilherme has attended a mental health update recently about research that has been undertaken around how to improve mental well-being and he has been asked by his manager to share with the team the key learning points from this. Guilherme begins by explaining how research has shown that there are five steps that can be taken to improve mental well-being and these are: 1) connecting with others, 2) keeping active, 3) keep learning skills, 4) giving to others, and 5) taking notice of yourself and others around you.

Evidencing AC2.1 to your assessor:

For AC2.1 you must evidence your knowledge of the steps that an individual may take to promote their mental well-being and mental health.

Assessment Methods:

Oral or **Written** Questioning or **Discussion** or a **Personal Statement** or **Reflection**

- You can **tell** your assessor about the steps that an individual may take to promote their mental well-being and mental health.
  Or
- You can **talk** to your assessor about the steps that an individual may take to promote their mental well-being and mental health.
  Or
- You can write a **personal statement** or **reflection** about your experience of the steps that an individual may take to promote their mental well-being and mental health.

REMEMBER TO:

- Provide an account and explain.
- Include details and examples of each of the five steps that can be taken.
- Think about **your work setting** and the steps that an individual may take to promote their mental well-being and mental health.

Learning Outcome 2: Know how to implement an effective strategy for promoting mental well-being and mental health with individuals and groups

Assessment Criterion 2.2: Explain how to support an individual in promoting their mental well-being and mental health

What does AC2.2 mean?

- The lead word **explain** means that you must **make clear** how to support an individual in promoting their mental well-being and mental health.
- Your **account** must **detail** how to support an individual.
- For the key word **support** you can think about how this may include providing individuals with practical and emotional support to connect with others, be active, keep learning skills, give to others and take notice of themselves and others around them.
- For the key words **mental well-being** you can think about how this involves an individual feeling good about themselves, enjoying how to live their life, being able to manage the different stresses of life and being an active part of their family, friends and community.
- For the key words **mental health** you can think about how this involves an individual's psychological and emotional well-being and how these can change throughout their lifespan.

Read the following **Real Work Setting** scenario and think about how it relates to your work setting and role:

Real Work Setting

Name: Guilherme

Job Role: Mental Health Support Worker in a mental health project
(See page 121 for a description of the role)

Supporting an individual: Guilherme then explains to the team how it is really important that the team promote a holistic and whole-person approach to understanding well-being and mental health. In terms of connecting with others, Guilherme explains how it is important for the team to spend time in getting to know the individual and who is in their support network. The availability of activities that appeal to individuals' interests and strengths will make them more likely to want to be active and learn new skills. Providing volunteering opportunities for individuals can improve their well-being, and opportunities to meet others and gain a greater insight into themselves and others can enable individuals to make positive changes in their lives and manage different stresses of life well.

Evidencing AC2.2 to your assessor:

For AC2.2 you must evidence your knowledge of how to support an individual in promoting their mental well-being and mental health.

Assessment Methods:

Oral or **Written** Questioning or **Discussion** or a **Personal Statement** or **Reflection**

- You can **tell** your assessor about how to support an individual in promoting their mental well-being and mental health.

  Or
- You can **talk** to your assessor about how to support an individual in promoting their mental well-being and mental health.

  Or
- You can write a **personal statement** or **reflection** about your experience of how to support an individual in promoting their mental well-being and mental health.

REMEMBER TO:

- Provide an account and explain.
- Include details and examples of how to support an individual.
- Think about **your work setting** and how to support an individual in promoting their mental well-being and mental health.

Learning Outcome 2: Know how to implement an effective strategy for promoting mental well-being and mental health with individuals and groups

Assessment Criterion 2.3: Evaluate a strategy for supporting an individual in promoting their mental well-being and mental health

What does AC2.3 mean?

- The lead word **evaluate** means that you must **assess** a strategy for supporting an individual in promoting their mental well-being and mental health.
- Your **account** must include how you assess the strengths and weaknesses of a strategy for supporting an individual.
- For the key word **strategy** you can think about how this involves putting a plan in place to support an individual to achieve good mental well-being and mental health.
- For the key words **mental well-being** you can think about how this involves feeling good about yourself, enjoying how you live your life, being able to manage the different stresses of life and being an active part of your family, friends and community.
- For the key words **mental health** you can think about how this involves your psychological and emotional well-being and how these can change throughout your lifespan.

Read the following **Real Work Setting** scenario and think about how it relates to your work setting and role:

Real Work Setting

Name: Guilherme

Job Role: Mental Health Support Worker in a mental health project
(See page 121 for a description of the role)

Evaluate a strategy for supporting an individual: Guilherme discusses with the team the strategy they have in place for an individual who has been accessing the mental health project for a number of weeks, including how effective it is in promoting this individual's mental well-being and mental health. Discussions ensue about the areas of support that are working well and the areas of support that require further development; the team conclude that they must ensure they take better account of this individual's personality, strengths, interests and aspirations.

Evidencing AC2.3 to your assessor:

For AC2.3 you must evidence your evaluation of a strategy for supporting an individual in promoting their mental well-being and mental health.

Assessment Methods:

Oral or **Written** Questioning or **Discussion** or a **Personal Statement**

- You can **tell** your assessor about your evaluation of a strategy for supporting an individual in promoting their mental well-being and mental health.
  Or
- You can **talk** to your assessor about your evaluation of a strategy for supporting an individual in promoting their mental well-being and mental health.
  Or
- You can write a **personal statement** about your evaluation of a strategy for supporting an individual in promoting their mental well-being and mental health.

REMEMBER TO:

- Provide an account and evaluate.
- Include details with examples about how you assess the strengths and weaknesses of a strategy for supporting an individual.
- Ensure your evidence includes promoting an individual's mental well-being and mental health.
- Think about **your work setting** and how to evaluate a strategy for supporting an individual in promoting their mental well-being and mental health.

Learning Outcome 2: Know how to implement an effective strategy for promoting mental well-being and mental health with individuals and groups

Assessment Criterion 2.4: Describe key aspects of a local, national or international strategy to promote mental well-being and mental health within a group or community

What does AC2.4 mean?

- The lead word **describe** means that you must provide an **account** that **details** the key aspects of a local, national or international strategy to promote mental well-being and mental health within a group or community.
- Your **account** must detail key aspects of a local, national or international strategy.
- For the key words **local, national or international strategy** you can think about how this involves plans of action to promote mental well-being and mental health within a group or community in a specific region, inside and outside the UK.

Read the following **Real Work Setting** scenario and think about how it relates to your work setting and role:

Real Work Setting

Name: Guilherme

Job Role: Mental Health Support Worker in a mental health project
(See page 121 for a description of the role)

Key aspects of a local, national or international strategy to promote mental well-being and mental health within a group or community: Guilherme provides the team with a brief overview of the UK government's mental health strategy 'No Health without Mental Health' and the subsequent guidance 'Closing the gap: priorities for essential change in mental health' that includes 25 priorities for change in local service planning and delivery, designed to make a difference to the lives of people with mental health problems in the next two or three years.

Evidencing AC2.4 to your assessor:

For AC2.4 you must evidence your knowledge of key aspects of a local, national or international strategy to promote mental well-being and mental health within a group or community.

Assessment Methods:

Oral or **Written** Questioning or **Discussion** or a **Personal Statement**

- You can **tell** your assessor about key aspects of a local, national or international strategy to promote mental well-being and mental health within a group or community.
  Or
- You can **talk** to your assessor about key aspects of a local, national or international strategy to promote mental well-being and mental health within a group or community.
  Or
- You can write a **personal statement** about key aspects of a local, national or international strategy to promote mental well-being and mental health within a group or community.

REMEMBER TO:

- Provide an account that details the key aspects.
- Include details about a local, national or international strategy.
- Ensure your evidence relates to promoting an individual's mental well-being and mental health within a group or community.
- Think about **your work setting** and key aspects of a local, national or international strategy to promote mental well-being and mental health within a group or community.

Learning Outcome 2: Know how to implement an effective strategy for promoting mental well-being and mental health with individuals and groups

Assessment Criterion 2.5: Evaluate a local, national or international strategy to promote mental well-being and mental health within a group or community

What does AC2.5 mean?

- The lead word **evaluate** means that you must **assess** a local, national or international strategy to promote mental well-being and mental health within a group or community.
- Your **account** must include how you assess the strengths and weaknesses of a local, national or international strategy.
- For the key words **local, national or international strategy** you can think about how this involves plans of action to promote mental well-being and mental health within a group or community in a specific region, inside and outside the UK.

Read the following **Real Work Setting** scenario and think about how it relates to your work setting and role:

Real Work Setting

Name: Guilherme

Job Role: Mental Health Support Worker in a mental health project
(See page 121 for a description of the role)

Evaluation of a local, national or international strategy to promote mental well-being and mental health within a group or community: Guilherme then discusses in detail with the team the strengths and areas for development of the UK government's mental health strategy 'No Health without Mental Health' and the subsequent guidance 'Closing the gap: priorities for essential change in mental health'. The team come to the conclusion that in some areas the quality of the lives of people with mental health problems in the next two or three years will improve but this will be dependent on the availability of funding and services to meet individuals' changing needs.

Evidencing AC2.5 to your assessor:

For AC2.5 you must evidence your evaluation of a local, national or international strategy to promote mental well-being and mental health within a group or community.

Assessment Methods:

Oral or **Written** Questioning or **Discussion** or a **Personal Statement**

- You can **tell** your assessor about your evaluation of a local, national or international strategy to promote mental well-being and mental health within a group or community.
  Or
- You can **talk** to your assessor about your evaluation of a local, national or international strategy to promote mental well-being and mental health within a group or community.
  Or
- You can write a **personal statement** about your evaluation of a local, national or international strategy to promote mental well-being and mental health within a group or community.

REMEMBER TO:

- Provide an account and evaluate.
- Include details with examples about your evaluation of a local, national or international strategy.
- Ensure your evidence relates to promoting mental well-being and mental health within a group or community.
- Think about **your work setting** and how to evaluate a local, national or international strategy to promote mental well-being and mental health within a group or community.

DEM201 Dementia awareness

Learning Outcome 1: Understand what dementia is

Assessment Criterion 1.1: Explain what is meant by the term 'dementia'

What does AC1.1 mean?

- The lead word **explain** means that you must **make clear** what is meant by the term 'dementia'.
- Your **account** must make clear the meaning of the term 'dementia'.
- For the key word **dementia** you can think about how this term refers to the way in which the main functions of the brain such as those related to memory, language, behaviour and movement are affected, as well as the different causes of these.

Read the following **Real Work Setting** scenario and think about how it relates to your work setting and role:

Real Work Setting

Name: Yiran

Job Role: Residential Worker for adults who have dementia

Yiran has been working as a Residential Worker for eight months. Her responsibilities include supporting individuals who have dementia with daily activities and living active lives.

The meaning of dementia: Yiran is working with a new Volunteer today who has never worked with individuals who have dementia. During their meeting prior to meeting the individuals, Linda, the new Volunteer, asks Yiran whether she could explain to her what the term 'dementia' actually means, as she is not sure she fully understands its meaning and is a little anxious about meeting with individuals who have dementia. Yiran begins by reassuring Linda that she has nothing to worry about and that it is important when she meets individuals that she gets to know them for who they are, rather than think first and foremost that they have dementia. Yiran begins by telling Linda that dementia affects over 800,000 people in the UK and it is thought that the number of individuals who have dementia in the UK will double over the next 40 years. Yiran then explains to her how dementia affects the way that the brain works and gives Yiran an information fact sheet that shows her the difference between the brains of an individual who has dementia and an individual who doesn't have dementia, including how dementia affects how the brain works and the way an individual remembers, uses language, behaves and moves around.

Evidencing AC1.1 to your assessor:

For AC1.1 you must evidence your understanding of the meaning of the term 'dementia'.

Assessment Methods:

Oral or **Written** Questioning or **Discussion** or a **Personal Statement** or **Reflection**

- You can **tell** your assessor about what is meant by the term 'dementia'.

  Or
- You can **talk** to your assessor about what is meant by the term 'dementia'.

  Or
- You can write a **personal statement** or **reflection** about your experience of what is meant by the term 'dementia'.

REMEMBER TO:

- Provide an account and explain the meaning.
- Include details about what dementia is and the main causes.
- Think about **your work setting** and what is meant by the term 'dementia'.

Learning Outcome 1: Understand what dementia is

Assessment Criterion 1.2: Describe the key functions of the brain that are affected by dementia

What does AC1.2 mean?

- The lead word **describe** means that you must provide an **account** that **details** the key functions of the brain that are affected by dementia.
- Your **account** must detail **different** key functions of the brain that are affected.
- For the key words **key functions** you can think about how the brain is divided into different parts such as the frontal lobe, the temporal lobe, the occipital lobe and the parietal lobe that control different functions of our bodies such as memory, speech, hearing, vision, movement and behaviour and how dementia can affect these.

Read the following **Real Work Setting** scenario and think about how it relates to your work setting and role:

Real Work Setting

Name: Yiran

Job Role: Residential Worker for adults who have dementia
(See page 126 for a description of the role)

How dementia affects the key functions of the brain: To help Linda, the new Volunteer, fully understand how dementia affects the key functions of the brain, Yiran talks to Linda about two individuals she will meet today, both of whom have different forms of dementia: one individual has Alzheimer's disease and another has vascular dementia. Yiran explains to Linda how over time she has observed a deterioration in both individuals' key functions but at slightly different rates and in different ways. Yiran has noted a deterioration in the ability of the individual who has Alzheimer's to remember information and conversations held with others; for the individual with vascular dementia, Yiran has noted this individual experiencing difficulties in mobilising and in her physical well-being.

Evidencing AC1.2 to your assessor:

For AC1.2 you must evidence your understanding of the key functions of the brain that are affected by dementia.

Assessment Methods:

Oral or **Written** Questioning or **Discussion** or a **Personal Statement** or **Reflection**

- You can **tell** your assessor about the key functions of the brain that are affected by dementia.
  Or
- You can **talk** to your assessor about the key functions of the brain that are affected by dementia.
  Or
- You can write a **personal statement** or **reflection** about your experience of the key functions of the brain that are affected by dementia.

REMEMBER TO:

- Provide a detailed **account**.
- Include details about different key functions of the brain that are affected by dementia.
- Include varied examples of the effects of dementia on the key functions of the brain.
- Think about **your work setting** and the key functions of the brain that are affected in individuals who have dementia.

Learning Outcome 1: Understand what dementia is

Assessment Criterion 1.3: Explain why depression, delirium and age-related memory impairment may be mistaken for dementia

What does AC1.3 mean?

- The lead word **explain** means that you must **make clear** the reasons why depression, delirium and age-related memory impairment may be mistaken for dementia.
- Your **account** must make clear the reasons why.
- For the key word **depression** you can think about how this refers to a condition characterised by feelings of hopelessness, sadness and a lack of interest in life.
- For the key word **delirium** you can think about how this refers to a condition characterised by restlessness, drowsiness, disorientation and hallucinations.
- For the key words **age-related memory impairment** you can think about how this refers to memory loss that may occur such as forgetting names and important events or difficulty in following conversations.
- For the key word **dementia** you can think about how this term refers to the way in which the main functions of the brain such as those related to memory, language, behaviour and movement are affected, as well as the different causes of these.

Read the following **Real Work Setting** scenario and think about how it relates to your work setting and role:

Real Work Setting

Name: Yiran

Job Role: Residential Worker for adults who have dementia
(See page 126 for a description of the role)

Why depression, delirium and age-related memory impairment may be mistaken for dementia: Yiran also explains to the new Volunteer, Linda, how some individuals may also experience depression, delirium and age-related memory impairment and as these conditions have symptoms that are like dementia they may cause added confusion and be mistaken for dementia.

Evidencing AC1.3 to your assessor:

For AC1.3 you must evidence your understanding of why depression, delirium and age-related memory impairment may be mistaken for dementia.

Assessment Methods:

Oral or **Written** Questioning or **Discussion** or a **Personal Statement** or **Reflection**

- You can **tell** your assessor about why depression, delirium and age-related memory impairment may be mistaken for dementia.
  Or
- You can **talk** to your assessor about why depression, delirium and age-related memory impairment may be mistaken for dementia.
  Or
- You can write a **personal statement** or **reflection** about your experience of why depression, delirium and age-related memory impairment may be mistaken for dementia.

REMEMBER TO:

- Provide an **account** and explain the reasons why.
- Include details about why depression, delirium and age-related memory impairment may be mistaken for dementia.
- Think about **your work setting** and why depression, delirium and age-related memory impairment may be mistaken for dementia.

Learning Outcome 2: Understand key features of the theoretical models of dementia

Assessment Criterion 2.1: Outline the medical model of dementia

What does AC2.1 mean?

- The lead word **outline** means that you must provide an **account** that includes brief **details** about the medical model of dementia.
- Your **account** must detail briefly the medical model of dementia.
- For the key words **medical model** you can think about how this model focuses on the individual's dementia.
- For the key word **dementia** you can think about how this term refers to the way in which the main functions of the brain such as those related to memory, language, behaviour and movement are affected, as well as the different causes of these.

Read the following **Real Work Setting** scenario and think about how it relates to your work setting and role:

Real Work Setting

Name: Nick

Job Role: Support Worker for an individual who has dementia and lives at home

Nick has been working as a Support Worker for three years. His responsibilities include: supporting an individual who has dementia in a way that promotes his and his family's well-being, supporting the individual to maintain his independence with physical and social activities and following the individual's support plan closely.

The medical model of dementia: Nick is being introduced today to a friend of the individual that he supports who has not seen this individual since before his diagnosis of dementia. The individual's family have asked Nick whether he would be able to explain to him what dementia is, including the person-centred and individualised support provided by Nick and his team. Nick agrees to do this and reflects on how he will use his knowledge of the medical model of dementia to explain to him what person-centred support is not and then show him positive ways that he can use to interact with this individual.

Evidencing AC2.1 to your assessor:

For AC2.1 you must evidence your understanding of the medical model of dementia.

Assessment Methods:

Oral or **Written** Questioning or **Discussion** or a **Personal Statement** or **Reflection**

- You can **tell** your assessor about the medical model of dementia.
  Or
- You can **talk** to your assessor about the medical model of dementia.
  Or
- You can write a **personal statement** or **reflection** about your experience of the medical model of dementia.

REMEMBER TO:

- Provide an **account** that includes brief details.
- Include brief details about what the medical model is and what it involves.
- Ensure your evidence relates to the medical model in relation to individuals who have dementia.
- Think about **your work setting** and the medical model of dementia.

Learning Outcome 2: Understand key features of the theoretical models of dementia

Assessment Criterion 2.2: Outline the social model of dementia

What does AC2.2 mean?

- The lead word **outline** means that you must provide an **account** that includes brief **details** about the social model of dementia.
- Your **account** must detail briefly the social model of dementia.
- For the key words **social model** you can think about how this model focuses on the individual.
- For the key word **dementia** you can think about how this term refers to the way in which the main functions of the brain such as those related to memory, language, behaviour and movement are affected, as well as the different causes of these.

Read the following **Real Work Setting** scenario and think about how it relates to your work setting and role:

Real Work Setting

Name: Nick

Job Role: Support Worker for an individual who has dementia and lives at home
(See page 129 for a description of the role)

The social model of dementia: Nick meets with a friend of the individual that he supports who has not seen this individual since before his diagnosis of dementia and while showing him positive ways that he can use to interact with this individual introduces the social model of dementia to him. Nick explains how it is useful to think about this model, as it focuses on the individual and can help to remind him about who the individual is, what he was like as a friend, the interests they both shared and the activities they enjoyed doing. The individual's friend thanks Nick for all his guidance and information about dementia and says to him how he still finds it difficult to relate to his friend, as he has changed so much in terms of his personality and the way he looks. Nick listens carefully to his concerns and reassures him that although there have been changes that getting to know his friend again will greatly improve his quality of life.

Evidencing AC2.2 to your assessor:

For AC2.2 you must evidence your understanding of the social model of dementia.

Assessment Methods:

Oral or **Written** Questioning or **Discussion** or a **Personal Statement** or **Reflection**

- You can **tell** your assessor about the social model of dementia.

  Or
- You can **talk** to your assessor about the social model of dementia.

  Or
- You can write a **personal statement** or **reflection** about your experience of the social model of dementia.

REMEMBER TO:

- Provide an **account** that includes brief details.
- Include brief details about what the social model is and what it involves.
- Ensure your evidence relates to the social model in relation to individuals who have dementia.
- Think about **your work setting** and the social model of dementia.

Learning Outcome 2: Understand key features of the theoretical models of dementia

Assessment Criterion 2.3: Explain why dementia should be viewed as a disability

What does AC2.3 mean?

- The lead word **explain** means that you must **make clear** the reasons why dementia should be viewed as a disability.
- Your **account** must make clear the reasons why.
- For the key word **dementia** you can think about how this term refers to the way in which the main functions of the brain such as those related to memory, language, behaviour and movement are affected, as well as the different causes of these.
- For the key word **disability** you can think about how this term refers to a physical or mental condition that as a result impairs a person's movements, senses, or activities.

Read the following **Real Work Setting** scenario and think about how it relates to your work setting and role:

Real Work Setting

Name: Nick

Job Role: Support Worker for an individual who has dementia and lives at home
(See page 129 for a description of the role)

The reasons why dementia should be viewed as a disability: Finally, Nick asks the individual's friend to view dementia as a disability since viewing his friend's condition in this way may help him to come to terms with it, as well as focus his attention back on to his friend rather than on the dementia. Nick then discusses with the individual's friend a range of ways of adapting the way he interacts and communicates with him and suggests he gives these some thought.

Evidencing AC2.3 to your assessor:

For AC2.3 you must evidence your understanding of why dementia should be viewed as a disability.

Assessment Methods:

Oral or **Written** Questioning or **Discussion** or a **Personal Statement** or **Reflection**

- You can **tell** your assessor about why dementia should be viewed as a disability.
  Or
- You can **talk** to your assessor about why dementia should be viewed as a disability.
  Or
- You can write a **personal statement** or **reflection** about your experience of why dementia should be viewed as a disability.

REMEMBER TO:

- Provide an **account** and explain the reasons why.
- Include details about why dementia should be viewed as a disability.
- Ensure your evidence includes details of the benefits to the individual when dementia is viewed as a disability.
- Think about **your work setting** and why dementia should be viewed as a disability.

Learning Outcome 3: Know the most common types of dementia and their causes

Assessment Criterion 3.1: List the most common causes of dementia

What does AC3.1 mean?

- The lead word **list** means that you must provide a list of the different causes of dementia syndrome.
- Your **list** must make clear the **different** most common causes of dementia.
- For the key word **dementia** you can think about how this term refers to the way in which the main functions of the brain such as those related to memory, language, behaviour and movement are affected, as well as the different causes of these such as a result of a specific disease, or several conditions, or damage to the brain.

Read the following **Real Work Setting** scenario and think about how it relates to your work setting and role:

Real Work Setting

Name: Latiesha
Job Role: Support Worker for young adults who have dementia
Latiesha has been working as a Support Worker for one year. Her responsibilities include: following individuals' care plans, assisting with practical support in all aspects of individuals' daily lives and supporting individuals to lead independent and fulfilling lives.
Common causes of dementia: Latiesha has recently attended a training update on the most common types of dementia and their causes. Latiesha has found the training update useful as it has improved her knowledge of the different types of dementia that exist, including how they are caused. Considering the different causes of dementia also enables Latiesha to gain a greater insight into why younger individuals and not just older individuals also have dementia.

Evidencing AC3.1 to your assessor:

For AC3.1 you must evidence your knowledge of the most common causes of dementia.

Assessment Methods:

Oral or **Written** Questioning or **Discussion** or a **Spidergram**

- You can **tell** your assessor about the most common causes of dementia.

  Or
- You can **talk** to your assessor about the most common causes of dementia.

  Or
- You can complete a **spidergram** of the most common causes of dementia.

REMEMBER TO:

- Provide a list.
- Include **varied examples** of the common causes of dementia.
- Think about **your work setting** and the most common causes of dementia.

Learning Outcome 3: Know the most common types of dementia and their causes

Assessment Criterion 3.2: Describe the likely signs and symptoms of the most common causes of dementia

What does AC3.2 mean?

- The lead word **describe** means that you must provide an **account** that **details** the likely signs and symptoms of the most common causes of dementia.
- Your **account** must detail **different** signs and symptoms.
- For the key word **signs** you can think about the visible changes that may be seen and/or noticed in individuals who have dementia.
- For the key word **symptoms** you can think about how individuals who have dementia may feel and how this may be expressed in a variety of ways.
- For the key word **dementia** you can think about how this term refers to the way in which the main functions of the brain such as those related to memory, language, behaviour and movement are affected, as well as the different causes such as a result of a specific disease, or several conditions, or damage to the brain.

Read the following **Real Work Setting** scenario and think about how it relates to your work setting and role:

Real Work Setting

Name: Latiesha

Job Role: Support Worker for young adults who have dementia
(See page 132 for a description of the role)

Signs and symptoms of the most common causes of dementia: During the training session Latiesha developed her knowledge of how each of the most common causes of dementia can present in different individuals. Latiesha was particularly interested in the common symptoms that individuals may experience and express in a variety of ways.

Evidencing AC3.2 to your assessor:

For AC3.2 you must evidence your knowledge of the likely signs and symptoms of the most common causes of dementia.

Assessment Methods:

Oral or **Written** Questioning or **Discussion** or a **Personal Statement** or **Reflection**

- You can **tell** your assessor about the likely signs and symptoms of the most common causes of dementia.
  Or
- You can **talk** to your assessor about the likely signs and symptoms of the most common causes of dementia.
  Or
- You can write a **personal statement** or **reflection** about your experience of the likely signs and symptoms of the most common causes of dementia.

REMEMBER TO:

- Provide a detailed account.
- Include details about different signs and symptoms.
- Include **varied examples** of the signs and symptoms.
- Ensure your evidence is related to the most common causes of dementia.
- Think about **your work setting** and the individuals you work with and the likely signs and symptoms of the most common causes of dementia.

Learning Outcome 3: Know the most common types of dementia and their causes

Assessment Criterion 3.3: Outline the risk factors for the most common causes of dementia

What does AC3.3 mean?

- The lead word **outline** means that you must provide an **account** that includes brief **details** about the risk factors for the most common causes of dementia.
- Your **account** must detail briefly the risk factors.
- For the key words **risk factors** you can think about what increases individuals' chances of developing the most common causes of dementia such as in relation to an individual's lifestyle, or medical conditions, or age, or genetics.
- For the key word **dementia** you can think about how this term refers to the way in which the main functions of the brain such as those related to memory, language, behaviour and movement are affected, as well as the different causes of these.

Read the following **Real Work Setting** scenario and think about how it relates to your work setting and role:

Real Work Setting

Name: Latiesha

Job Role: Support Worker for young adults who have dementia
(See page 132 for a description of the role)

The risk factors for the most common causes of dementia: While learning more about the most common causes of dementia, Latiesha and the rest of the participants in the training session also discussed the range of risk factors that may make individuals more likely to develop the most common causes of dementia such as the way individuals live their lives in relation to their diet, consumption of alcohol and the amount they exercise, or other factors such as individuals' age, gender, genetics or medical history.

Evidencing AC3.3 to your assessor:

For AC3.3 you must evidence your knowledge of the risk factors for the most common causes of dementia.

Assessment Methods:

Oral or **Written** Questioning or **Discussion** or a **Personal Statement** or **Reflection**

- You can **tell** your assessor about the risk factors for the most common causes of dementia.
  Or
- You can **talk** to your assessor about the risk factors for the most common causes of dementia.
  Or
- You can write a **personal statement** or **reflection** about your experience of the risk factors for the most common causes of dementia.

REMEMBER TO:

- Provide an account that includes brief details.
- Include brief details about what the risk factors are.
- Ensure your evidence relates to the most common causes of dementia.
- Think about **your work setting** and the individuals you work with, as well as the risk factors for the most common causes of dementia.

Learning Outcome 3: Know the most common types of dementia and their causes

Assessment Criterion 3.4: Identify prevalence rates for different types of dementia

What does AC3.4 mean?

- The lead word **identify** means that you must provide a list of the prevalence rates for different types of dementia.
- Your **list** must make clear the different prevalence rates.
- For the key words **prevalence rates** you can think about the statistics that refer to the number of cases of the different types of dementia that are present in a particular population at a given time.
- For the key word **dementia** you can think about the different types of dementia there are such as Alzheimer's disease, vascular dementia, dementia with Lewy bodies, fronto-temporal dementia and Creutzfeldt–Jakob disease (CJD).

Read the following **Real Work Setting** scenario and think about how it relates to your work setting and role:

Real Work Setting

Name: Latiesha

Job Role: Support Worker for young adults who have dementia
(See page 132 for a description of the role)

Prevalence rates for different types of dementia: For the final part of the training update, Latiesha and the rest of the participants were asked to share with the group what types of dementia they thought had the highest prevalence rates and then were asked to research the actual prevalence rates for the most common types of dementia using the Alzheimer's society website. Latiesha found it interesting to complete this activity and see how her views of the types of the dementia that had the highest prevalence rates compared with the actual statistics available.

Evidencing AC3.4 to your assessor:

For AC3.4 you must evidence your knowledge of the prevalence rates for different types of dementia.

Assessment Methods:

Oral or **Written** Questioning or **Discussion** or a **Spidergram**

- You can **tell** your assessor about the prevalence rates for different types of dementia.
  Or
- You can **talk** to your assessor about the prevalence rates for different types of dementia.
  Or
- You can complete a **spidergram** of the prevalence rates for different types of dementia.

REMEMBER TO:

- Provide a list of the prevalence rates.
- Include varied examples of the prevalence rates that exist for different types of dementia.
- Think about **your work setting** and the individuals you work with and the prevalence rates for different types of dementia.

Learning Outcome 4: Understand factors relating to an individual's experience of dementia

Assessment Criterion 4.1: Describe how different individuals may experience living with dementia depending on age, type of dementia and level of ability and disability

What does AC4.1 mean?

- The lead word **describe** means that you must provide an **account** that **details** how different individuals may experience living with dementia depending on age, type of dementia and level of ability and disability.
- Your **account** must detail how **different** individuals may experience living with dementia.
- For the key word **age** you can think about how the experiences between young and older adults who have dementia may vary and impact on how they experience dementia.
- For the key words **type of dementia** you can think about how different types of dementia may present differently and will impact on individuals in different ways.
- For the key words **level of ability and disability** you can think about how the level of impairment of individuals' movements, sense, or activities may vary and impact on individuals in different ways.

Read the following **Real Work Setting** scenario and think about how it relates to your work setting and role:

Real Work Setting

Name: Dillon

Job Role: Support Worker for older adults who have dementia

Dillon has been working as a Support Worker for eight years. His responsibilities include: providing assistance with continence management, household tasks, social and leisure activities, empowering individuals to participate in daily activities and maintaining individuals' skills and interests as specified in their care plans.

Individuals' experiences of dementia: Dillon reflects on the different experiences of living with dementia that two individuals he works with are going through and considers the different factors that have played a part in their being positive for one and negative for the other individual.

Evidencing AC4.1 to your assessor:

For AC4.1 you must evidence your understanding of how different individuals may experience living with dementia depending on age, type of dementia and level of ability and disability.

Assessment Methods:

Oral or **Written** Questioning or **Discussion** or a **Personal Statement** or **Reflection**

- You can **tell** your assessor about how different individuals may experience living with dementia depending on age, type of dementia and level of ability and disability.
  Or
- You can **talk** to your assessor about how different individuals may experience living with dementia depending on age, type of dementia and level of ability and disability.
  Or
- You can write a **personal statement** or **reflection** about your experience of how different individuals may experience living with dementia depending on age, type of dementia and level of ability and disability.

REMEMBER TO:

- Provide a detailed account.
- Include details about the experiences of different individuals.
- Ensure your evidence is related to individuals' age, type of dementia and level of ability and disability.
- Think about **your work setting** and the individuals you work with and how different individuals may experience living with dementia depending on age, type of dementia and level of ability and disability.

Learning Outcome 4: Understand factors relating to an individual's experience of dementia

Assessment Criterion 4.2: Outline the impact that the attitudes and behaviours of others may have on an individual with dementia

What does AC4.2 mean?

- The lead word **outline** means that you must provide an **account** that includes brief **details** about the impact that the attitudes and behaviours of others may have on an individual who has dementia.
- Your **account** must detail briefly the impact on an individual who has dementia.
- For the key words **attitudes and behaviours** you can think about how others' attitudes and behaviours towards individuals who have dementia will vary and impact on individuals both positively and negatively.
- For the key word **others** you can think about how this may include care workers, colleagues, managers, social worker, occupational therapist, GP, speech and language therapist, physiotherapist, pharmacist, nurse, psychologist, Admiral nurses, independent mental capacity advocate, community psychiatric nurse, dementia care advisors, advocate and support groups.

Read the following **Real Work Setting** scenario and think about how it relates to your work setting and role:

Real Work Setting

Name: Dillon

Job Role: Support Worker for older adults who have dementia
(See page 136 for a description of the role)

The impact of the attitudes and behaviours of others: While reflecting on the different experiences of two individuals he works with, Dillon also reflects on how the positive and negative attitudes have impacted on each of them. The negative attitude of a nurse in relation to one of the individuals who has dementia and a dependent family made the individual fearful for him and his family of losing his independence, whereas the positive attitude of the other individual's advocate enabled him to feel more in control of his life and future.

Evidencing AC4.2 to your assessor:

For AC4.2 you must evidence your understanding of the impact that attitudes and behaviours of others may have on an individual who has dementia.

Assessment Methods:

Oral or **Written** Questioning or **Discussion** or a **Personal Statement** or **Reflection**

- You can **tell** your assessor about the impact that attitudes and behaviours of others may have on an individual who has dementia.
  Or
- You can **talk** to your assessor about the impact that attitudes and behaviours of others may have on an individual who has dementia.
  Or
- You can write a **personal statement** or **reflection** about the impact that attitudes and behaviours of others may have on an individual who has dementia.

REMEMBER TO:

- Provide an account that includes brief details.
- Include brief details about the impact on an individual who has dementia.
- Ensure your evidence relates to the attitudes and behaviours of others.
- Think about **your work setting** and the individuals you work with, as well as the impact that attitudes and behaviours of others may have on an individual who has dementia.

IC01 The principles of infection prevention and control

Learning Outcome 1: Understand roles and responsibilities in the prevention and control of infections

Assessment Criterion 1.1: Explain employees' roles and responsibilities in relation to the prevention and control of infection

What does AC1.1 mean?

- The lead word **explain** means that you must **make clear** what is meant by employees' roles and responsibilities in relation to the prevention and control of infection.
- Your **account** must make clear the employees' roles and responsibilities.
- For the key word **roles** you can think about the duties that health and social care workers have in relation to preventing and controlling infections.
- For the key word **responsibilities** you can think about the legal obligations that health and social care workers have in relation to preventing and controlling infections.

Read the following **Real Work Setting** scenario and think about how it relates to your work setting and role:

Real Work Setting

Name: Wayne

Job Role: Residential Care Worker for older people

Wayne has been working as a Residential Care Worker for eight years. His responsibilities include: supporting individuals with all aspects of daily living, meeting individuals' physical, emotional and spiritual care needs, acting as a key worker for nominated individuals and assisting individuals in maintaining their current interests and hobbies.

Employees' roles and responsibilities: Wayne is very aware of the role and responsibilities he has in relation to infection prevention and control in his day-to-day work. Wayne ensures that his working practices are in line with his employer's infection prevention and control procedures and always reports any working practices he observes that are not in line with agreed ways of working. Wayne always attends the infection control training he is booked on by his manager and ensures he seeks advice if there are any areas relevant to preventing and controlling infections that he is unsure about.

Evidencing AC1.1 to your assessor:

For AC1.1 you must evidence your understanding of employees' roles and responsibilities in relation to the prevention and control of infection.

Assessment Methods:

Oral or **Written** Questioning or **Discussion** or a **Personal Statement** or **Reflection**

- You can **tell** your assessor about employees' roles and responsibilities in relation to the prevention and control of infection.
  Or
- You can **talk** to your assessor about employees' roles and responsibilities in relation to the prevention and control of infection.
  Or
- You can write a **personal statement** or **reflection** about your experience of employees' roles and responsibilities in relation to the prevention and control of infection.

REMEMBER TO:

- Provide an **account** and **explain** the roles and responsibilities.
- Include **details** about what these involve in relation to preventing and controlling infections.
- Include **examples** of employees' roles and responsibilities in relation to the prevention and control of infection.
- Think about **your work setting** and employees' roles and responsibilities in relation to the prevention and control of infection.

Learning Outcome 1: Understand roles and responsibilities in the prevention and control of infections

Assessment Criterion 1.2: Explain employers' responsibilities in relation to the prevention and control of infection

What does AC1.2 mean?

- The lead word **explain** means that you must **make clear** what is meant by employers' responsibilities in relation to the prevention and control of infection.
- Your **account** must make clear the employers' responsibilities.
- For the key word **responsibilities** you can think about the legal obligations that employers have in relation to preventing and controlling infections.

Read the following **Real Work Setting** scenario and think about how it relates to your work setting and role:

Real Work Setting

Name: Wayne

Job Role: Residential Care Worker for older people
(See page 138 for a description of the role)

Employers' responsibilities: Wayne is also aware that his employer is responsible for the prevention and control of infections and this is why there is an infection control policy in place, procedures for how to prevent and control infections, and specific guidance for working with individuals who may be vulnerable to infections or have an infection. Infection control and prevention training is provided to the team by Wayne's employer and up-to-date information updates are also made available to the team and posted up on both the staff intranet and the noticeboard in the staff office. The team members, including Wayne, have also been encouraged to complete a distance learning course based on infection control and prevention that explores good working practices in depth.

Evidencing AC1.2 to your assessor:

For AC1.2 you must evidence your understanding of employers' responsibilities in relation to the prevention and control of infection.

Assessment Methods:

Oral or **Written** Questioning or **Discussion** or a **Personal Statement** or **Reflection**

- You can **tell** your assessor about employers' responsibilities in relation to the prevention and control of infection.
  Or
- You can **talk** to your assessor about employers' responsibilities in relation to the prevention and control of infection.
  Or
- You can write a **personal statement** or **reflection** about your experience of employers' responsibilities in relation to the prevention and control of infection.

REMEMBER TO:

- Provide an **account** and **explain** the responsibilities.
- Include **details** about what these involve in relation to preventing and controlling infections.
- Include **examples** of employers' responsibilities in relation to the prevention and control of infection.
- Think about **your work setting** and your employer's responsibilities in relation to the prevention and control of infection.

Learning Outcome 2: Understand legislation and policies relating to prevention and control of infections

Assessment Criterion 2.1: Outline current legislation and regulatory body standards which are relevant to the prevention and control of infection

What does AC2.1 mean?

- The lead word **outline** means that you must provide an **account** that includes brief **details** about current legislation and regulatory body standards which are relevant to the prevention and control of infection.
- Your **account** must detail briefly current legislation and regulatory body standards.
- For the key words **current legislation** you can think about the laws that currently exist and are relevant to the prevention and control of infection.
- For the key words **regulatory body standards** you can think about organisations that have been set up by the government to put in place national standards that are relevant to the prevention and control of infection such as the Care Quality Commission in England (CQC), the Nursing and Midwifery Council (NMC) and the Health and Care Professions Council (HCPC).

Read the following **Real Work Setting** scenario and think about how it relates to your work setting and role:

Real Work Setting

Name: Glenda

Job Role: Support Worker for adults who have learning disabilities

Glenda has been working as a Support Worker for ten years. Her responsibilities include: supporting individuals with personal care and household tasks, enabling individuals to access work and education placements, as well as community facilities.

Current legislation and regulatory body standards: Glenda reads through an information handout provided by her employer, which gives a brief overview of the current legislation and regulatory body standards that are relevant to the prevention and control of infection. Glenda decides that she would like to find out more information about these and the handout signposts her to accessing the Health and Care Professions Council website.

Evidencing AC2.1 to your assessor:

For AC2.1 you must evidence your understanding of current legislation and regulatory body standards which are relevant to the prevention and control of infection.

Assessment Methods:

Oral or **Written** Questioning or **Discussion** or a **Personal Statement**

- You can **tell** your assessor about the current legislation and regulatory body standards which are relevant to the prevention and control of infection.
  Or
- You can **talk** to your assessor about the current legislation and regulatory body standards which are relevant to the prevention and control of infection.
  Or
- You can write a **personal statement** of the current legislation and regulatory body standards which are relevant to the prevention and control of infection.

REMEMBER TO:

- Provide an **account** that includes brief **details**.
- Include brief details about current legislation and regulatory body standards.
- Ensure your evidence relates to the prevention and control of infection.
- Think about **your work setting** and the current legislation and regulatory body standards which are relevant to the prevention and control of infection.

Learning Outcome 2: Understand legislation and policies relating to prevention and control of infections

Assessment Criterion 2.2: Describe local and organisational policies relevant to the prevention and control of infection

What does AC2.2 mean?

- The lead word **describe** means that you must provide an **account** that **details** local and organisational policies relevant to the prevention and control of infection.
- Your **account** must detail local and organisational policies.
- For the key words **local policies** you can think about the policies relevant to the prevention and control of infection developed by local authorities for ensuring health and social care settings in different areas comply with legislation.
- For the key words **organisational policies** you can think about the policies relevant to the prevention and control of infection developed by organisations for ensuring health and social care settings comply with legislation.

Read the following **Real Work Setting** scenario and think about how it relates to your work setting and role:

Real Work Setting

Name: Glenda

Job Role: Support Worker for adults who have learning disabilities
(See page 140 for a description of the role)

Local and organisational policies: After accessing the Health and Care Professions Council's (HCPC) website, Glenda reads through her work setting's policies for infection prevention and control and the arrangements that are in place, should there be an infection outbreak in the local area. Reading through these again has reminded Glenda of both her responsibilities and those of her employer and how together the team and the organisation she works for have important roles to play in ensuring infections are minimised and do not spread.

Evidencing AC2.2 to your assessor:

For AC2.2 you must evidence your understanding of local and organisational policies relevant to the prevention and control of infection.

Assessment Methods:

Oral or **Written** Questioning or **Discussion** or a **Personal Statement**

- You can **tell** your assessor about the local and organisational policies relevant to the prevention and control of infection.
  Or
- You can **talk** to your assessor about the local and organisational policies relevant to the prevention and control of infection.
  Or
- You can write a **personal statement** of the local and organisational policies relevant to the prevention and control of infection.

REMEMBER TO:

- Provide an **account** that includes **details**.
- Include details about local and organisational policies.
- Ensure your evidence relates to the prevention and control of infection.
- Think about **your work setting** and the local and organisational policies relevant to the prevention and control of infection.

Learning Outcome 3: Understand systems and procedures relating to the prevention and control of infections

Assessment Criterion 3.1: Describe procedures and systems relevant to the prevention and control of infection

What does AC3.1 mean?

- The lead word **describe** means that you must provide an **account** that **details** procedures and systems relevant to the prevention and control of infection.
- Your **account** must detail both procedures and systems.
- For the key word **procedures** you can think about the processes and activities you and others must follow in your work setting for the prevention and control of infections.
- For the key word **systems** you can think about the methods used by organisations and work settings for managing and monitoring the prevention and control of infections.

Read the following **Real Work Setting** scenario and think about how it relates to your work setting and role:

Real Work Setting

Name: Royson

Job Role: Care Worker for adults who live in supported living

Royson has been working as a Care Worker for five years. His responsibilities include: assisting individuals to get up and dressed, preparing meals, shopping, completing general household tasks, and keeping accurate records

Procedures and systems: Royson has up-to-date knowledge of his work setting's procedures for the prevention and control of infections. These set out clearly the standard working practices that are expected of Royson and others when carrying out their day-to-day duties in relation to maintaining effective hand hygiene, wearing personal protective equipment, handling and disposing of waste including body fluids, and keeping themselves and their environment clean. Royson is also aware of his duty to report and record immediately to his manager any dangerous or unsafe practices he may come across.

Evidencing AC3.1 to your assessor:

For AC3.1 you must evidence your understanding of procedures and systems relevant to the prevention and control of infection.

Assessment Methods:

Oral or **Written** Questioning or **Discussion** or a **Personal Statement**

- You can **tell** your assessor about the procedures and systems relevant to the prevention and control of infection.
  Or
- You can **talk** to your assessor about the procedures and systems relevant to the prevention and control of infection.
  Or
- You can write a **personal statement** about the procedures and systems relevant to the prevention and control of infection.

REMEMBER TO:

- Provide an **account** that includes **details**.
- Include details about both procedures and systems.
- Ensure your evidence relates to the prevention and control of infection.
- Think about **your work setting** and the procedures and systems relevant to the prevention and control of infection.

Learning Outcome 3: Understand systems and procedures relating to the prevention and control of infections

Assessment Criterion 3.2: Explain the potential impact of an outbreak of infection on the individual and the organisation

What does AC3.2 mean?

- The lead word **explain** means that you must **make clear** the potential impact of an outbreak of infection on the individual and the organisation.
- Your **account** must **detail** the potential impact of an outbreak of infection.
- For the key words **potential impact** you can think about how an outbreak of infection can affect an individual's well-being and how their relatives feel about the health and social care setting, as well as the demand on an organisation's time and staff and their reputation.
- For the key words **outbreak of infection** you can think about how having two or more people being affected by infections such as norovirus or MRSA can impact on the individuals infected, those who work with them and know them, as well as the organisation.

Read the following **Real Work Setting** scenario and think about how it relates to your work setting and role:

Real Work Setting

Name: Royson

Job Role: Care Worker for adults who live in supported living
(See page 142 for a description of the role)

The impact of an outbreak of infection: Royson reflects on when there was an outbreak of norovirus in his work setting and how this began with three individuals and two Care Workers suddenly experiencing diarrhoea and vomiting. Isolating the individuals concerned in their rooms made them feel anxious and their relatives concerned. Sending the affected Care Workers home meant an immediate staff shortage and put additional work pressures on Care Workers that remained working at the home; in fact, Royson remembers how this led to another Care Worker not wanting to come to work the following day in case she, too, fell ill with the norovirus.

Evidencing AC3.2 to your assessor:

For AC3.2 you must evidence your understanding of the potential impact of an outbreak of infection on the individual and the organisation.

Assessment Methods:

Oral or **Written** Questioning or **Discussion** or a **Personal Statement** or **Reflection**

- You can **tell** your assessor about the potential impact of an outbreak of infection on the individual and the organisation.
  Or
- You can **talk** to your assessor about the potential impact of an outbreak of infection on the individual and the organisation.
  Or
- You can write a **personal statement** or **reflection** about the potential impact of an outbreak of infection on the individual and the organisation.

REMEMBER TO:

- Provide an **account** and **explain** the potential impact of an outbreak of infection.
- Include **details** about the potential impact on the individual and the organisation.
- Include **examples** of how an outbreak of infection can affect the individual and the organisation.
- Think about **your work setting** and the potential impact of an outbreak of infection on the individual and the organisation.

Learning Outcome 4: Understand the importance of risk assessment in relation to the prevention and control of infections

Assessment Criterion 4.1: Define the term 'risk'

What does AC4.1 mean?

- The lead word **define** means that you must **make clear** what is meant by the term 'risk'.
- Your **definition** must make clear your understanding of the term 'risk'.
- For the key word **risk** you can think about how infections occur, as well as the factors that can increase the likelihood of these occurring.

Read the following **Real Work Setting** scenario and think about how it relates to your work setting and role:

Real Work Setting

Name: Colette

Job Role: Support Worker for an older adult who has dementia

Colette has been working as a Support Worker for one year. Her responsibilities include: supporting an adult who has dementia with her personal care, continence, eating and drinking and general household tasks including cleaning, laundry, ironing and shopping.

The meaning of risk: Colette is attending a training update on infection prevention and control and discusses with a colleague the meaning of the term 'risk' in relation to preventing and controlling infections. Both discuss how the risks of infections spreading can vary from day to day because the likelihood of this happening will very much depend on factors such as the consistency of work practices being followed by all care workers, the hygiene practices being observed by all visitors to the individual's home, as well as the health of the individual and the activities the individual takes part in. Both agree that risks can present as low or high.

Evidencing AC4.1 to your assessor:

For AC4.1 you must evidence your understanding of the meaning of the term 'risk'.

Assessment Methods:

Oral or **Written** Questioning or **Discussion** or a **Spidergram**

- You can **tell** your assessor about the meaning of the term 'risk'.
  Or
- You can **talk** to your assessor about the meaning of the term 'risk'.
  Or
- You can complete a **spidergram** of the meaning of the term 'risk'.

REMEMBER TO:

- Provide the **meaning** of the term 'risk'.
- Include **details** about your understanding of this term.
- Provide details that relate specifically to the prevention and control of infections.
- Think about **your work setting** and the meaning of the term 'risk'.

Learning Outcome 4: Understand the importance of risk assessment in relation to the prevention and control of infections

Assessment Criterion 4.2: Outline potential risks of infection within the workplace

What does AC4.2 mean?

- The lead word **outline** means that you must provide an **account** that includes brief **details** about the potential risks of infection within the workplace.
- Your **account** must detail briefly the potential risks of infection.
- For the key words **potential risks of infection** you can think about how infections may occur through direct contact between people such as when supporting an individual with personal care tasks, indirect contact with items people have used such as handling laundry that contains body fluids, inhalation such as working closely in confined spaces with others, engaging in activities that involve eating and drinking and through the use of equipment such as hoists, commodes and needles.

Read the following **Real Work Setting** scenario and think about how it relates to your work setting and role:

Real Work Setting

Name: Colette

Job Role: Support Worker for an older adult who has dementia
(See page 144 for a description of the role)

Potential risks of infection: Colette and her colleague then continue to think about the areas of potential risk in their work setting, where a team of Care Workers and others provide care and support to an individual who has dementia and lives at home with her daughter. Both agree that there are many daily activities they carry out that could be potential high-risk activities for spreading infection, such as when supporting the individual with showering and toileting, when preparing and clearing away food, when cleaning the bathroom and toilet areas, when emptying the bins and the commode, and when doing the laundry.

Evidencing AC4.2 to your assessor:

For AC4.2 you must evidence your understanding of the potential risks of infection within the workplace.

Assessment Methods:

Oral or **Written** Questioning or **Discussion** or a **Personal Statement**

- You can **tell** your assessor about the potential risks of infection within the workplace.
  Or
- You can **talk** to your assessor about the potential risks of infection within the workplace.
  Or
- You can write a **personal statement** of the potential risks of infection within the workplace.

REMEMBER TO:

- Provide an **account** that includes brief **details**.
- Include brief details about the potential risks of infection.
- Ensure your evidence relates to infections.
- Think about the potential risks of infection within **your work setting**.

Learning Outcome 4: Understand the importance of risk assessment in relation to the prevention and control of infections

Assessment Criterion 4.3: Describe the process of carrying out a risk assessment

What does AC4.3 mean?

- The lead word **describe** means that you must provide an **account** that **details** the process of carrying out a risk assessment.
- Your **account** must detail the process.
- For the key word **process** you can think about the five steps that are involved in carrying out a risk assessment: **Step 1** Identify the hazards; **Step 2** Evaluate the risks; **Step 3** Take precautions to remove, reduce or contain the risks; **Step 4** Report on and record the risk assessment's outcomes; and **Step 5** Review the risk assessment.
- For the key words **risk assessment** you can think about how this is a way of identifying, preventing and controlling risks of infections that could cause harm to yourself or other people.

Read the following **Real Work Setting** scenario and think about how it relates to your work setting and role:

Real Work Setting

Name: Colette

Job Role: Support Worker for an older adult who has dementia
(See page 144 for a description of the role)

Carrying out a risk assessment: During the training update Colette updates her knowledge of the steps involved in carrying out a risk assessment and this makes her think again about what each of the five steps to carrying out a risk assessment involves.

Step 1: Identify the hazards. What dangers exist in the work setting that could cause the spread of infections? Step 2: Evaluate the risks .Who might be harmed, how and why by the spread of infections in the work setting? Step 3: Take precautions. How can the risks identified be removed, reduced and contained? Step 4: Report and record. How can everyone be informed of the outcomes of the risk assessment? Step 5: Review. How can you review the risk assessment regularly and make revisions to it if necessary?

Evidencing AC4.3 to your assessor:

For AC4.3 you must evidence your understanding of the process of carrying out a risk assessment.

Assessment Methods:

Oral or **Written** Questioning or **Discussion** or a **Personal Statement**

- You can **tell** your assessor about the process of carrying out a risk assessment.
  Or
- You can **talk** to your assessor about the process of carrying out a risk assessment.
  Or
- You can write a **personal statement** about the process of carrying out a risk assessment.

REMEMBER TO:

- Provide an **account** that includes **details**.
- Include details about the process.
- Ensure your evidence relates to carrying out a risk assessment in relation to the prevention and control of infections.
- Think about **your work setting** and the process of carrying out a risk assessment.

Learning Outcome 4: Understand the importance of risk assessment in relation to the prevention and control of infections

Assessment Criterion 4.4: Explain the importance of carrying out a risk assessment

What does AC4.4 mean?

- The lead word **explain** means that you must **make clear** the importance of carrying out a risk assessment.
- Your **account** must detail the importance.
- For the key words **risk assessment** you can think about the importance of identifying, preventing and controlling risks of infections that could cause harm to yourself or other people.

Read the following **Real Work Setting** scenario and think about how it relates to your work setting and role:

Real Work Setting

Name: Colette

Job Role: Support Worker for an older adult who has dementia
(See page 144 for a description of the role)

The importance of carrying out a risk assessment: At the end of the training update, each of the participants is then asked to make a short presentation to the rest of the group to explain the importance of carrying out a risk assessment for the prevention and control of infections. When putting together her presentation Colette makes a list of the five key reasons why carrying out a risk assessment is important: 1) to comply with legal and organisational health and safety requirements; 2) to protect the health of everyone; 3) to carry out work responsibilities and duty of care to a high standard; 4) to maintain professional work settings; and 5) to maintain safe environments for individuals to live in.

Evidencing AC4.4 to your assessor:

For AC4.4 you must evidence your understanding of the importance of carrying out a risk assessment.

Assessment Methods:

Oral or **Written** Questioning or **Discussion** or a **Personal Statement** or **Reflection**

- You can **tell** your assessor about the importance of carrying out a risk assessment.
  Or
- You can **talk** to your assessor about the importance of carrying out a risk assessment.
  Or
- You can write a **personal statement** or **reflection** about the importance of carrying out a risk assessment.

REMEMBER TO:

- Provide an **account** and **explain** the importance.
- Include details about the reasons why it is important to carry out a risk assessment.
- Ensure your evidence relates to the prevention and control of infections.
- Think about **your work setting** and the importance of carrying out a risk assessment.

Learning Outcome 5: Understand the importance of using personal protective equipment (PPE) in the prevention and control of infections

Assessment Criterion 5.1: Demonstrate the correct use of PPE

What does AC5.1 mean?

- The lead word **demonstrate** means that you must be able to **show through your work practices** how to use PPE correctly.
- Your **observations of your work practices** must include you using PPE correctly.
- For the key words **correct use** you can think about the procedures to follow to ensure that PPE is correctly put on, taken off and disposed of.
- For the key words **personal protective equipment (PPE)** you can think about the different personal protective equipment that is worn to protect against risks of infections in your work setting, such as uniforms, aprons and gloves.

Read the following **Real Work Setting** scenario and think about how it relates to your work setting and role:

Real Work Setting

Name: David
Job Role: Mental Health Support Worker
David has been working as a Mental Health Support Worker for two-and-a-half years. His responsibilities include: supporting individuals to make informed choices, increasing individuals' independence, enabling individuals to make and maintain relationships of their choice, and supporting individuals to actively participate in their individual support plans.
Correct use of PPE: David always ensures he follows his work setting's procedures for PPE correctly, as not doing so can put himself and others at risk of infection. David receives ongoing infection control training and his work practices are regularly observed by the Senior Support Workers in the team to ensure that he understands how to use PPE correctly. David uses different-coloured plastic aprons for various tasks such as for supporting individuals with personal care, or when serving food to individuals; and disposes carefully of his apron after each task and individual he has contact with. David always ensures he washes his hands both before and after using gloves and that he disposes of these after use in the clinical waste bins provided in his work setting.

Evidencing AC5.1 to your assessor:

For AC5.1 you must evidence your skills of the correct use of PPE.

Assessment Method:

Direct Observation of your work practices

- You can **show** your assessor the correct use of PPE.

REMEMBER TO:

- Make arrangements for **observation** of your **work practices**.
- Include evidence of you putting on, taking off and disposing of PPE.
- Include evidence of different types of PPE.
- Include evidence of you correctly following your work setting's procedures for using PPE.
- Think about **your work setting** and the correct use of PPE.

Learning Outcome 5: Understand the importance of using personal protective equipment (PPE) in the prevention and control of infections

Assessment Criterion 5.2: Describe different types of PPE

What does AC5.2 mean?

- The lead word **describe** means that you must provide an **account** that **details** the different types of PPE.
- Your **account** must detail **different** types.
- For the key word **types** you can think about the different functions of PPE in terms of protecting your body, your eyes, your face, your hands and your feet from infections.
- For the key words **personal protective equipment (PPE)** you can think about the different personal protective equipment that is worn to protect against risks of infections in your work setting, such as uniforms, aprons and gloves.

Read the following **Real Work Setting** scenario and think about how it relates to your work setting and role:

Real Work Setting

Name: Colette

Job Role: Mental Health Support Worker
(See page 148 for a description of the role)

Different types of PPE: David is being job shadowed this morning by a new Support Worker and is showing him the different types of PPE that are used, including what they are and when they are worn. David begins by discussing with the new Support Worker the full uniform that he is required to wear at work and change out of at the end of his shift. In terms of the plastic aprons that are used, David shows the new Support Worker the different-coloured aprons that are used for various tasks and then where the disposable gloves are located and must be disposed of after use. Finally, David shows the new Support Worker the paper hats that must be worn to cover hair when serving food to individuals.

Evidencing AC5.2 to your assessor:

For AC5.2 you must evidence your understanding of different types of PPE.

Assessment Methods:

Oral or **Written** Questioning or **Discussion** or a **Personal Statement**

- You can **tell** your assessor about the different types of PPE.
  Or
- You can **talk** to your assessor about the different types of PPE.
  Or
- You can write a **personal statement** about the different types of PPE.

REMEMBER TO:

- Provide an **account** that includes **details**.
- Include details about the different types of PPE.
- Ensure your evidence relates to preventing the spread of infections.
- Think about **your work setting** and the different types of PPE that you and others wear.

Learning Outcome 5: Understand the importance of using personal protective equipment (PPE) in the prevention and control of infections

Assessment Criterion 5.3: Explain the reasons for the use of PPE

What does AC5.3 mean?

- The lead word **explain** means that you must **make clear** the reasons for the use of PPE.
- Your **account** must **detail** the reasons.
- For the key words **personal protective equipment (PPE)** you can think about the reasons why different personal protective equipment such as uniforms, aprons and gloves are worn to protect against risks of infections in your work setting, such as complying with legislation, following organisational policies and procedures, and to prevent the spread of infections.

Read the following **Real Work Setting** scenario and think about how it relates to your work setting and role:

Real Work Setting

Name: David

Job Role: Mental Health Support Worker
(See page 148 for a description of the role)

Reasons for use of PPE: The new Support Worker thanks David for showing him the different types of PPE that are used and then asks him whether it is important to always remember to wear these and use them when completing different tasks. David explains that, as he would have learnt in his infection control training, not doing so could potentially have serious consequences not just for himself but also for the individuals he supports, others he works with and all those who visit the work setting. David then reinforces this with him by explaining why the full uniform that is provided must be worn, why different-coloured aprons must be used for various tasks, why disposable gloves must always be used for carrying out tasks and why paper hats must be worn when serving food to individuals.

Evidencing AC5.3 to your assessor:

For AC5.3 you must evidence your understanding of the reasons for the use of PPE.

Assessment Methods:

Oral or **Written** Questioning or **Discussion** or a **Personal Statement** or **Reflection**

- You can **tell** your assessor about the reasons for the use of PPE.
  Or
- You can **talk** to your assessor about the reasons for the use of PPE.
  Or
- You can write a **personal statement** or **reflection** about the reasons for the use of PPE.

REMEMBER TO:

- Provide an **account** and **explain** the reasons.
- Include details about the reasons why it is important to use PPE.
- Ensure you include examples of the use of different types of PPE.
- Ensure your evidence relates to the prevention and control of infections.
- Think about **your work setting** and the reasons for the use of PPE.

Learning Outcome 5: Understand the importance of using personal protective equipment (PPE) in the prevention and control of infections

Assessment Criterion 5.4: State current relevant regulations and legislation relating to PPE

What does AC5.4 mean?

- The lead word **state** means that you must **specify** the current relevant regulations and legislation relating to PPE.
- Your **list** must include relevant regulations and legislation.
- For the key word **regulations** you can think about the laws that come under the main Acts related to PPE.
- For the key word **legislation** you can think about the main Acts that have been developed by the government for PPE.

Read the following **Real Work Setting** scenario and think about how it relates to your work setting and role:

Real Work Setting

Name: David

Job Role: Mental Health Support Worker
(See page 148 for a description of the role)

PPE regulations and legislation: David then shows the new Support Worker a copy of the work setting's policy and procedure for using PPE in the prevention and control of infections and points out to him the laws and regulations that relate to the use of PPE and are relevant in terms of protecting everyone from infections, preventing and controlling the spread of infections. The new Support Worker asks David how he could find out more details about the relevant regulations and legislation relating to PPE; David suggests that he could read through the information provided on the Health and Safety Executive's, Health and Care Professions Council's (HCPC) and Department of Health's websites.

Evidencing AC5.4 to your assessor:

For AC5.4 you must evidence your understanding of current relevant regulations and legislation relating to PPE.

Assessment Methods:

Oral or **Written** Questioning or **Discussion** or a **Spidergram**

- You can **tell** your assessor about the current relevant regulations and legislation relating to PPE.
  Or
- You can **talk** to your assessor about the current relevant regulations and legislation relating to PPE.
  Or
- You can complete a **spidergram** of the current relevant regulations and legislation relating to PPE.

REMEMBER TO:

- Provide a **list.**
- Include **examples** of both relevant regulations and legislation.
- Ensure your evidence relates to PPE.
- Think about **your work setting** and the relevant regulations and legislation relating to PPE.

Learning Outcome 5: Understand the importance of using personal protective equipment (PPE) in the prevention and control of infections

Assessment Criterion 5.5: Describe employees' responsibilities regarding the use of PPE

What does AC5.5 mean?

- The lead word **describe** means that you must provide an **account** that **details** employees' responsibilities regarding the use of PPE.
- Your **account** must detail different responsibilities.
- For the key word **responsibilities** you can think about how and why tasks that relate to the use of PPE are carried out in the work setting, such as to protect employees and others from infections, to comply with legal requirements and to follow the work setting's policies and procedures.
- For the key words **personal protective equipment (PPE)** you can think about the different responsibilities of employees relating to the use of personal protective equipment that is worn to protect against risks of infections in your work setting, such as uniforms, aprons and gloves.

Read the following **Real Work Setting** scenario and think about how it relates to your work setting and role:

Real Work Setting

Name: David

Job Role: Mental Health Support Worker
(See page 148 for a description of the role)

PPE and employees' responsibilities: The following day David and the new Support Worker talk over the responsibilities they and others who work in the setting have in relation to the use of PPE, in terms of the prevention and control of infections. David explains that it is important for employees to understand the PPE that must be used, why and when. It is also important to follow the correct procedures to comply with both organisational and legal requirements. David and the new Support Worker also discuss the ongoing training that the organisation provides for them, which they must attend, as well as the importance of being vigilant when PPE is not being used correctly and the correct actions that must be taken when this occurs, in line with the work setting's agreed ways of working.

Evidencing AC5.5 to your assessor:

For AC5.5 you must evidence your understanding of employees' responsibilities regarding PPE.

Assessment Methods:

Oral or **Written** Questioning or **Discussion** or a **Personal Statement**

- You can **tell** your assessor about employees' responsibilities regarding PPE.
  Or
- You can **talk** to your assessor about employees' responsibilities regarding PPE.
  Or
- You can write a **personal statement** about employees' responsibilities regarding the use of PPE.

REMEMBER TO:

- Provide an **account** that includes **details**.
- Include details about employees' responsibilities.
- Ensure your evidence relates to the use of PPE.
- Think about **your work setting** and employees' responsibilities regarding the use of PPE.

Learning Outcome 5: Understand the importance of using personal protective equipment (PPE) in the prevention and control of infections

Assessment Criterion 5.6: Describe employers' responsibilities regarding the use of PPE

What does AC5.6 mean?

- The lead word **describe** means that you must provide an **account** that **details** employers' responsibilities regarding the use of PPE.
- Your **account** must detail **different** responsibilities.
- For the key word **responsibilities** you can think about how and why tasks that relate to the use of PPE are carried out in the work setting.
- For the key words **personal protective equipment (PPE)** you can think about the different responsibilities of employers relating to the use of personal protective equipment that is worn to protect against risks of infections in your work setting, such as uniforms, aprons and gloves.

Read the following **Real Work Setting** scenario and think about how it relates to your work setting and role:

Real Work Setting

Name: David

Job Role: Mental Health Support Worker
(See page 148 for a description of the role)

PPE and employers' responsibilities: David and the new Support Worker then discuss the responsibilities employers have in relation to the use of PPE in terms of the prevention and control of infections. David explains that it is also important for employees to understand the responsibilities of their employers in terms of providing PPE, ensuring safe procedures are in place and followed for the use of PPE, providing information and training to employees on the safe use of PPE, as well as monitoring employees' practices for the use of PPE by carrying out regular risk assessments. Finally, David and the new Support Worker talk through the relevant legislation and regulations that relate to employers' responsibilities regarding the use of PPE.

Evidencing AC5.6 to your assessor:

For AC5.6 you must evidence your understanding of employers' responsibilities regarding PPE.

Assessment Methods:

Oral or **Written** Questioning or **Discussion** or a **Personal Statement**

- You can **tell** your assessor about employers' responsibilities regarding PPE.
  Or
- You can **talk** to your assessor about employers' responsibilities regarding PPE.
  Or
- You can write a **personal statement** about employers' responsibilities regarding the use of PPE.

REMEMBER TO:

- Provide an **account** that includes **details**.
- Include details about employers' responsibilities.
- Ensure your evidence relates to the use of PPE.
- Think about **your work setting** and employers' responsibilities regarding the use of PPE.

Learning Outcome 5: Understand the importance of using personal protective equipment (PPE) in the prevention and control of infections

Assessment Criterion 5.7: Describe the correct practice in the application and removal of PPE

What does AC5.7 mean?

- The lead word **describe** means that you must provide an **account** that **details** the correct practice in the application and removal of PPE.
- Your **account** must detail the correct practice.
- For the key words **correct practice** you can think about the correct practice to follow in line with your work setting's agreed ways of working for wearing and removing PPE.
- For the key words **personal protective equipment (PPE)** you can think about the correct practice to follow for wearing and removing personal protective equipment in your work setting, such as uniforms, aprons and gloves.

Read the following **Real Work Setting** scenario and think about how it relates to your work setting and role:

Real Work Setting

Name: David

Job Role: Mental Health Support Worker
(See page 148 for a description of the role)

Applying and removing PPE: The new Support Worker clarifies with David the correct practice in the application and removal of PPE. David shares with him how there are a number of factors to consider when putting on and taking off PPE. David details how it is important to take into account the order in which you put on PPE, that is, uniform on first, apron second and gloves last. David also details how careful attention must be paid to how each item is worn, as well as the precautions to take both before and after wearing PPE. The correct method of removing each item of PPE must also be observed in order to avoid the spread of infections.

Evidencing AC5.7 to your assessor:

For AC5.7 you must evidence your understanding of the correct practice in the application and removal of PPE.

Assessment Methods:

Oral or **Written** Questioning or **Discussion** or a **Personal Statement** or **Reflection**

- You can **tell** your assessor about the correct practice in the application and removal of PPE.
  Or
- You can talk to your assessor about the correct practice in the application and removal of PPE.
  Or
- You can write a **personal statement** or **reflection** about the correct practice in the application and removal of PPE.

REMEMBER TO:

Provide an **account** that includes **details**.

- Include details about the correct practice to follow.
- Ensure your evidence relates to the application and removal of PPE.
- Think about **your work setting** and the correct practice in the application and removal of PPE.

Learning Outcome 5: Understand the importance of using personal protective equipment (PPE) in the prevention and control of infections

Assessment Criterion 5.8: Describe the correct procedure for the disposal of used PPE

What does AC5.8 mean?

- The lead word **describe** means that you must provide an **account** that **details** the correct procedure for the disposal of used PPE.
- Your **account** must detail the correct procedure.
- For the key words **correct procedure** you can think about the correct process you must follow in line with your work setting's agreed ways of working for disposing of used PPE.
- For the key words **personal protective equipment (PPE)** you can think about the correct process to follow for disposing of used personal protective equipment in your work setting, such as aprons and gloves.

Read the following **Real Work Setting** scenario and think about how it relates to your work setting and role:

Real Work Setting

Name: David

Job Role: Mental Health Support Worker
(See page 148 for a description of the role)

Disposal of used PPE: Finally, David and the new Support Worker discuss the correct procedure for the disposal of used PPE. Both discuss where, when and how PPE should be disposed of, depending on whether it has been contaminated by bodily fluids and infectious waste. David also discusses with the new Support Worker the procedure to follow in the work setting for emptying and securing waste awaiting collection, including the area where it is kept and how the area should be maintained clean and secure.

Evidencing AC5.8 to your assessor:

For AC5.8 you must evidence your understanding of the correct procedure for the disposal of used PPE.

Assessment Methods:

Oral or **Written** Questioning or **Discussion** or a **Personal Statement** or **Reflection**

- You can **tell** your assessor about the correct procedure for the disposal of used PPE.
  Or
- You can **talk** to your assessor about the correct procedure for the disposal of used PPE.
  Or
- You can write a **personal statement** or **reflection** about the correct procedure for the disposal of used PPE.

REMEMBER TO:

- Provide an **account** that includes **details**.
- Include details about the correct procedure to follow.
- Ensure your evidence relates to the disposal of used PPE.
- Think about **your work setting** and the correct procedure for the disposal of used PPE.

Learning Outcome 6: Understand the importance of good personal hygiene in the prevention and control of infections

Assessment Criterion 6.1: Describe the key principles of good personal hygiene

What does AC6.1 mean?

- The lead word **describe** means that you must provide an **account** that **details** the key principles of good personal hygiene.
- Your **account** must detail the key principles.
- For the key word **principles** you can think about the high standards that are necessary for maintaining good personal hygiene.
- For the key words **good personal hygiene** you can think about how this involves keeping the body clean and well groomed to avoid the risk of infections.

Read the following **Real Work Setting** scenario and think about how it relates to your work setting and role:

Real Work Setting

Name: Sabrina
Job Role: Care Assistant in a residential care home
Sabrina has been working as a Care Assistant for five years. Her responsibilities include: supporting individuals to maintain good personal hygiene, assisting individuals at meal times with eating and drinking, cleaning and maintaining equipment, as well as moving and handling individuals.
The key principles of good personal hygiene: Sabrina is a good role model to others, as she always maintains high standards of good personal hygiene for both herself and the individuals she supports. Sabrina always arrives at work with a clean uniform, her hair tied back and wearing enclosed shoes; she also ensures that she removes any jewellery at the beginning of her shift, as she is aware that not doing so can lead to infections spreading. Sabrina ensures that she supports individuals to shower, bath or wash regularly and to maintain good grooming practices in relation to their hair, nails and clothes.

Evidencing AC6.1 to your assessor:

For AC6.1 you must evidence your understanding of the key principles of good personal hygiene.

Assessment Methods:

Oral or **Written** Questioning or **Discussion** or a **Personal Statement** or **Reflection**

- You can **tell** your assessor about the key principles of good personal hygiene.
  Or
- You can **talk** to your assessor about the key principles of good personal hygiene.
  Or
- You can write a **personal statement** or **reflection** about the key principles of good personal hygiene.

REMEMBER TO:

- Provide an **account** that includes **details**.
- Include details about the key principles of good personal hygiene.
- Ensure your evidence relates to the prevention and control of infections.
- Think about **your work setting** and the key principles of good personal hygiene.

Learning Outcome 6: Understand the importance of good personal hygiene in the prevention and control of infections

Assessment Criterion 6.2: Demonstrate good hand-washing technique

What does AC6.2 mean?

- The lead word **demonstrate** means that you must be able to **show through your work practices** how to use a good hand-washing technique.
- Your **observations of your work practices** must include you using a good hand-washing technique.
- For the key words **good hand-washing technique** you can think about your work setting's hand-washing policy and the occasions when you must wash your hands, all the preparations that must be made before and after washing your hands, as well as the correct technique to use.

Read the following **Real Work Setting** scenario and think about how it relates to your work setting and role:

Real Work Setting

Name: Sabrina

Job Role: Care Assistant in a residential care home
(See page 156 for a description of the role)

Good hand-washing technique: Sabrina has been asked by her manager to demonstrate to the team at their meeting today a good hand-washing technique to use, as it has been noted that some team members do not wash their hands thoroughly on every occasion. Sabrina shows the team the preparations she makes prior to washing her hands, including removing her rings and watch, rolling her sleeves up to her elbows, ensuring she runs the water so that it is neither too hot nor too cold before following the steps outlined in the World Health Organization's diagrams for washing her hands thoroughly. Sabrina demonstrates that she takes time to wash her hands thoroughly and to ensure that all areas of her hands are washed effectively.

Evidencing AC6.2 to your assessor:

For AC6.2 you must evidence your skills of using a good hand-washing technique.

Assessment Method:

Direct Observation of your work practices

- You can **show** your assessor how to use a good hand-washing technique.

REMEMBER TO:

- Make arrangements for **observation** of your **work practices**.
- Include evidence of you using a good hand-washing technique.
- Include evidence of you correctly following your work setting's procedures for good hand washing.
- Think about **your work setting** and how to use a good hand-washing technique.

Learning Outcome 6: Understand the importance of good personal hygiene in the prevention and control of infections

Assessment Criterion 6.3: Describe the correct sequence for hand washing

What does AC6.3 mean?

- The lead word **describe** means that you must provide an **account** that **details** the correct sequence for hand washing.
- Your **account** must detail the correct sequence.
- For the key words **correct sequence** you can think about the approved guidelines in place for washing your hands.

Read the following **Real Work Setting** scenario and think about how it relates to your work setting and role:

Real Work Setting

Name: Sabrina

Job Role: Care Assistant in a residential care home
(See page 156 for a description of the role)

The correct sequence for hand washing: Sabrina then talks to the team about how she washes her hands in line with the steps that are outlined in the World Health Organization's diagrams for maintaining effective and thorough hand-washing standards. To test the team's knowledge of the correct sequence to follow Sabrina asks the team to fill in the blanks on the information handout she gives them.
1) Wet hands with ------------ 2) Apply ----- 3) ----- hands together, palm to ------ 4) Rub the right palm and then the left palm over the other hand with -------------- fingers 5) Rub hands --------------, palm to palm with fingers interlaced 6) Rub --------- of palms together with fingers interlocked 7) Rotationally --- left thumb clasped in right palm and then right thumb in left palm 8) Rotational rub, ------------- and -------------- with clasped fingers of right hand in left palm and left hand in right palm 9) --------- hands with water and 10) Dry ---------------------- with paper towels.

Evidencing AC6.3 to your assessor:

For AC6.3 you must evidence your understanding of the correct sequence for hand washing.

Assessment Methods:

Oral or **Written** Questioning or **Discussion** or a **Personal Statement** or **Reflection**

- You can **tell** your assessor about the correct sequence for hand washing.
  Or
- You can **talk** to your assessor about the correct sequence for hand washing.
  Or
- You can write a **personal statement** or **reflection** about the correct sequence for hand washing.

REMEMBER TO:

- Provide an **account** that includes **details**.
- Include details about the correct sequence for hand washing.
- Ensure your evidence relates to the correct process to follow to effectively wash your hands.
- Think about **your work setting** and the correct sequence for hand washing.

Learning Outcome 6: Understand the importance of good personal hygiene in the prevention and control of infections

Assessment Criterion 6.4: Explain when and why hand washing should be carried out

What does AC6.4 mean?

- The lead word **explain** means that you must **make clear** when and why hand washing should be carried out.
- Your **account** must **detai**l both the occasions and the reasons why.
- For the key word **when** you can think about the different occasions when you must wash your hands such as before and after your shift at work, before and after contact with an individual, before and after handling, serving and eating food and drink, after handling laundry and waste, and after removing disposable gloves.
- For the key word **why** you can think about the reasons why hand washing must be carried out, as well as the consequences of not doing so for you, the individuals and others you work with.

Read the following **Real Work Setting** scenario and think about how it relates to your work setting and role:

Real Work Setting

Name: Sabrina

Job Role: Care Assistant in a residential care home
(See page 156 for a description of the role)

When and why hand washing should be carried out: Sabrina then asks the team whether they have any questions about effective hand washing and the technique to use; three of the team indicate that they have questions for her. The first team member asks Sabrina whether she can explain when and why hand washing should be carried out. Sabrina begins by asking the team to consider all the activities and occasions when they think hand washing should be done and then goes through each in turn and includes some other occasions that the team do not mention, such as after removing disposable gloves and at the end of their shifts. Sabrina then discusses with the team for each activity and occasion mentioned the reasons why hand washing should be carried out.

Evidencing AC6.4 to your assessor:

For AC6.4 you must evidence your understanding of when and why hand washing should be carried out.

Assessment Methods:

Oral or **Written** Questioning or **Discussion** or a **Personal Statement** or **Reflection**

- You can **tell** your assessor about when and why hand washing should be carried out.
  Or
- You can **talk** to your assessor about when and why hand washing should be carried out.
  Or
- You can write a **personal statement** or **reflection** about when and why hand washing should be carried out.

REMEMBER TO:

- Provide an account and explain when and why hand washing should be carried out.
- Include details about both the occasions and the reasons.
- Ensure you include examples of both different occasions and the reasons.
- Ensure your evidence relates to hand washing.
- Think about **your work setting** and when and why hand washing should be carried out.

Learning Outcome 6: Understand the importance of good personal hygiene in the prevention and control of infections

Assessment Criterion 6.5: Describe the types of products that should be used for hand washing

What does AC6.5 mean?

- The lead word **describe** means that you must provide an **account** that **details** the types of products that should be used for hand washing.
- Your **account** must detail the types of products that should be used.
- For the key words **types of products** you can think about how and when soap, antiseptics and alcohol-based hand gels are used for hand washing.

Read the following **Real Work Setting** scenario and think about how it relates to your work setting and role:

Real Work Setting

Name: Sabrina

Job Role: Care Assistant in a residential care home
(See page 156 for a description of the role)

Types of products that are used for hand washing: The second team member asks Sabrina whether she can talk her through the different types of products that should be used for hand washing. Sabrina provides details about various different soaps that can be used and how the liquid soap used in their work setting is the recommended type of soap to use. Sabrina then discusses the use of antiseptics and alcohol-based hand gels with the team. Antiseptic or anti-bacterial soap and gels can also be used, Sabrina explains, for tasks where there is a high risk of infection. Alcohol-based hand gels, Sabrina adds, must never be used instead of hand washing but are useful in addition to hand washing for providing extra protection against infections.

Evidencing AC6.5 to your assessor:

For AC6.5 you must evidence your understanding of the types of products that should be used for hand washing.

Assessment Methods:

Oral or **Written** Questioning or **Discussion** or a **Personal Statement** or **Reflection**

- You can **tell** your assessor about the types of products that should be used for hand washing.
  Or
- You can **talk** to your assessor about the types of products that should be used for hand washing.
  Or
- You can write a **personal statement** or **reflection** about the types of products that should be used for hand washing.

REMEMBER TO:

- Provide an **account** that includes **details**.
- Include details about the types of products that should be used for hand washing.
- Ensure your evidence relates to hand washing.
- Think about **your work setting** and the types of products that should be used for hand washing.

Learning Outcome 6: Understand the importance of good personal hygiene in the prevention and control of infections

Assessment Criterion 6.6: Describe correct procedures that relate to skincare

What does AC6.6 mean?

- The lead word **describe** means that you must provide an **account** that **details** the correct procedures that relate to skincare.
- Your **account** must detail the correct procedures.
- For the key words **correct procedures** you can think about your work setting's hand-washing procedures, as well as the guidelines in place for effective hand washing.
- For the key word **skincare** you can think about the correct procedures to follow for skin to remain moisturised and in good condition.

Read the following **Real Work Setting** scenario and think about how it relates to your work setting and role:

Real Work Setting

Name: Sabrina

Job Role: Care Assistant in a residential care home
(See page 156 for a description of the role)

Correct procedures that relate to skincare: The third team member asks Sabrina whether she can talk through the correct procedures that relate to maintaining skin in good condition. Sabrina discusses with the team how skin, particularly on hands, can become dry and irritated owing to frequent washing and drying that can cause infections that can spread to others. The team discuss different ways of keeping their hands in good condition, such as the use of hand creams, and then read through together the work setting's procedures to follow for maintaining skin in good condition.

Evidencing AC6.6 to your assessor:

For AC6.6 you must evidence your understanding of the correct procedures that relate to skincare.

Assessment Methods:

Oral or **Written** Questioning or **Discussion** or a **Personal Statement** or **Reflection**

- You can **tell** your assessor about the correct procedures that relate to skincare.
  Or
- You can **talk** to your assessor about the correct procedures that relate to skincare.
  Or
- You can write a **personal statement** or **reflection** about the correct procedures that relate to skincare.

REMEMBER TO:

- Provide an **account** that includes **details**.
- Include details about the correct procedures that relate to skincare.
- Ensure your evidence relates to skincare.
- Think about **your work setting** and the correct procedures that relate to skincare.

IC02 Causes and spread of infection

Learning Outcome 1: Understand the causes of infection

Assessment Criterion 1.1: Identify the differences between bacteria, viruses, fungi and parasites

What does AC1.1 mean?

- The lead word **identify** means that you must **make clear** the differences between bacteria, viruses, fungi and parasites.
- Your **list** must make clear the differences.
- For the key word **bacteria** you can think about how these include different types of harmful and harmless pathogens.
- For the key word **viruses** you can think about how these include pathogens that cause disease.
- For the key word **fungi** you can think about how these include different types of harmful and harmless pathogens.
- For the key word **parasites** you can think about how these include living organisms that are present in or on the body.

Read the following **Real Work Setting** scenario and think about how it relates to your work setting and role:

Real Work Setting

Name: Lucy

Job Role: Care Assistant for older people

Lucy has been working as a Care Assistant for two years. Her responsibilities include: meeting individuals' physical, emotional and social needs in line with their care plans, ensuring individuals' safety, dignity and control over their lives and reporting any changes or concerns regarding individuals' needs, abilities or well-being.

Differences between bacteria, viruses, fungi and parasites: Lucy is attending a mandatory training update today about the causes of infection. The course begins by explaining that infections are caused by micro-organisms that are known as pathogens and that many different types of pathogens exist, some of which are harmful and can cause diseases, infections and illnesses and others that are not harmful.

Evidencing AC1.1 to your assessor:

For AC1.1 you must evidence your understanding of the differences between bacteria, viruses, fungi and parasites.

Assessment Methods:

Oral or **Written** Questioning or **Discussion** or a **Spidergram**

- You can **tell** your assessor about the differences between bacteria, viruses, fungi and parasites.
  Or
- You can **talk** to your assessor about the differences between bacteria, viruses, fungi and parasites.
  Or
- You can complete a **spidergram** of the differences between bacteria, viruses, fungi and parasites.

REMEMBER TO:

- Include a list of the differences.
- Ensure the list relates to the differences between bacteria, viruses, fungi and parasites.
- Think about **your work setting** and the differences between bacteria, viruses, fungi and parasites.

Learning Outcome 1: Understand the causes of infection

Assessment Criterion 1.2: Identify common illnesses and infections caused by bacteria, viruses, fungi and parasites

What does AC1.2 mean?

- The lead word **identify** means that you must **make clear** the common illnesses and infections caused by bacteria, viruses, fungi and parasites.
- Your **list** must make clear the common illnesses and infections.
- For the key words **common illnesses** you can think about the common diseases that can affect the body and that are caused by bacteria, viruses, fungi and parasites.
- For the key words **common infections** you can think about how bacteria, viruses, fungi and parasites can enter the body and cause individuals to feel unwell.
- For the key word **bacteria** you can think about how these include different types of harmful and harmless pathogens.
- For the key word **viruses** you can think about how these include pathogens that cause disease.
- For the key word **fungi** you can think about how these include different types of harmful and harmless pathogens.
- For the key word **parasites** you can think about how these include living organisms that are present in or on the body.

Read the following **Real Work Setting** scenario and think about how it relates to your work setting and role:

Real Work Setting

Name: Lucy

Job Role: Care Assistant for older people
(See page 162 for a description of the role)

Common illnesses and infections: Lucy also learns more about the common illnesses and infections that are widespread in the UK and are caused by bacterial infections, viral illnesses, fungal conditions, internal parasites and external parasites.

Evidencing AC1.2 to your assessor:

For AC1.2 you must evidence your understanding of the common illnesses and infections caused by bacteria, viruses, fungi and parasites.

Assessment Methods:

Oral or **Written** Questioning or **Discussion** or a **Spidergram**

- You can **tell** your assessor about the common illnesses and infections caused by bacteria, viruses, fungi and parasites.
  Or
- You can **talk** to your assessor about the common illnesses and infections caused by bacteria, viruses, fungi and parasites.
  Or
- You can complete a **spidergram** of the common illnesses and infections caused by bacteria, viruses, fungi and parasites.

REMEMBER TO:

- Include a list of the common illnesses and infections.
- Ensure the list relates to those caused by bacteria, viruses, fungi and parasites.
- Think about **your work setting** and the common illnesses and infections caused by bacteria, viruses, fungi and parasites.

Learning Outcome 1: Understand the causes of infection

Assessment Criterion 1.3: Describe what is meant by 'infection' and 'colonisation'

What does AC1.3 mean?

- The lead word **describe** means that you must provide an **account** that **details** what is meant by 'infection' and 'colonisation'.
- Your **account** must detail the meanings of 'infection' and 'colonisation'.
- For the key word **infection** you can think about how this involves pathogens entering the body and causing individuals to feel unwell.
- For the key word **colonisation** you can think about how this involves a pathogen existing without causing any immediate disease or adverse effects.

Read the following **Real Work Setting** scenario and think about how it relates to your work setting and role:

Real Work Setting

Name: Lucy
Job Role: Care Assistant for older people (See page 162 for a description of the role)
Infection and colonisation meanings: The training course then moves on to explain the various different details that are common to infections and also provides some detailed information about the colonisation process. Lucy finds the information she learns about the colonisation process very interesting as she now understands how infections can transfer from one person to another without anyone realising that this is the case, or there being any visible signs that infection is present in a person.

Evidencing AC1.3 to your assessor:

For AC1.3 you must evidence your understanding of what is meant by 'infection' and 'colonisation'.

Assessment Methods:

Oral or **Written** Questioning or **Discussion** or a **Personal Statement**

- You can **tell** your assessor about what is meant by 'infection' and 'colonisation'.
  Or
- You can **talk** to your assessor about what is meant by 'infection' and 'colonisation'.
  Or
- You can write a **personal statement** about what is meant by 'infection' and 'colonisation'.

REMEMBER TO:

- Provide an account that details the meanings of 'infection' and 'colonisation'.
- Ensure your evidence is related to both infection and colonisation.
- Think about **your work setting** and what is meant by 'infection' and 'colonisation'.

Learning Outcome 1: Understand the causes of infection

Assessment Criterion 1.4: Explain what is meant by 'systemic infection' and 'localised infection'

What does AC1.4 mean?

- The lead word **explain** means that you must **make clear** what is meant by 'systemic infection' and 'localised infection'.
- Your **account** must detail the meanings of 'systemic infection' and 'localised infection'.
- For the key words **systemic infection** you can think about how this type of infection can affect all parts of your body.
- For the key words **localised infection** you can think about how this type of infection can affect a specific part of your body.

Read the following **Real Work Setting** scenario and think about how it relates to your work setting and role:

Real Work Setting

Name: Lucy

Job Role: Care Assistant for older people
(See page 162 for a description of the role)

Systemic and localised infections meanings: During the afternoon session of the training Lucy learns more about how infections are classified as falling under two types: localised or systemic. A systemic infection would affect all parts of your body and the symptoms associated with this type of infection would reflect this and may include a fever and whole-body aches and pains. A localised infection would affect a specific part of your body only.

Evidencing AC1.4 to your assessor:

For AC1.4 you must evidence your understanding of what is meant by 'systemic infection' and 'localised infection'.

Assessment Methods:

Oral or **Written** Questioning or **Discussion** or a **Personal Statement** or **Reflection**

- You can **tell** your assessor about what is meant by 'systemic infection' and 'localised infection'.
  Or
- You can **talk** to your assessor about what is meant by 'systemic infection' and 'localised infection'.
  Or
- You can write a **personal statement** or **reflection** about what is meant by 'systemic infection' and 'localised infection'.

REMEMBER TO:

- Provide an account and explain.
- Include details with examples of what is meant by 'systemic infection' and 'localised infection'.
- Think about **your work setting** and what is meant by 'systemic infection' and 'localised infection'.

Learning Outcome 1: Understand the causes of infection

Assessment Criterion 1.5: Identify poor practices that may lead to the spread of infection

What does AC1.5 mean?

- The lead word **identify** means that you must **make clear** the poor practices that may lead to the spread of infection.
- Your **list** must make clear poor practices.
- For the key words **poor practices** you can think about how these include working practices that may lead to the spread of infection, such as not following the correct procedures when coming into contact with body fluids, when handling food, or when supporting individuals who are vulnerable to infections.
- For the key word **infection** you can think about how this involves pathogens entering the body and causing individuals to feel unwell.

Read the following **Real Work Setting** scenario and think about how it relates to your work setting and role:

Real Work Setting

Name: Lucy

Job Role: Care Assistant for older people
(See page 162 for a description of the role)

Poor practices that may lead to the spread of infection: Lucy then discusses with the other participants in her group a range of poor practices that may lead to the spread of infection. Lucy reflects on her role as a Care Assistant and thinks about how her actions can lead to the spread of infection in her work setting amongst the individuals and others she works with, due to the nature of the daily tasks she supports individuals with and the vulnerability of some individuals to infections. Taking part in this group activity reinforced to Lucy the importance of ensuring that she follows her work setting's policy and procedure.

Evidencing AC1.5 to your assessor:

For AC1.5 you must evidence your understanding of poor practices that may lead to the spread of infection.

Assessment Methods:

Oral or **Written** Questioning or **Discussion** or a **Spidergram**

- You can **tell** your assessor about poor practices that may lead to the spread of infection.
  Or
- You can **talk** to your assessor about poor practices that may lead to the spread of infection.
  Or
- You can complete a **spidergram** of poor practices that may lead to the spread of infection.

REMEMBER TO:

- Include a list of poor practices.
- Ensure the list relates to practices that may lead to the spread of infection.
- Think about **your work setting** and the poor practices that may lead to the spread of infection.

Learning Outcome 2: Understand the transmission of infection

Assessment Criterion 2.1: Explain the conditions needed for the growth of micro-organisms

What does AC2.1 mean?

- The lead word **explain** means that you must **make clear** the conditions needed for the growth of micro-organisms.
- Your **account** must detail the conditions needed.
- For the key word **conditions** you can think about how bacteria, viruses, fungi and parasites all require different factors to grow such as moisture, temperature, nutrients, time, oxygen, no oxygen, a location.

Read the following **Real Work Setting** scenario and think about how it relates to your work setting and role:

Real Work Setting

Name: Abdulah

Job Role: Personal Assistant for adults with physical disabilities

Abdulah has been working as a Personal Assistant for five years. His responsibilities include: supporting individuals with personal care tasks such as washing, dressing and grooming, as well as assisting individuals with household activities such as, for example, cooking, cleaning, doing the laundry and ironing.

The conditions needed for the growth of micro-organisms: Abdulah is reading through a book that his manager has suggested he read about how infection is spread, as Abdulah requested an infection control update in his supervision and although he has been booked on the next available training course, this will take place in four months' time. Abdulah begins by updating his knowledge around how bacteria, viruses, fungi and parasites all thrive in the right conditions and how these conditions vary between these different pathogens.

Evidencing AC2.1 to your assessor:

For AC2.1 you must evidence your understanding of conditions needed for the growth of micro-organisms.

Assessment Methods:

Oral or **Written** Questioning or **Discussion** or a **Personal Statement**

- You can **tell** your assessor about the conditions needed for the growth of micro-organisms.
  Or
- You can **talk** to your assessor about the conditions needed for the growth of micro-organisms.
  Or
- You can write a **personal statement** about the conditions needed for the growth of micro-organisms.

REMEMBER TO:

- Provide an account and explain.
- Include details about the conditions needed for the growth of micro-organisms.
- Think about **your work setting** and the conditions needed for the growth of micro-organisms.

Learning Outcome 2: Understand the transmission of infection

Assessment Criterion 2.2: Explain the ways an infective agent might enter the body

What does AC2.2 mean?

- The lead word **explain** means that you must **make clear** the ways an infective agent might enter the body.
- Your **account** must detail the ways an infective agent might enter the body.
- For the key words **infective agent** you can think about the different ways an infection might enter the body by: 1) ingesting pathogens, 2) touch, 3) pathogens entering via the blood circulation, 4) inhaling pathogens, 5) pathogens entering via the umbilical cord, 6) via body fluids, and 7) via the genital route.

Read the following **Real Work Setting** scenario and think about how it relates to your work setting and role:

Real Work Setting

Name: Abdulah

Job Role: Personal Assistant for adults with physical disabilities
(See page 167 for a description of the role)

The ways an infective agent might enter the body: Abdulah then continues to read up about the different routes through which an infection may enter the body: digestive route, via touch, blood circulation route, respiratory route, placenta route, body fluids route and genital route, including the reasons why these are the main routes that cause infections to spread through both natural breaks in the skin such as, for example, our mouths and ears and unnatural breaks in the skin such as, for example, cuts and wounds.

Evidencing AC2.2 to your assessor:

For AC2.2 you must evidence your understanding of the ways an infective agent might enter the body.

Assessment Methods:

Oral or **Written** Questioning or **Discussion** or a **Personal Statement**

- You can **tell** your assessor about the ways an infective agent might enter the body.
  Or
- You can **talk** to your assessor about the ways an infective agent might enter the body.
  Or
- You can write a **personal statement** about the ways an infective agent might enter the body.

REMEMBER TO:

- Provide an account and explain.
- Include details with examples about the ways an infective agent might enter the body.
- Think about **your work setting** and the ways an infective agent might enter the body.

Learning Outcome 2: Understand the transmission of infection

Assessment Criterion 2.3: Identify common sources of infection

What does AC2.3 mean?

- The lead word **identify** means that you must **make clear** the common sources of infection.
- Your **list** must make clear the sources.
- For the key words **common sources** you can think about how pathogens need a location in which to thrive and grow such as those that include moisture, the correct temperature, a supply of nutrients, sufficient time, oxygen and no oxygen.

Read the following **Real Work Setting** scenario and think about how it relates to your work setting and role:

Real Work Setting

Name: Abdulah
Job Role: Personal Assistant for adults with physical disabilities (See page 167 for a description of the role)
The common sources of infection: Abdulah finds it interesting to read about the common sources of infection and the types of locations that provide a 'good home' for pathogens to thrive in and grow, such as those that fully meet the conditions needed for the growth of pathogens. In light of Abdulah's Personal Assistant role and the various high-risk tasks he undertakes as part of his day-to-day work activities, it is important for him to be aware of the main sources of infections.

Evidencing AC2.3 to your assessor:

For AC2.3 you must evidence your understanding of the common sources of infection.

Assessment Methods:

Oral or **Written** Questioning or **Discussion** or a **Spidergram**

- You can **tell** your assessor about the common sources of infection.

  Or
- You can **talk** to your assessor about the common sources of infection.

  Or
- You can complete a **spidergram** of the common sources of infection.

REMEMBER TO:

- Include a list of the sources of infection.
- Ensure the list relates to different and common sources of infection.
- Think about **your work setting** and the common sources of infection.

Learning Outcome 2: Understand the transmission of infection

Assessment Criterion 2.4: Explain how infective agents can be transmitted to a person

What does AC2.4 mean?

- The lead word **explain** means that you must **make clear** how infective agents can be transmitted to a person.
- Your **account** must detail how infective agents can be transmitted.
- For the key words **infective agents** you can think about how infections can be passed on to a person through a series of steps: Step 1) Pathogens cause an infection. Step 2) Pathogens find a source in which to thrive and grow. Step 3) Pathogens find a route into the body. Step 4) Pathogens find ways of spreading around the body. Step 5) Pathogens find a route out of the body and then a new source in which to thrive and grow.

Read the following **Real Work Setting** scenario and think about how it relates to your work setting and role:

Real Work Setting

Name: Abdulah

Job Role: Personal Assistant for adults with physical disabilities
(See page 167 for a description of the role)

How infective agents can be transmitted to a person: Abdulah also learns more about how pathogens can be harmful and cause an infection in a person by going through a series of steps, often referred to as the 'chain of infection'. Reading up on the chain of infection and how it occurs reinforces to Abdulah the causes of infections, the conditions needed for the growth of pathogens, the different routes and sources of infection, as well as how these link to each other and can enable pathogens to spread rapidly once in the body.

Evidencing AC2.4 to your assessor:

For AC2.4 you must evidence your understanding of how infective agents can be transmitted to a person.

Assessment Methods:

Oral or **Written** Questioning or **Discussion** or a **Personal Statement**

- You can **tell** your assessor about how infective agents can be transmitted to a person.
  Or
- You can **talk** to your assessor about how infective agents can be transmitted to a person.
  Or
- You can write a **personal statement** about how infective agents can be transmitted to a person.

REMEMBER TO:

- Provide an account and explain.
- Include details with examples about how infective agents can be transmitted to a person.
- Think about **your work setting** and how infective agents can be transmitted to a person.

Learning Outcome 2: Understand the transmission of infection

Assessment Criterion 2.5: Identify the key factors that will make it more likely that infections will occur

What does AC2.5 mean?

- The lead word **identify** means that you must **make clear** the key factors that will make it more likely that infections will occur.
- Your **list** must make clear the key factors.
- For the key word **factors** you can think about what aspects will make it more likely that infections will occur such as in relation to contact with others, the activities that are involved in the tasks that you carry out, the different situations and environments.

Read the following **Real Work Setting** scenario and think about how it relates to your work setting and role:

Real Work Setting

Name: Abdulah

Job Role: Personal Assistant for adults with physical disabilities
(See page 167 for a description of the role)

The key factors that will make it more likely that infections will occur: Abdulah then finally considers the factors that can make it more likely that infections will occur by thinking about these in terms of his job role and activities, such as the different individuals he provides care and support to, the different tasks that he carries out and are seen as high risk in terms of spreading infections, the different accidents and incidents that may occur in his day-to-day work, as well as the different settings where individuals live and he works in.

Evidencing AC2.5 to your assessor:

For AC2.5 you must evidence your understanding of the key factors that will make it more likely that infections will occur.

Assessment Methods:

Oral or **Written** Questioning or **Discussion** or a **Spidergram**

- You can **tell** your assessor about the key factors that will make it more likely that infections will occur.
  Or
- You can **talk** to your assessor about the key factors that will make it more likely that infections will occur.
  Or
- You can complete a **spidergram** of the key factors that will make it more likely that infections will occur.

REMEMBER TO:

- Include a list of the key factors.
- Ensure the list relates to making it more likely that infections will occur.
- Think about **your work setting** and the key factors that will make it more likely that infections will occur.

LD201 Understand the context of supporting individuals with learning disabilities

Learning Outcome 1: Understand the legislation and policies that support the human rights and inclusion of individuals with learning disabilities

Assessment Criterion 1.1: Identify legislation and policies that are designed to promote the human rights, inclusion, equal life chances and citizenship of individuals with learning disabilities

What does AC1.1 mean?

- The lead word **identify** means that you must **make clear** legislation and policies that are designed to promote the human rights, inclusion, equal life chances and citizenship of individuals with learning disabilities.
- Your **list** must make clear both legislation and policies.
- For the key words **legislation and policies** you can think about the laws, guidance and agreed ways of working that are in place.
- For the key words **human rights** you can think about the legislation and policies that promote the freedoms to which all humans are entitled such as the right to life and equality, freedom of thought and expression.
- For the key word **inclusion** you can think about the legislation and policies that promote individuals who have learning disabilities to be full and active participants in their lives.
- For the key words **equal life chances** you can think about the legislation and policies that relate to making opportunities available to individuals who have learning disabilities.
- For the key word **citizenship** you can think about the legislation and policies that relate to promoting individuals who have learning disabilities to be members of society.

Read the following **Real Work Setting** scenario and think about how it relates to your work setting and role:

Real Work Setting

Name: Lorraine
Job Role: Carer for adults who have learning disabilities
Lorraine has been working as a Carer for eight years. Her responsibilities include enabling individuals to lead fulfilling lives and actively participate in their communities.
Legislation and policies: Lorraine is attending a training course this morning to learn more about the legislation and policies that support the human rights, inclusion, equal life chances and citizenship of individuals with learning disabilities

Evidencing AC1.1 to your assessor:

For AC1.1 you must evidence your understanding of legislation and policies that are designed to promote the human rights, inclusion, equal life chances and citizenship of individuals with learning disabilities.

Assessment Methods:

Oral or **Written** Questioning or **Discussion** or a **Spidergram**

- You can **tell** your assessor about legislation and policies.

  Or
- You can **talk** to your assessor about legislation and policies.

  Or
- You can complete a **spidergram** of legislation and policies.

REMEMBER TO:

- Include a list of both legislation and policies.
- Ensure the list relates to human rights, inclusion, equal life chances and citizenship of individuals who have learning disabilities.
- Think about **your work setting** and legislation and policies that are designed to promote the human rights, inclusion, equal life chances and citizenship of individuals with learning disabilities.

Learning Outcome 1: Understand the legislation and policies that support the human rights and inclusion of individuals with learning disabilities

Assessment Criterion 1.2: Explain how this legislation and policies influence the day-to-day experiences of individuals with learning disabilities and their families

What does AC1.2 mean?

- The lead word **explain** means that you must **make clear** how this legislation and policies influence the day-to-day experiences of individuals with learning disabilities and their families.
- Your **account** must detail how.
- For the key words **legislation and policies** you can think about the laws, guidance and agreed ways of working that influence the day-to-day experiences of individuals who have learning disabilities and their families.

Read the following **Real Work Setting** scenario and think about how it relates to your work setting and role:

Real Work Setting

Name: Lorraine

Job Role: Carer for adults who have learning disabilities
(See page 172 for a description of the role)

Influence of legislation and policies: During the training course Lorraine reflects on her own experiences of working as a Carer with adults who have learning disabilities and considers how the legislation, guidance and agreed ways of working that are in place have enabled her in her role as a Carer to support the human rights of individuals who have learning disabilities, as well as empower individuals to be active members of society and enable them to be included as part of their communities and families, access equal life opportunities in relation to areas such as work, education, leisure, family and social networking.

Evidencing AC1.2 to your assessor:

For AC1.2 you must evidence your understanding of how this legislation and policies influence the day-to-day experiences of individuals with learning disabilities and their families.

Assessment Methods:

Oral or **Written** Questioning or **Discussion** or a **Personal Statement** or **Reflection**

- You can **tell** your assessor about how this legislation and policies influence the day-to-day experiences of individuals with learning disabilities and their families.
  Or
- You can **talk** to your assessor about how this legislation and policies influence the day-to-day experiences of individuals with learning disabilities and their families.
  Or
- You can write a **personal statement** or **reflection** about your experience of how this legislation and policies influence the day-to-day experiences of individuals with learning disabilities and their families.

REMEMBER TO:

- Provide an account and explain how.
- Include details about different legislation and policies.
- Include examples of how this legislation and policies influence the day-to-day experiences of both individuals who have learning disabilities and their families.
- Think about your work setting and how this legislation and policies influence the day-to-day experiences of individuals with learning disabilities and their families.

Learning Outcome 2: Understand the nature and characteristics of learning disability

Assessment Criterion 2.1: Explain what is meant by 'learning disability'

What does AC2.1 mean?

- The lead word **explain** means that you must **make clear** what is meant by 'learning disability'.
- Your account must detail the meaning of 'learning disability'.
- For the key words **learning disability** you can think about how this is related to an individual's ability to understand information, learn skills, be independent and the effects on an individual's development throughout their life.

Read the following **Real Work Setting** scenario and think about how it relates to your work setting and role:

Real Work Setting

Name: Andreas

Job Role: Residential Carer for older adults who have learning disabilities

Andreas has been working as a Residential Carer for 13 years. His responsibilities include: supporting individuals to maximise their independence, maintain family relationships and friendships, as well as access community opportunities.

The meaning of learning disability: During Andreas's shift one of the recently recruited Residential Carers asks Andreas whether he could suggest some reading that she could do around working with individuals who have learning disabilities, as this is the first time she has worked in this field. Andreas suggests for her to consider reading the Department of Health's 2001 policy document called 'Valuing People: A New Strategy for Learning Disability for the 21st Century' in which they include details about the meaning of learning disability. Andreas then discusses with her how the term 'learning disability' is a generic term but how all individuals who have learning disabilities are unique and therefore will also have varying abilities and skills.

Evidencing AC2.1 to your assessor:

For AC2.1 you must evidence your understanding of what is meant by 'learning disability'.

Assessment Methods:

Oral or **Written** Questioning or **Discussion** or a **Personal Statement**

- You can **tell** your assessor about what is meant by 'learning disability'.
  Or
- You can **talk** to your assessor about what is meant by 'learning disability'.
  Or
- You can write a **personal statement** about what is meant by 'learning disability'.

REMEMBER TO:

- Provide an account and explain.
- Include details about what is meant by 'learning disability'.
- Think about **your work setting** and explain what is meant by 'learning disability'.

Learning Outcome 2: Understand the nature and characteristics of learning disability

Assessment Criterion 2.2: Give examples of causes of learning disability

What does AC2.2 mean?

- The lead words **give examples** mean that you must provide **details** about examples of causes of learning disability.
- Your **account** must detail the causes of learning disability.
- For the key word **causes** you can think about the reasons for learning disabilities occurring in individuals before birth, during birth and after birth.
- For the key words **learning disabilities** you can think about the causes of individuals' varying development and abilities to understand information, learn skills, be independent.

Read the following **Real Work Setting** scenario and think about how it relates to your work setting and role:

Real Work Setting

Name: Andreas

Job Role: Residential Carer for older adults who have learning disabilities
(See page 174 for a description of the role)

The causes of learning disability: Andreas and the newly recruited Residential Carer then spend some time looking at the Foundation for People with Learning Disabilities and the British Institute of Learning Disabilities websites and discuss the information available there in relation to the causes of learning disabilities occurring in individuals. Both discuss how the cause of learning disability before birth may be in relation to the individual's mother being unwell or having an unhealthy lifestyle or to genetics; learning disability may occur during birth when an individual's mother experiences difficulties that reduce the amount of oxygen supplied to the individual's brain; and after birth such as, for example, when an individual has a sudden illness or accident.

Evidencing AC2.2 to your assessor:

For AC2.2 you must evidence your understanding of examples of causes of learning disability.

Assessment Methods:

Oral or **Written** Questioning or **Discussion** or a **Personal Statement**

- You can **tell** your assessor about examples of causes of learning disability.
  Or
- You can **talk** to your assessor about examples of causes of learning disability.
  Or
- You can write a **personal statement** about examples of causes of learning disability.

REMEMBER TO:

- Provide an account and give examples of causes.
- Include details about the causes of learning disability.
- Think about **your work setting** and give examples of causes of learning disability .

Derby Teaching Hospitals
NHS Foundation Trust
Library and Knowledge Centre

Learning Outcome 2: Understand the nature and characteristics of learning disability

Assessment Criterion 2.3: Describe the medical and social models of disability

What does AC2.3 mean?

- The lead word **describe** means that you must provide an **account** that **details** the medical and social models of disability.
- Your **account** must detail both the medical and social models of disability.
- For the key words **medical model** you can think about how this model focuses on the individual's learning disability and their condition.
- For the key words **social model** you can think about how this model focuses on the individual and who they are.

Read the following **Real Work Setting** scenario and think about how it relates to your work setting and role:

Real Work Setting

Name: Andreas

Job Role: Residential Carer for older adults who have learning disabilities
(See page 174 for a description of the role)

The medical and social models of disability: Andreas and the newly recruited Residential Carer then have a discussion about the medical and social models of disability to assist with gaining an insight into how individuals who have learning disabilities experience their disability. They discuss how both models are very different and how the social model of disability supports the working practices and approaches used in their work setting.

Evidencing AC2.3 to your assessor:

For AC2.3 you must evidence your understanding of the medical and social models of disability.

Assessment Methods:

Oral or **Written** Questioning or **Discussion** or a **Personal Statement**

- You can **tell** your assessor about the medical and social models of disability.
  Or
- You can **talk** to your assessor about the medical and social models of disability.
  Or
- You can write a **personal statement** about the medical and social models of disability.

REMEMBER TO:

- Provide an account that details both models of disability.
- Include details about the medical model of disability.
- Include details about the social model of disability.
- Think about **your work setting** and the medical and social models of disability.

Learning Outcome 2: Understand the nature and characteristics of learning disability

Assessment Criterion 2.4: State the approximate proportion of individuals with a learning disability for whom the cause is 'not known'

What does AC2.4 mean?

- The lead word **state** means that you must provide an **account** that **details** the approximate proportion of individuals with a learning disability for whom the cause is 'not known'.
- Your **account** must detail the approximate proportion of individuals with a learning disability.
- For the key words **approximate proportion** you can think about finding out the number of individuals with a learning disability for whom the cause of their learning disability is not known.
- For the key word **cause** you can think about the approximate proportion of individuals with a learning disability for whom the reason for their learning disabilities is not known.

Read the following **Real Work Setting** scenario and think about how it relates to your work setting and role:

Real Work Setting

Name: Andreas

Job Role: Residential Carer for older adults who have learning disabilities
(See page 174 for a description of the role)

The approximate proportion of individuals with a learning disability for whom the cause is not known: Andreas continues to discuss with the newly recruited Residential Carer how although they previously talked about the reasons for learning disabilities occurring in individuals before birth, during birth and after birth that sometimes there is no known cause for a learning disability. Both again look at the British Institute of Learning Disabilities website to find out more information about the current numbers of individuals who have learning disabilities and for whom the cause is unknown.

Evidencing AC2.4 to your assessor:

For AC2.4 you must evidence your understanding of the approximate proportion of individuals with a learning disability for whom the cause is 'not known'.

Assessment Methods:

Oral or **Written** Questioning or **Discussion** or a **Personal Statement**

- You can **tell** your assessor about the approximate proportion of individuals with a learning disability for whom the cause is 'not known'.
  Or
- You can **talk** to your assessor about the approximate proportion of individuals with a learning disability for whom the cause is 'not known'.
  Or
- You can write a **personal statement** about the approximate proportion of individuals with a learning disability for whom the cause is 'not known'.

REMEMBER TO:

- Provide an account that details the approximate proportion.
- Include details about the number of individuals who have learning disabilities for whom the cause is 'not known'.
- Think about **your work setting** and the approximate proportion of individuals with a learning disability for whom the cause is 'not known'.

Learning Outcome 2: Understand the nature and characteristics of learning disability

Assessment Criterion 2.5: Describe the possible impact on a family of having a member with a learning disability

What does AC2.5 mean?

- The lead word **describe** means that you must provide an **account** that **details** the possible impact on a family of having a member with a learning disability.
- Your **account** must detail the possible impact on a family.
- For the key words **possible impact** you can think about the effect on a family of having a member with a learning disability such as the emotional impact on a family, or the physical demands that exist in terms of care and support, and how these can impact on a family's economic and social well-being, as well as on individual family members' relationships, health and well-being.

Read the following **Real Work Setting** scenario and think about how it relates to your work setting and role:

Real Work Setting

Name: Andreas

Job Role: Residential Carer for older adults who have learning disabilities
(See page 174 for a description of the role)

The possible impact on a family: Andreas and the newly recruited Residential Carer then consider the different families of the individuals they provide care and support to and discuss how having a family member with a learning disability can put additional pressures on a family, in terms of making additional demands on their time, resources, health and well-being. Both agree that the demands will vary from one family to another, depending on the relationships within that family, the support that has been made available and accessed by the family, as well as the individual's needs, requirements and preferences.

Evidencing AC2.5 to your assessor:

For AC2.5 you must evidence your understanding of the possible impact on a family of having a member with a learning disability.

Assessment Methods:

Oral or **Written** Questioning or **Discussion** or a **Personal Statement**

- You can **tell** your assessor about the possible impact on a family of having a member with a learning disability.
  Or
- You can **talk** to your assessor about the possible impact on a family of having a member with a learning disability.
  Or
- You can write a **personal statement** about the possible impact on a family of having a member with a learning disability.

REMEMBER TO:

- Provide an account that details the possible impact.
- Include details of the possible impact on a family of having a member with a learning disability.
- Think about **your work setting** and the possible impact on a family of having a member with a learning disability.

Learning Outcome 3: Understand the historical context of learning disability

Assessment Criterion 3.1: Explain the types of services that have been provided for individuals with learning disabilities over time

What does AC3.1 mean?

- The lead word **explain** means that you must **make clear** what is meant by the types of services that have been provided for individuals with learning disabilities over time.
- Your **account** must detail the types of services that have been provided.
- For the key words **types of services** you can think about how the services that have been provided for individuals with learning disabilities over time have varied throughout the years as society's understanding of the meaning of learning disabilities has changed over the nineteenth, twentieth and twenty-first centuries such as providing assistance to individuals in the form of 'asylums', 'institutions', 'long-stay hospitals' and then in their own homes in the community.

Read the following **Real Work Setting** scenario and think about how it relates to your work setting and role:

Real Work Setting

Name: Jacinta

Job Role: Home Carer for young adults who have learning disabilities

Jacinta has worked as a Home Carer for seven years. Her responsibilities include empowering and enabling individuals to make their own choices about how they want to live their lives and the support they require to do this.

The types of services provided: Jacinta is working on Unit LD201 as part of her L2 Diploma in Health and Social Care (Adults) for England qualification. Jacinta found it very interesting but also quite upsetting to explore in the workshop she attended how people with learning disabilities were treated over time. The building of asylums in the nineteenth century reflected society's perceptions at that time of individuals who had learning disabilities as unstable and worthless. The introduction of institutions in the twentieth century reflected society's desire to segregate all individuals who have learning disabilities and then to 'cure' them in the provision of 'long-stay' hospitals. Jacinta considered how these services compare to the personal and individual support provided now to individuals who have learning disabilities and who live in their own homes and with their own families.

Evidencing AC3.1 to your assessor:

For AC3.1 you must evidence your understanding of the types of services that have been provided for individuals with learning disabilities over time.

Assessment Methods:

Oral or **Written** Questioning or **Discussion** or a **Personal Statement**

- You can **tell** your assessor about the types of services that have been provided for individuals with learning disabilities over time.
  Or
- You can **talk** to your assessor about the types of services that have been provided for individuals with learning disabilities over time.
  Or
- You can write a **personal statement** about the types of services that have been provided for individuals with learning disabilities over time.

REMEMBER TO:

- Provide an account and explain.
- Include details about the types of services that have been provided.
- Think about **your work setting** and explain the types of services that have been provided for individuals with learning disabilities over time.

Learning Outcome 3: Understand the historical context of learning disability

Assessment Criterion 3.2: Describe how past ways of working may affect present services

What does AC3.2 mean?

- The lead word **describe** means that you must provide an **account** that **details** how past ways of working may affect present services.
- Your **account** must detail how.
- For the key words **present services** you can think about how this may include a range of provision such as supported living schemes, self-directed support for people who have learning disabilities to make choices about how to live their lives, access to employment, leisure, social opportunities and personalised support services.

Read the following **Real Work Setting** scenario and think about how it relates to your work setting and role:

Real Work Setting

Name: Jacinta

Job Role: Home Carer for young adults who have learning disabilities
(See page 179 for a description of the role)

Effects of past ways of working on present services: Jacinta also took part in group discussions about how past ways of working may affect the services that are provided even now to people who have learning disabilities. Jacinta considered how although there are more individuals who have learning disabilities who now live either in their own homes or with their families, the support and services provided by the organisations and people who work in these may still perceive individuals who have learning disabilities in a negative way, or may have adopted poor ways of working from the past that are not person-centred and that do not empower individuals or recognise their rights to live their lives as they wish.

Evidencing AC3.2 to your assessor:

For AC3.2 you must evidence your understanding of how past ways of working may affect present services.

Assessment Methods:

Oral or **Written** Questioning or **Discussion** or a **Personal Statement** or **Reflection**

- You can **tell** your assessor about how past ways of working may affect present services.
  Or
- You can **talk** to your assessor about how past ways of working may affect present services.
  Or
- You can write a **personal statement** or **reflection** about your experience of how past ways of working may affect present services.

REMEMBER TO:

- Provide an account that details how past ways of working may affect present services.
- Include details of past ways of working and their possible effects on present day services.
- Ensure your evidence is related to services for people who have learning disabilities.
- Think about **your work setting** and how past ways of working may affect present services.

Learning Outcome 3: Understand the historical context of learning disability

Assessment Criterion 3.3: Identify some of the key changes in the following areas of the lives of individuals who have learning disabilities: where people live, daytime activities, employment, sexual relationships and parenthood, and the provision of healthcare

What does AC3.3 mean?

- The lead word **identify** means that you must **make clear** some of the key changes in the following areas of the lives of individuals who have learning disabilities: where people live, daytime activities, employment, sexual relationships and parenthood, and the provision of healthcare.
- Your **list** must make clear some of the key changes.
- For the key words **where people live** you can think about changes such as in terms of the support available to enable individuals to live more independently.
- For the key words **daytime activities** you can think about changes such as in terms of the support available to enable individuals to make their own choices about what to do during the daytime.
- For the key word **employment** you can think about changes such as in terms of the support available to enable individuals to access valued employment opportunities.
- For the key words **sexual relationships and parenthood** you can think about changes such as in terms of the support and services available to enable individuals to have personal relationships and be parents.
- For the key words **provision of healthcare** you can think about changes such as in terms of the services and support available to enable individuals to meet their healthcare needs.

Read the following **Real Work Setting** scenario and think about how it relates to your work setting and role:

Real Work Setting

Name: Jacinta

Job Role: Home Carer for young adults who have learning disabilities
(See page 179 for a description of the role)

Key changes: As part of Jacinta's final piece of work for Learning Outcome 3 of Unit LD201 she designs a poster to show some of the key changes that have occurred in the lives of individuals who have learning disabilities.

Evidencing AC3.3 to your assessor:

For AC3.3 you must evidence your understanding of the key changes in the following areas of the lives of individuals who have learning disabilities: where people live, daytime activities, employment, sexual relationships and parenthood, and the provision of healthcare.

Assessment Methods:

Oral or **Written** Questioning or **Discussion** or a **Spidergram**

- You can **tell** your assessor about the key changes.
  Or
- You can **talk** to your assessor about the key changes.
  Or
- You can complete a **spidergram** of the key changes.

REMEMBER TO:

- Include a list of the key changes.
- Think about your work setting and the key changes in the following areas of the lives of individuals who have learning disabilities: where people live, daytime activities, employment, sexual relationships and parenthood, and the provision of healthcare.

Learning Outcome 4: Understand the basic principles and practice of advocacy, empowerment and active participation in relation to supporting individuals with learning disabilities and their families

Assessment Criterion 4.1: Explain the meaning of the term 'social inclusion'

What does AC4.1 mean?

- The lead word **explain** means that you must **make clear** the meaning of the term 'social inclusion'.
- Your **account** must detail the meaning of 'social inclusion'.
- For the key words **social inclusion** you can think about how this involves supporting individuals who have learning disabilities and their families to feel valued, respected, their individuality and needs met.

Read the following **Real Work Setting** scenario and think about how it relates to your work setting and role:

Real Work Setting

Name: Malcolm

Job Role: Home Carer for older adults who have learning disabilities

Malcolm has been working as a Home Carer for four years. His responsibilities include: delivering individualised person-centred support, to promote and develop their independent living skills, as well as planning activities to engage the individuals while at home and accessing the community.

The meaning of the term 'social inclusion': After visiting Sean, who has a learning disability, at home, Malcolm and his colleague discuss on their way back to the office how best to enable individuals like Sean and their families to feel valued and respected. Malcolm explains to his colleague how, like him, he always ensures he doesn't make any assumptions or judgements about the individuals and their families that he provides support to and treats each individual as a unique person with their own needs, wishes and preferences and checks with individuals' families when appropriate to do so that the support being provided is also in line with their expectations, beliefs and lifestyle.

Evidencing AC4.1 to your assessor:

For AC4.1 you must evidence your understanding of the meaning of the term 'social inclusion'.

Assessment Methods:

Oral or **Written** Questioning or **Discussion** or a **Personal Statement**

- You can **tell** your assessor about the meaning of the term 'social inclusion'.

  Or
- You can **talk** to your assessor about the meaning of the term 'social inclusion'.

  Or
- You can write a **personal statement** about the meaning of the term 'social inclusion'.

REMEMBER TO:

- Provide an account and explain.
- Include details with examples about what is meant by 'social inclusion'.
- Think about your work setting and explain the meaning of the term 'social inclusion'.

Learning Outcome 4: Understand the basic principles and practice of advocacy, empowerment and active participation in relation to supporting individuals with learning disabilities and their families

Assessment Criterion 4.2: Explain the meaning of the term 'advocacy'

What does AC4.2 mean?

- The lead word **explain** means that you must make clear the meaning of the term 'advocacy'.
- Your **account** must detail the meaning of 'advocacy'.
- For the key word **advocacy** you can think about how this involves supporting individuals to have their views taken into account, accessing information and services, safeguarding their rights and finding out about different options available when making decisions about their lives.

Read the following **Real Work Setting** scenario and think about how it relates to your work setting and role:

Real Work Setting

Name: Malcolm

Job Role: Home Carer for older adults who have learning disabilities
(See page 182 for a description of the role)

The meaning of the term 'advocacy': Malcolm and his colleague then move on to discuss the role of Sean's advocate who was present today, as Sean was going to be attending a meeting this afternoon with his social worker and family to discuss how he would like his care needs to be met in the future if his health continues to deteriorate. Malcolm has noted that Sean's advocate is a good support to Sean, as he is able to present information to him in a way that he can understand and make his own decisions about how he wants to live his life. Sean has also told Malcolm that having his advocate present at meetings helps him to say what he really thinks, rather than what he thinks his family would want him to say.

Evidencing AC4.2 to your assessor:

For AC4.2 you must evidence your understanding of the meaning of the term 'advocacy'.

Assessment Methods:

Oral or **Written** Questioning or **Discussion** or a **Personal Statement**

- You can **tell** your assessor about the meaning of the term 'advocacy'.

  Or
- You can **talk** to your assessor about the meaning of the term 'advocacy'.

  Or
- You can write a **personal statement** about the meaning of the term 'advocacy'.

REMEMBER TO:

- Provide an account and explain.
- Include details with examples about what is meant by 'advocacy'.
- Think about your work setting and explain the meaning of the term 'advocacy'.

LD201

AC 4.3

Learning Outcome 4: Understand the basic principles and practice of advocacy, empowerment and active participation in relation to supporting individuals with learning disabilities and their families

Assessment Criterion 4.3: Describe different types of advocacy

What does AC4.3 mean?

- The lead word **describe** means that you must provide an **account** that **details** the different types of advocacy.
- Your **account** must detail different types.
- For the key words **types of advocacy** you can think about how individuals' needs are unique and how different forms of advocacy are necessary at different times in an individual's life such as self-advocacy, case advocacy, peer advocacy, paid independent advocacy, citizen advocacy and statutory advocacy.

Read the following **Real Work Setting** scenario and think about how it relates to your work setting and role:

Real Work Setting

Name: Malcolm

Job Role: Home Carer for older adults who have learning disabilities
(See page 182 for a description of the role)

Different types of advocacy: Malcolm's colleague tells him how he has thought about becoming an advocate to an individual with a learning disability but is unsure what type of advocate he would like to be, as he is aware that there are different types of advocacy available. Malcom discusses with his colleague how he is aware of the different types of advocacy that exist and how each type varies, depending on an individual's needs and requirements. For example, Malcolm shares with his colleague how case advocacy is offered on a relatively short-term basis and is usually provided when there is a conflict or a difficulty that can't be resolved. Other types of advocacy involve the development of a more long-term type of relationship with the individual.

Evidencing AC4.3 to your assessor:

For AC4.3 you must evidence your understanding of the different types of advocacy.

Assessment Methods:

Oral or **Written** Questioning or **Discussion** or a **Personal Statement**

- You can tell your assessor about the different types of advocacy.
  Or
- You can **talk** to your assessor about the different types of advocacy.
  Or
- You can write a **personal statement** about the different types of advocacy.

REMEMBER TO:

- Provide an account that details different types of advocacy.
- Include details about each type of advocacy.
- Think about your work setting and the different types of advocacy.

Learning Outcome 4: Understand the basic principles and practice of advocacy, empowerment and active participation in relation to supporting individuals with learning disabilities and their families

Assessment Criterion 4.4: Describe ways to build empowerment and active participation into everyday support with individuals with learning disabilities

What does AC4.4 mean?

- The lead word **describe** means that you must provide an **account** that **details** ways to build empowerment and active participation into everyday support with individuals with learning disabilities.
- Your **account** must detail different ways to build empowerment and active participation.
- For the key words **ways to build empowerment** you can think about how you can support individuals with learning disabilities to take control of their lives such as by person-centred thinking, maximising individuals' choices, enabling individuals to make their own decisions and promoting individuals' rights.
- For the key words **active participation** you can think about how you can enable individuals with learning disabilities to be fully involved in all aspects of their lives such as by enabling them to express what they think, to achieve their goals and to live their lives as they wish.

Read the following **Real Work Setting** scenario and think about how it relates to your work setting and role:

Real Work Setting

Name: Malcolm

Job Role: Home Carer for older adults who have learning disabilities
(See page 182 for a description of the role)

Ways to build empowerment and active participation: Following their discussion about the different types of advocacy that are available to people who have learning disabilities, Malcolm suggests to his colleague that he puts into practice some of the concepts on which advocacy is based, as doing so will enable the individuals he supports to be fully involved in all aspects of their day-to-day living.

Evidencing AC4.4 to your assessor:

For AC4.4 you must evidence your understanding of ways to build empowerment and active participation into everyday support with individuals with learning disabilities.

Assessment Methods:

Oral or **Written** Questioning or **Discussion** or a **Personal Statement** or **Reflection**

- You can **tell** your assessor about the ways to build empowerment and active participation into everyday support with individuals with learning disabilities.
  Or
- You can **talk** to your assessor about the ways to build empowerment and active participation into everyday support with individuals with learning disabilities.
  Or
- You can write a **personal statement** or **reflection** about the ways to build empowerment and active participation into everyday support with individuals with learning disabilities.

REMEMBER TO:

- Provide an account that details different ways.
- Include details about ways to build empowerment.
- Include details about ways to build active participation.
- Ensure your evidence is related to everyday support with individuals who have learning disabilities.
- Think about your work setting and the ways to build empowerment and active participation into everyday support with individuals with learning disabilities.

Learning Outcome 5: Understand how views and attitudes impact on the lives of individuals with learning disabilities and their family carers

Assessment Criterion 5.1: Explain how attitudes are changing in relation to individuals with learning disabilities

What does AC5.1 mean?

- The lead word **explain** means that you must **make clear** how attitudes are changing in relation to individuals with learning disabilities.
- Your **account** must detail how attitudes are changing.
- For the key word **attitudes** you can think about how the way people view and feel in relation to individuals with learning disabilities is changing, such as by people becoming more understanding and empathetic towards individuals with learning disabilities through having more contact with individuals, as well as hearing and reading about positive ways of working and aspects of the lives of individuals who have learning disabilities.

Read the following **Real Work Setting** scenario and think about how it relates to your work setting and role:

Real Work Setting

Name: Tashina

Job Role: Personal Assistant for adults who have learning disabilities

Tashina has been working as a Personal Assistant for four years. Her responsibilities include: supporting individuals with personal care and household tasks within the home, as well as enabling individuals to access their local community facilities and services, maintain friendships and relationships.

Attitudes in relation to people who have learning disabilities: Tashina has worked with people who have learning disabilities for over 15 years in a variety of different work settings and in her current role as a Personal Assistant has in the main experienced positive attitudes from others towards individuals who have learning disabilities such as, for example, when out shopping or in the park or at the swimming pool or the gym.

Evidencing AC5.1 to your assessor:

For AC5.1 you must evidence your understanding of how attitudes are changing in relation to individuals with learning disabilities.

Assessment Methods:

Oral or **Written** Questioning or **Discussion** or a **Personal Statement** or **Reflection**

- You can **tell** your assessor about how attitudes are changing in relation to individuals with learning disabilities.
  Or
- You can **talk** to your assessor about how attitudes are changing in relation to individuals with learning disabilities.
  Or
- You can write a **personal statement** or **reflection** about your experience of how attitudes are changing in relation to individuals with learning disabilities.

REMEMBER TO:

- Provide an account and explain.
- Include details with examples about how attitudes are changing.
- Ensure your evidence is related to individuals with learning disabilities.
- Think about your work setting and how attitudes are changing in relation to individuals with learning disabilities.

Learning Outcome 5: Understand how views and attitudes impact on the lives of individuals with learning disabilities and their family carers

Assessment Criterion 5.2: Give examples of positive and negative aspects of being labelled as having a learning disability

What does AC5.2 mean?

- The lead words **give examples** mean that you must provide **details** about positive and negative aspects of being labelled as having a learning disability.
- Your **account** must detail both positive and negative aspects.
- For the key word **positive** you can think about how being labelled as having a learning disability can be beneficial to individuals and their family carers such as by being able to have their individual needs met.
- For the key word **negative** you can think about how being labelled as having a learning disability can be obstructive for individuals and their family carers such as by making the individual's disability the focus.
- For the key word **labelled** you can think about how this can involve being both helpful and restrictive to individuals who have a learning disability and their family carers.

Read the following **Real Work Setting** scenario and think about how it relates to your work setting and role:

Real Work Setting

Name: Tashina

Job Role: Personal Assistant for adults who have learning disabilities
(See page 186 for a description of the role)

Positive and negative aspects of being labelled: Tashina remembers attending a training course many years ago that was hosted by a People First group who stated that 'Labels are for jars not people.' Tashina agrees that labelling an individual as having a learning disability can draw attention to their disability rather than who they are as an individual. Equally though, through her different roles in working with individuals who have learning disabilities she can see how it is also important for those who provide care and support to know about the individual and how their learning disability affects them so that they can ensure the individual's needs are fully met.

Evidencing AC5.2 to your assessor:

For AC5.2 you must evidence your understanding of examples of positive and negative aspects of being labelled as having a learning disability.

Assessment Methods:

Oral or **Written** Questioning or **Discussion** or a **Personal Statement**

- You can **tell** your assessor about examples of positive and negative aspects of being labelled as having a learning disability.
  Or
- You can **talk** to your assessor about examples of positive and negative aspects of being labelled as having a learning disability.
  Or
- You can write a **personal statement** about examples of positive and negative aspects of being labelled as having a learning disability.

REMEMBER TO:

- Provide an account and give examples.
- Include details about both positive and negative aspects.
- Ensure your evidence is related to being labelled as having a learning disability.
- Think about **your work setting** and give examples of positive and negative aspects of being labelled as having a learning disability.

Learning Outcome 5: Understand how views and attitudes impact on the lives of individuals with learning disabilities and their family carers

Assessment Criterion 5.3: Describe steps that can be taken to promote positive attitudes towards individuals who have learning disabilities and their family carers

What does AC5.3 mean?

- The lead word **describe** means that you must provide an **account** that **details** steps that can be taken to promote positive attitudes towards individuals who have learning disabilities and their family carers.
- Your **account** must detail different steps that can be taken.
- For the key word **steps** you can think about the process that can be followed to promote positive attitudes such as by raising awareness of the meaning of learning disabilities, recognising the role of family carers in individuals' lives and celebrating positive aspects of the lives of individuals who have learning disabilities and their family carers.
- For the key words **positive attitudes** you can think about the process that can be followed to promote positive views and feelings about individuals who have learning disabilities and their family carers such as through maximising opportunities and their access to a range of services and facilities.

Read the following **Real Work Setting** scenario and think about how it relates to your work setting and role:

Real Work Setting

Name: Tashina

Job Role: Personal Assistant for adults who have learning disabilities
(See page 186 for a description of the role)

Steps that can be taken to promote positive attitudes: Tashina reflects on how promoting positive attitudes towards individuals who have learning disabilities and their family carers is an ongoing process and believes that this can be achieved through providing people with clear information, positive role models and sharing good news stories of individuals who have learning disabilities and their family carers.

Evidencing AC5.3 to your assessor:

For AC5.3 you must evidence your understanding of steps that can be taken to promote positive attitudes towards individuals who have learning disabilities and their family carers.

Assessment Methods:

Oral or **Written** Questioning or **Discussion** or a **Personal Statement** or **Reflection**

- You can **tell** your assessor about the steps that can be taken to promote positive attitudes towards individuals who have learning disabilities and their family carers.
  Or
- You can **talk** to your assessor about the steps that can be taken to promote positive attitudes towards individuals who have learning disabilities and their family carers.
  Or
- You can write a **personal statement** or **reflection** about your experience of steps that can be taken to promote positive attitudes towards individuals who have learning disabilities and their family carers.

REMEMBER TO:

- Provide an account that details different steps to follow.
- Include details about how to promote positive attitudes.
- Ensure your evidence is related to individuals who have learning disabilities and their family carers.
- Think about **your work setting** and the steps that can be taken to promote positive attitudes towards individuals who have learning disabilities and their family carers.

Learning Outcome 5: Understand how views and attitudes impact on the lives of individuals with learning disabilities and their family carers

Assessment Criterion 5.4: Explain the roles of external agencies and others in changing attitudes, policy and practice

What does AC5.4 mean?

- The lead word **explain** means that you must **make clear** the roles of external agencies and others in changing attitudes, policy and practice.
- Your **account** must **detail** the roles of external agencies and others.
- For the key words **external agencies** you can think about how advocacy services, parent and carer support groups, campaign groups and organisations that provide services to people who have learning disabilities can change attitudes, policy and practice such as by expressing the views and concerns of people who have learning disabilities and their family carers on, for example, funding available and the types of services required.
- For the key word **others** you can think about how individuals who have learning disabilities, their colleagues, families or carers, friends, other professionals, members of the public and advocates can change attitudes, policy and practice such as by sharing at both local and national levels aspects of individuals' lives, the support or services that are provided that are working well and those that need further improvement.

Read the following **Real Work Setting** scenario and think about how it relates to your work setting and role:

Real Work Setting

Name: Tashina

Job Role: Personal Assistant for adults who have learning disabilities
(See page 186 for a description of the role)

The roles of external agencies and others: Tashina is also aware of the role that the many external agencies and others who work with people who have learning disabilities play in ensuring individuals are able to lead their lives as they wish and continue to improve the quality of support, services and facilities that are available.

Evidencing AC5.4 to your assessor:

For AC5.4 you must evidence your understanding of the roles of external agencies and others in changing attitudes, policy and practice.

Assessment Methods:

Oral or **Written** Questioning or **Discussion** or a **Personal Statement** or **Reflection**

- You can **tell** your assessor about the roles of external agencies and others in changing attitudes, policy and practice.
  Or
- You can **talk** to your assessor about the roles of external agencies and others in changing attitudes, policy and practice.
  Or
- You can write a **personal statement** or **reflection** about your experience of the roles of external agencies and others in changing attitudes, policy and practice.

REMEMBER TO:

- Provide an account and explain.
- Include details with examples about the roles of external agencies and others.
- Ensure your evidence is related to changing attitudes, policy and practice.
- Think about **your work setting** and the roles of external agencies and others in changing attitudes, policy and practice.

Learning Outcome 6: Know how to promote communication with individuals with learning disabilities

Assessment Criterion 6.1: Identify ways of adapting each of the following when communicating with individuals who have learning disabilities: verbal communication and non-verbal communication

What does AC6.1 mean?

- The lead word **identify** means that you must **make clear** ways of adapting each of the following when communicating with individuals who have learning disabilities: verbal communication and non-verbal communication.
- Your **list** must make clear ways of adapting both verbal communication and non-verbal communication.
- For the key words **verbal communication** you can think about how you can adapt your vocabulary, linguistic tone and pitch when communicating with people who have learning disabilities.
- For the key words **non-verbal communication** you can think about how you can adapt the way you use eye contact, touch, physical gestures, your body language and behaviour when communicating with people who have learning disabilities.

Read the following **Real Work Setting** scenario and think about how it relates to your work setting and role:

Real Work Setting

Name: Akihiko

Job Role: Support Worker for adults who have learning disabilities

Akihiko has been working as a Support Worker for two years. His responsibilities include: delivering person-centred and individualised support, promoting individuals' choice, rights and independence and enabling individuals to play an active role in the community.

Verbal and non-verbal communication: Akihiko supports different individuals who have mild, moderate and severe learning disabilities. With some individuals Akihiko communicates by speaking with them on a one-to-one basis, with others he communicates by writing down short phrases, or by using signs and symbol communication systems such as Makaton and British Sign Language.

Evidencing AC6.1 to your assessor:

For AC6.1 you must evidence your knowledge of ways of adapting each of the following when communicating with individuals who have learning disabilities: verbal communication and non-verbal communication.

Assessment Methods:

Oral or **Written** Questioning or **Discussion** or a **Spidergram**

- You can **tell** your assessor about ways of adapting each of the following when communicating with individuals who have learning disabilities: verbal communication and non-verbal communication.

  Or
- You can **talk** to your assessor about ways of adapting each of the following when communicating with individuals who have learning disabilities: verbal communication and non-verbal communication.

  Or
- You can complete a **spidergram** of ways of adapting each of the following when communicating with individuals who have learning disabilities: verbal communication and non-verbal communication.

REMEMBER TO:

- Include a list of different ways.
- Ensure the list relates to both verbal and non-verbal communication.
- Include details about ways of adapting communication with people who have learning disabilities.
- Think about **your work setting** and ways of adapting each of the following when communicating with individuals who have learning disabilities: verbal communication and non-verbal communication.

Learning Outcome 6: Know how to promote communication with individuals with learning disabilities

Assessment Criterion 6.2: Explain why it is important to use language that is both 'age appropriate' and 'ability appropriate' when communicating with individuals with learning disabilities

What does AC6.2 mean?

- The lead word **explain** means that you must **make clear** why it is important to use language that is both 'age appropriate' and 'ability appropriate' when communicating with individuals who have learning disabilities.
- Your **account** must detail why it is important to use language that is both 'age appropriate' and 'ability appropriate'.
- For the key words **age appropriate** you can think about why it is important to use language that is suitable for the age of the individuals who have learning disabilities that you are communicating with, such as in terms of promoting their identity, self-esteem and dignity.
- For the key words **ability appropriate** you can think about why it is important to use language that is suitable for the level of skills of the individuals who have learning disabilities that you are communicating with, such as in terms of promoting their understanding and active involvement.

Read the following **Real Work Setting** scenario and think about how it relates to your work setting and role:

Real Work Setting

Name: Akihiko

Job Role: Support Worker for adults who have learning disabilities
(See page 190 for a description of the role)

Using language that is age appropriate and ability appropriate: Akihiko ensures that the language he uses to communicate with different individuals is chosen and led by them so that individuals feel that they are able to express what they think and feel in their own unique way and at their own pace.

Evidencing AC6.2 to your assessor:

For AC6.2 you must evidence your knowledge of why it is important to use language that is both 'age appropriate' and 'ability appropriate' when communicating with individuals who have learning disabilities.

Assessment Methods:

Oral or **Written** Questioning or **Discussion** or a **Personal Statement** or **Reflection**

- You can **tell** your assessor about why it is important to use language that is both 'age appropriate' and 'ability appropriate'.
  Or
- You can **talk** to your assessor about why it is important to use language that is both 'age appropriate' and 'ability appropriate'.
  Or
- You can write a **personal statement** or **reflection** about your experience of why it is important to use language that is both 'age appropriate' and 'ability appropriate'.

REMEMBER TO:

- Provide an account and explain.
- Include details with examples about the reasons why it is important to use language that is both 'age appropriate' and 'ability appropriate'.
- Ensure your evidence is related to when communicating with individuals who have learning disabilities.
- Think about **your work setting** and why it is important to use language that is both 'age appropriate' and 'ability appropriate' when communicating with individuals who have learning disabilities.

Learning Outcome 6: Know how to promote communication with individuals with learning disabilities

Assessment Criterion 6.3: Describe ways of checking whether an individual has understood a communication and how to address any misunderstandings

What does AC6.3 mean?

- The lead word **describe** means that you must provide an **account** that **details** ways of checking whether an individual has understood a communication and how to address any misunderstandings.
- Your **account** must detail different ways of checking and how to address any misunderstandings.
- For the key word **checking** you can think about the different ways of clarifying whether an individual has understood a communication such as by listening to the individual, observing the individual's body language, facial expressions, signs used, or by seeking advice from someone who knows the individual well.
- For the key word **misunderstandings** you can think about the different ways of addressing any difficulties that you may experience when communicating with individuals who have learning disabilities such as the individual not fully understanding you, or you not being able to understand the individual, or you not being sure about the way the individual uses to communicate with others.

Read the following **Real Work Setting** scenario and think about how it relates to your work setting and role:

Real Work Setting

Name: Akihiko

Job Role: Support Worker for adults who have learning disabilities
(See page 190 for a description of the role)

Checking understanding and addressing misunderstandings: Akihiko always checks with each individual by observing them carefully and actively listening to how and what they express to avoid any misunderstandings which can be frustrating and upsetting. When misunderstandings do occur Akihiko immediately seeks advice from someone who knows the individual well.

Evidencing AC6.3 to your assessor:

For AC6.3 you must evidence your knowledge of ways of checking whether an individual has understood a communication and how to address any misunderstandings.

Assessment Methods:

Oral or **Written** Questioning or **Discussion** or a **Personal Statement** or **Reflection**

- You can **tell** your assessor about the ways of checking whether an individual has understood a communication and how to address any misunderstandings.
  Or
- You can **talk** to your assessor about the ways of checking whether an individual has understood a communication and how to address any misunderstandings.
  Or
- You can write a **personal statement** or **reflection** about your experience of ways of checking whether an individual has understood a communication and how to address any misunderstandings.

REMEMBER TO:

- Provide an account that details different ways.
- Include details about how to check whether an individual has understood a communication.
- Include details about how to address any misunderstandings.
- Ensure your evidence is related to communication with people who have learning disabilities.
- Think about **your work setting** and the ways of checking whether an individual has understood a communication and how to address any misunderstandings.

ASM34 Administer medication to individuals and monitor the effects

Learning Outcome 1: Understand legislation, policy and procedures relevant to administration of medication

Assessment Criterion 1.1: Identify current legislation, guidelines, policies and protocols relevant to administration of medication

What does AC1.1 mean?

- The lead word **identify** means that you must **make clear** the current legislation, guidelines, policies and protocols relevant to administration of medication.
- Your **list** must make clear current legislation, guidelines, policies and protocols.
- For the key word **legislation** you can think about the relevant laws in place that relate to administering medication.
- For the key word **guidelines** you can think about relevant guidance in place such as that from the Nursing and Midwifery Council's Standards.
- For the key words **policies and protocols** you can think about the medication policies and procedures available in your work setting.

Read the following **Real Work Setting** scenario and think about how it relates to your work setting and role:

Real Work Setting

Name: Samuel
Job Role: Personal Assistant for an adult who has physical disabilities
Samuel has been working as a Personal Assistant for three months. His responsibilities include: assisting with personal care, administering medication, preparing meals, using the computer and going out.
Identifying current legislation, guidelines, policies and protocols: As part of Samuel's initial training he completed an in-depth course that focused on administering medication. The course had been designed with the individual Samuel supports and was focused on meeting his needs and requirements. The training also involved updating Samuel's knowledge of the current legislation and guidelines that are relevant to the administration of medication and provided Samuel with an opportunity to read through and clarify his understanding of the work setting's medication policy and procedures.

Evidencing AC1.1 to your assessor:

For AC1.1 you must evidence your knowledge of current legislation, guidelines, policies and protocols relevant to administration of medication.

Assessment Methods:

Oral or **Written** Questioning or **Discussion** or a **Spidergram**

- You can **tell** your assessor about current legislation, guidelines, policies and protocols relevant to administration of medication.
  Or
- You can **talk** to your assessor about current legislation, guidelines, policies and protocols relevant to administration of medication.
  Or
- You can complete a **spidergram** of current legislation, guidelines, policies and protocols relevant to administration of medication.

REMEMBER TO:

- Include a **list** of current legislation, guidelines, policies and protocols relevant to administration of medication.
- Ensure the list relates to the administration of medication.
- Think about **your work setting** and current legislation, guidelines, policies and protocols relevant to administration of medication.

Learning Outcome 2: Know about common types of medication and their use

Assessment Criterion 2.1: Describe common types of medication including their effects and potential side effects

What does AC2.1 mean?

- The lead word **describe** means that you must provide an **account** that **details** common types of medication including their effects and potential side effects.
- Your **account** must detail common types of medication.
- For the key words **types of medication** you can think about how the Medicines Act 1968 classifies medication into different groups.
- For the key word **effects** you can think about the different purposes of medications, how they are used and how they work.
- For the key words **potential side effects** you can think about the ways that medications may impact both positively and negatively on an individual's physical, mental or emotional well-being.

Read the following **Real Work Setting** scenario and think about how it relates to your work setting and role:

Real Work Setting

Name: Candice

Job Role: Home Carer for older people

Candice has been working as a Home Carer for two years. Her responsibilities include: supporting individuals with daily activities such as washing, dressing, undressing, using the toilet, medication, eating and drinking, as well as household tasks such as laundry and cleaning and other general tasks such as paying bills and budgeting.

Common types of medications: Today, Candice is visiting Heidi who lives at home on her own. Heidi explains to Candice that she has been given some new medication and has been told that it is an analgesic but does not fully understand what this means. Candice explains to Heidi that common types of medications fall under four main groups: analgesics, antibiotics, antidepressants and anticoagulants and that analgesics are medications for the relief of pain. Heidi and Candice read through the leaflet that has come with the medication, which indicates it contains ibuprofen; this means that it comes under the group of analgesic medications called non-steroidal anti-inflammatory drugs. Heidi thanks Candice for the information and they both continue to read through the medication's leaflet to find out more about its effects and potential side effects.

Evidencing AC2.1 to your assessor:

For AC2.1 you must evidence your knowledge of common types of medication including their effects and potential side effects.

Assessment Methods:

Oral or **Written** Questioning or **Discussion** or a **Personal Statement** or **Reflection**

- You can **tell** your assessor about common types of medication including their effects and potential side effects.

  Or
- You can **talk** to your assessor about common types of medication including their effects and potential side effects.

  Or
- You can write a **personal statement** or **reflection** about your experience of common types of medication including their effects and potential side effects.

REMEMBER TO:

- Provide an account that details **common types of medication**.
- Ensure your evidence includes both their **effects** and **potential side effects**.
- Think about **your work setting** and common types of medication including their effects and potential side effects.

Learning Outcome 2: Know about common types of medication and their use

Assessment Criterion 2.2: Identify medication which demands the measurement of specific physiological measurements

What does AC2.2 mean?

- The lead word **identify** means that you must **make clear** the medications that require the measurement of specific physiological measurements.
- Your **list** must make clear different medications that require the measurement of specific physiological measurements.
- For the key words **specific physiological measurements** you can think about the requirements of some medications to make checks of how well the body is working before and after they are administered or used.

Read the following **Real Work Setting** scenario and think about how it relates to your work setting and role:

Real Work Setting

Name: Candice

Job Role: Home Carer for older people
(See page 194 for a description of the role)

Specific physiological measurements: This afternoon, Candice visits Angelina who tells her all about her GP appointment which took place this morning and how her GP has told her that it is very important that checks are made both before and after administering her medication. Candice listens carefully to Angelina and then confirms the information that she has been given by her GP, explaining that as she is taking different medications this is why she has to go to her GP to have regular blood tests and also have her pulse taken by the Carers before taking her heart medication. Candice then continues to read through with her the information contained within the leaflet that has come with both medications to explain to her in more detail the reasons why specific physiological measurements are required for these.

Evidencing AC2.2 to your assessor:

For AC2.2 you must evidence your knowledge of the medication which demands the measurement of specific physiological measurements.

Assessment Methods:

Oral or **Written** Questioning or **Discussion** or a **Spidergram**

- You can **tell** your assessor about the medication which demands the measurement of specific physiological measurements.
  Or
- You can **talk** to your assessor about the medication which demands the measurement of specific physiological measurements.
  Or
- You can complete a **spidergram** of the medication which demands the measurement of specific physiological measurements.

REMEMBER TO:

- List examples of **different medications**.
- Ensure that your list is for medications that require **specific physiological measurements**.
- Think about **your work setting** and the medication which demands the measurement of specific physiological measurements.

Learning Outcome 2: Know about common types of medication and their use

Assessment Criterion 2.3: Describe the common adverse reactions to medication, how each can be recognised and the appropriate action(s) required

What does AC2.3 mean?

- The lead word **describe** means that you must provide an account that **details** the common adverse reactions to medication, how each can be recognised and the appropriate action(s) required.
- Your **account** must detail different common adverse reactions to medication.
- For the key words **adverse reactions** you can think about the negative side effects that a medication may have on an individual's physical, mental or emotional well-being.
- For the key words **appropriate actions required** you can think about the actions to take in line with your work setting's agreed ways of working and your job role and responsibilities.

Read the following **Real Work Setting** scenario and think about how it relates to your work setting and role:

Real Work Setting

Name: Candice

Job Role: Home Carer for older people
(See page 194 for a description of the role)

Common adverse reactions to medication: Towards the end of Candice's visit, Angelina tells Candice that having read through both medications' leaflets with her she was unaware of how many adverse reactions to medication there are and is a little concerned that she may experience some of these. Candice reassures Angelina and explains to her that not all these adverse reactions are experienced by everyone who takes the medications but that the team of Carers have regular medication training and are experienced in recognising any of these adverse reactions and are fully aware of the immediate actions that must be taken should any of these be observed in her. Angelina thanks Candice for the information and says she feels a lot better now.

Evidencing AC2.3 to your assessor:

For AC2.3 you must evidence your knowledge of the common adverse reactions to medication, how each can be recognised and the appropriate action(s) required.

Assessment Methods:

Oral or **Written** Questioning or **Discussion** or a **Personal Statement** or **Reflection**

- You can **tell** your assessor about the common adverse reactions to medication, how each can be recognised and the appropriate action(s) required.
  Or
- You can **talk** to your assessor about the common adverse reactions to medication, how each can be recognised and the appropriate action(s) required.
  Or
- You can write a **personal statement** or **reflection** about your experience of the common adverse reactions to medication, how each can be recognised and the appropriate action(s) required.

REMEMBER TO:

- Provide a detailed **account**.
- Include **details** about common adverse reactions to medication.
- Ensure your evidence includes how to recognise each one and the actions that must be taken.
- Think about **your work setting** and the common adverse reactions to medication, how each can be recognised and the appropriate action(s) required.

Learning Outcome 2: Know about common types of medication and their use

Assessment Criterion 2.4: Explain the different routes of medicine administration

What does AC2.4 mean?

- The lead word **explain** means that you must **make clear** the different routes of medicine administration.
- Your **account** must detail different routes.
- For the key word **routes** you can think about how medication can be administered in different ways such as via inhalation, instillation, orally, transdermally, topically, intravenously, rectally, vaginally, subcutaneously and intramuscularly.

Read the following **Real Work Setting** scenario and think about how it relates to your work setting and role:

Real Work Setting

Name: Candice

Job Role: Home Carer for older people
(See page 194 for a description of the role)

Routes of medicine administration: Candice's final visit today is to Naomi, who is having difficulties taking the medication she has recently been prescribed. Naomi explains that she does not like swallowing the tablets she has been given to take every morning, as they seem to get stuck in her throat and then she panics because she feels that she is going to choke. Candice reassures Naomi and explains to her that some medications, but not all, also come in liquids, suspensions and syrups. Candice suggests to Naomi that when she visits her GP this afternoon with her daughter she explains to him that she has difficulty in swallowing her medication. Naomi asks Candice whether she thinks that a cream may be better rather than medication that she has to swallow; Candice explains to Naomi that she does not know if her medication can be given via the topical route and that again she will need to seek advice from her GP in relation to this.

Evidencing AC2.4 to your assessor:

For AC2.4 you must evidence your knowledge of the different routes of medicine administration.

Assessment Methods:

Oral or **Written** Questioning or **Discussion** or a **Personal Statement** or **Reflection**

- You can **tell** your assessor about the different routes of medicine administration.
  Or
- You can **talk** to your assessor about the different routes of medicine administration.
  Or
- You can write a **personal statement** or **reflection** about your experience of the different routes of medicine administration.

REMEMBER TO:

- Provide an **account** and **explain** the different routes.
- Include **details** about what each route involves.
- Provide **examples** of medications that can be administered by each of the different routes.
- Include details of any **special requirements** that must be followed.
- Think about **your work setting** and the different routes of medicine administration.

Learning Outcome 3: Understand procedures and techniques for the administration of medication

Assessment Criterion 3.1: Explain the types, purpose and function of materials and equipment needed for the administration of medication via the different routes

What does AC3.1 mean?

- The lead word **explain** means that you must **make clear** the different routes of medicine administration.
- Your **account** must detail different routes.
- For the key words **materials and equipment** you can think about the range of items that can help in the administration of medication such as gloves, inhalers, nebulisers, medication cups and spoons: what they are, why they are used and how.
- For the key word **routes** you can think about how medication can be administered in different ways such as via inhalation, instillation, orally, transdermally, topically, intravenously, rectally, vaginally, subcutaneously and intramuscularly and the materials and equipment needed.

Read the following **Real Work Setting** scenario and think about how it relates to your work setting and role:

Real Work Setting

Name: Jason

Job Role: Home Carer for young adults

Jason has been working as a Home Carer for one year. His responsibilities include: promoting individuals' independence, assisting individuals with their medication, as well as supporting individuals to complete household tasks such as vacuuming, dusting and washing dishes.

Materials and equipment needed for medicine administration: Jason has recently attended a training update on medication and received useful information about the types, purpose and functions of materials and equipment needed for the administration of medication via the different routes. Jason was able to use his own experiences of the individuals he supports to explain the range of materials and equipment he uses for different medication routes.

Evidencing AC3.1 to your assessor:

For AC3.1 you must evidence your knowledge of the types, purpose and function of materials and equipment needed for the administration of medication via the different routes.

Assessment Methods:

Oral or **Written** Questioning or **Discussion** or a **Personal Statement** or **Reflection**

- You can **tell** your assessor about the types, purpose and function of materials and equipment needed for the administration of medication via the different routes.

  Or
- You can **talk** to your assessor about the types, purpose and function of materials and equipment needed for the administration of medication via the different routes.

  Or
- You can write a **personal statement** or **reflection** about your experience of the types, purpose and function of materials and equipment needed for the administration of medication via the different routes.

REMEMBER TO:

- Provide an **account** and **explain** the different materials and equipment needed.
- Include details about what these are, why they are used and how.
- Provide **examples** of both different materials and equipment.
- Think about **your work setting** and the types, purpose and function of materials and equipment needed for the administration of medication via the different routes.

Learning Outcome 3: Understand procedures and techniques for the administration of medication

Assessment Criterion 3.2: Identify the required information from prescriptions and medication administration charts

What does AC3.2 mean?

- The lead word **identify** means that you must **list** the information that is required from prescriptions or medication charts.
- Your **list** must include the information that is required.
- For the key words **prescriptions and medication administration charts** you can think about the information that is required about both the individual and the medication to be able to administer the medication.

Read the following **Real Work Setting** scenario and think about how it relates to your work setting and role:

Real Work Setting

Name: Jason

Job Role: Home Carer for young adults
(See page 198 for a description of the role)

Information required from prescriptions and medication administration charts: Jason also found the medication training update he attended useful in terms of updating his knowledge around the required information from prescriptions and medication administration charts. Jason was able to update his knowledge specifically around the information required about the individual, the medication itself, as well as about other specific instructions that may need to be observed. Jason has found that the medication training update has enabled him to feel more confident about the information he needs to check on the prescriptions that the individuals he supports collect from their GPs and, occasionally, from the dentist.

Evidencing AC3.2 to your assessor:

For AC3.2 you must evidence your understanding of the required information from prescriptions and medication administration charts.

Assessment Methods:

Oral or **Written** Questioning or **Discussion** or a **Spidergram**

- You can **tell** your assessor about the required information from prescriptions and medication administration charts.
  Or
- You can **talk** to your assessor about the required information from prescriptions and medication administration charts.
  Or
- You can complete a **spidergram** of the required information from prescriptions and medication administration charts.

REMEMBER TO:

- List **different** items of information.
- Include **examples** of information items.
- Ensure that your list includes the details required from prescriptions and medication administration charts.
- Think about **your work setting** and the required information from prescriptions and medication administration charts.

Learning Outcome 4: Prepare for the administration of medication

Assessment Criterion 4.1: Apply standard precautions for infection control

What does AC4.1 mean?

- The lead word **apply** means that you must be able to **show through your work practices** how to put into practice standard precautions for infection control.
- Your **observations of your work practices** must include you putting into practice standard precautions for infection control.
- For the key words **standard precautions** you can think about the different ways that exist to protect you, individuals and others from the spread of infections.
- For the key words **infection control** you can think about your work setting's policies and procedures used to minimise the risk of spreading infections.

Read the following **Real Work Setting** scenario and think about how it relates to your work setting and role:

Real Work Setting

Name: Tara

Job Role: Residential Carer for older adults who have dementia

Tara has been working as a Residential Carer for eight years. Her responsibilities include: supporting individuals with personal care tasks such as washing, dressing, using the toilet, eating, drinking, assisting with medication, enabling individuals to maintain relationships with family and friends, accompanying individuals to appointments and supporting individuals to take part in recreational and social activities.

Applying standard precautions for infection control: Tara is being observed today by the manager as part of her monitoring of Carers' working practices when administering medication. Tara and a Senior Residential Carer discuss confidentially in the office the medication administration to individuals that will need to take place this morning. Tara's manager observes Tara using the recommended hand-washing technique prior to putting on a pair of disposable gloves. Tara then shows her manager and the Senior the medication cups they will use this morning, which she prepared earlier on in the day by ensuring they were clean and thoroughly dried. Tara's Senior asks her to fetch a glass for Marion, who is first to take her medication this morning; Tara washes the glass in the medication sink and then, once thoroughly dried, hands this to her Senior. Tara then removes her disposable gloves, disposes of these in the waste bin in the medication room and then washes her hands thoroughly before putting on another pair of gloves.

Evidencing AC4.1 to your assessor:

For AC4.1 you must evidence your skills in applying standard precautions for infection control.

Assessment Method:

Direct Observation of your work practices

- You can **show** your assessor how to apply standard precautions for infection control.

REMEMBER TO:

- Make arrangements for **observation** of your work practices.
- Include evidence of you applying **different** standard precautions.
- Ensure the evidence you include relates to infection control.
- Think about **your work setting** and how to apply standard precautions for infection control.

Learning Outcome 4: Prepare for the administration of medication

Assessment Criterion 4.2: Explain the appropriate timing of medication, e.g. check that the individual has not taken any medication recently

What does AC4.2 mean?

- The lead word **explain** means that you must **make clear** the appropriate timing of medication.
- Your **account** must detail why the appropriate timing of medication is necessary and how to do this.
- For the key words **appropriate timing** you can think about the reasons why it is necessary to administer medication at the correct time as prescribed and how to ensure that this is done, including how much time should be left between administering one dose and the next.

Read the following **Real Work Setting** scenario and think about how it relates to your work setting and role:

Real Work Setting

Name: Tara

Job Role: Residential Carer for older adults who have dementia
(See page 200 for a description of the role)

Appropriate timing of medication: Tara then checks with the Senior that the second individual, Ulamila, has not taken any medication this morning by reading through this individual's medication administration record; it is confirmed that Ulamila has not taken any medication, so Tara confirms that it will be being given at the correct time this morning, as agreed with her GP.

Evidencing AC4.2 to your assessor:

For AC4.2 you must evidence your knowledge of the appropriate timing of medication, e.g. check that the individual has not taken any medication recently.

Assessment Methods:

Oral or **Written** Questioning or **Discussion** or a **Personal Statement** or **Reflection**

- You can **tell** your assessor about the appropriate timing of medication, e.g. check that the individual has not taken any medication recently.
  Or
- You can **talk** to your assessor about the appropriate timing of medication, e.g. check that the individual has not taken any medication recently.
  Or
- You can write a **personal statement** or **reflection** about your experience of the appropriate timing of medication, e.g. check that the individual has not taken any medication recently.

REMEMBER TO:

- Provide an account and explain the appropriate timing of medication.
- Include details about what is involved in administering medication at the correct times.
- Provide examples of how to do this and reasons why.
- Think about your work setting and the appropriate timing of medication, for example check that the individual has not taken any medication recently.

Learning Outcome 4: Prepare for the administration of medication

Assessment Criterion 4.3: Obtain the individual's consent and offer information, support and reassurance throughout in a manner which encourages their co-operation and which is appropriate to their needs and concerns

What does AC4.3 mean?

- The lead word **obtain** means that you must be able to **show through your work practices** how to gain the individual's consent and offer information, support and reassurance throughout in a manner which encourages their co-operation and which is appropriate to their needs and concerns.
- Your **observations of your work practices** must include you gaining the individual's consent and offering information, support and reassurance throughout.
- For the key word **consent** you can think about the different ways of seeking an individual's agreement for you to administer their medication.
- For the key words **needs and concerns** you can think about how the way you provide information, support and reassurance will vary depending on an individual's communication needs and concerns.

Read the following **Real Work Setting** scenario and think about how it relates to your work setting and role:

Real Work Setting

Name: Tara

Job Role: Residential Carer for older adults who have dementia
(See page 200 for a description of the role)

Obtaining consent, offering information, support and reassurance: Tara approaches Ulamila, who tells her that she doesn't want to take her medication this morning as she is about to go out with her friend. Tara sits down next to Ulamila and together both discuss what her medication is for and the importance of her taking it regularly and on time. Tara leaves Ulamila on her own for a few minutes to think about their discussion and then when she returns Ulamila tells Tara that she thinks she should take her medication straightaway.

Evidencing AC4.3 to your assessor:

For AC4.3 you must evidence your skills in obtaining the individual's consent and offering information, support and reassurance throughout in a manner which encourages their co-operation and which is appropriate to their needs and concerns.

Assessment Method:

Direct Observation of your work practices

- You can **show** your assessor how to obtain the individual's consent and offer information, support and reassurance throughout in a manner which encourages their co-operation and which is appropriate to their needs and concerns.

REMEMBER TO:

- Make arrangements for **observation** of your **work practices**.
- Include evidence of you obtaining consent and offering information, support and reassurance.
- Think about **your work setting** and how to obtain the individual's consent and offer information, support and reassurance throughout in a manner which encourages their co-operation and which is appropriate to their needs and concerns.

Learning Outcome 4: Prepare for the administration of medication

Assessment Criterion 4.4: Select, check and prepare correctly the medication according to the medication administration record or medication information leaflet

What does AC4.4 mean?

- The lead words **select, check and prepare** mean that you must be able to **show through your work practices** how to prepare medication for administration correctly and according to the medication administration record or medication information leaflet.
- Your **observations of your work practices** must include you selecting, checking and preparing correctly the medication according to the medication administration record or medication information leaflet.
- For the key words **select, check and prepare** you can think about the procedures you must follow in your work setting to ensure that you administer the correct medication to individuals including the checks you must carry out and any special instructions that must be followed.

Read the following **Real Work Setting** scenario and think about how it relates to your work setting and role:

Real Work Setting

Name: Tara
Job Role: Residential Carer for older adults who have dementia (See page 200 for a description of the role)
Selecting, checking and preparing: Tara's manager then observes Tara and the Senior read through Janet's medication profile and medication administration record. While doing so, the details and information included on these are checked against those on the box of tablets. Tara's manager observes her check that the following details are accurate: the name indicated on the box of tablets, the name of the medication, the dose and time to be given, as well as how it must be taken with water. Tara prepares a glass of water to take to the individual with her tablets.

Evidencing AC4.4 to your assessor:

For AC4.4 you must evidence your skills in selecting, checking and preparing correctly the medication according to the medication administration record or medication information leaflet.

Assessment Method:

Direct Observation of your work practices

- You can **show** your assessor how to select, check and prepare correctly the medication according to the medication administration record or medication information leaflet.

REMEMBER TO:

- Make arrangements for **observation** of your **work practices**.
- Include evidence of you selecting, checking and preparing correctly the medication.
- Ensure the evidence you provide is in line with the medication administration record or medication information leaflet.
- Think about **your work setting** and how to select, check and prepare correctly the medication according to the medication administration record or medication information leaflet.

Learning Outcome 5: Administer and monitor individuals' medication

Assessment Criterion 5.1: Select the route for the administration of medication, according to the individual's plan of care and the drug to be administered, and prepare the site if necessary

What does AC5.1 mean?

- The lead word **select** means that you must be able to **show through your work practices** how to choose the route of administration of medication, according to the individual's plan of care and the drug to be administered, and prepare the site if necessary.
- Your **observations of your work practices** must include you selecting the route for the administration of medication.
- For the key word **select** you can think about the procedures you must follow in your work setting to ensure that you choose the route of administration of medication, according to the individual's plan of care and the drug to be administered, and prepare the site if necessary.
- For the key word **route** you can think about how medication can be administered in different ways such as via inhalation, instillation, orally, transdermally, topically, intravenously, rectally, vaginally, subcutaneously and intramuscularly and the preparations required.

Read the following **Real Work Setting** scenario and think about how it relates to your work setting and role:

Real Work Setting

Name: Andy
Job Role: Carer for adults who have mental health needs
Andy has been working as a Carer for nine years. His responsibilities include: supporting individuals' plans of care and treatment, assisting with the administering of medication to individuals and supporting individuals to maintain links with their families and friends.
Selecting the route of administration of medication: All medication administered is supervised by the Senior Carer on duty and although medication is administered using different routes such as oral, topical or subcutaneous routes, Andy is aware that the route of administering medication must be as agreed in the individual's plan of care and that any requests by either the individual or their family to change this must be reported to the manager.

Evidencing AC5.1 to your assessor:

For AC5.1 you must evidence your skills in selecting the route for the administration of medication, according to the individual's plan of care and the drug to be administered, and prepare the site if necessary.

Assessment Method:

Direct Observation of your work practices

- You can **show** your assessor how to select the route for the administration of medication, according to the individual's plan of care and the drug to be administered, and prepare the site if necessary.

REMEMBER TO:

- Make arrangements for observation of your work practices.
- Include evidence of you selecting the route for the administration of medication and of preparing the site if necessary.
- Ensure the evidence you provide is according to the individual's plan of care and the drug to be administered.
- Think about your work setting and how to select, check and prepare correctly the medication according to the medication administration record or medication information leaflet.

Learning Outcome 5: Administer and monitor individuals' medication

Assessment Criterion 5.2: Safely administer the medication in line with legislation and local policies, in a way which minimises pain, discomfort and trauma to the individual

What does AC5.2 mean?

- The lead words **safely administer** mean that you must be able to **show through your work practices** how to administer medication using safe practices and in line with legislation and local policies, in a way which minimises pain, discomfort and trauma to the individual.
- Your **observations of your work practices** must include you safely administering the medication in line with legislation and local policies.
- For the key word **legislation** you can think about relevant laws in place that relate to the safe administration of medication.
- For the key words **local policies** you can think about the policies, procedures and ways of working available in your work setting for the safe administration of medication.

Read the following **Real Work Setting** scenario and think about how it relates to your work setting and role:

Real Work Setting

Name: Andy

Job Role: Carer for adults who have mental health needs
(See page 204 for a description of the role)

Safely administering medication: Andy always ensures he safely administers all medication to individuals in line with the work setting's medication policy and procedures and relevant legislation. One individual that Andy supports has an eye condition and requires the help of carers to apply the eye ointment he has been prescribed. Andy always wears disposable gloves to apply this and ensures that the individual is sitting comfortably and ready to have the eye ointment applied. Andy applies a small amount of ointment along the individual's lower lid and then asks the individual to blink a few times and continues to talk with him until the individual confirms that he is fine.

Evidencing AC5.2 to your assessor:

For AC5.2 you must evidence your skills in safely administering the medication in line with legislation and local policies, in a way which minimises pain, discomfort and trauma to the individual.

Assessment Method:

Direct Observation of your work practices

- You can **show** your assessor how to safely administer the medication in line with legislation and local policies, in a way which minimises pain, discomfort and trauma to the individual.

REMEMBER TO:

- Make arrangements for **observation** of your **work practices**.
- Include evidence of you safely administering the medication in line with legislation and local policies.
- Ensure the evidence you provide shows how you do this in a way which minimises pain, discomfort and trauma to the individual.
- Think about **your work setting** and how to safely administer the medication in line with legislation and local policies, in a way which minimises pain, discomfort and trauma to the individual.

Learning Outcome 5: Administer and monitor individuals' medication

Assessment Criterion 5.3: Describe how to report any immediate problems with the administration of medication

What does AC5.3 mean?

- The lead word **describe** means that you must provide an **account** that **details** how to report any immediate problems with the administration of medication.
- Your **account** must detail how to report any immediate problems.
- For the key word **report** you can think about how to provide a verbal and/or written account to an appointed person in your work setting about any immediate problems with the administration of medication.
- For the key word **problems** you can think about difficulties that may arise with the administration of medication such as when medication is missing or has been dropped or spilt, an individual refusal to take medication, difficulties in taking medication in its prescribed form, adverse reactions or anomalies in the medication administration records or in directions for use.

Read the following **Real Work Setting** scenario and think about how it relates to your work setting and role:

Real Work Setting

Name: Andy

Job Role: Carer for adults who have mental health needs
(See page 204 for a description of the role)

Reporting any immediate problems: Andy reflects on the occasion when he was assisting with administering medication to Martha and how she dropped the medication cup he handed to her and the tablets inside this fell onto the floor. As Andy was unsure what to do in this situation, he immediately reported what had happened to the Senior on duty. Andy recalls the Senior telling him that the tablets must not be thrown away but instead placed in the medication envelopes that are returned to the pharmacist, who will then dispose of these safely. Andy was also then advised to administer new tablets and to record what had happened on the medication administration record for this individual.

Evidencing AC5.3 to your assessor:

For AC5.3 you must evidence your knowledge of how to report any immediate problems with the administration of medication.

Assessment Methods:

Oral or **Written** Questioning or **Discussion** or a **Personal Statement** or **Reflection**

- You can **tell** your assessor about how to report any immediate problems with the administration of medication.
  Or
- You can **talk** to your assessor about how to report any immediate problems with the administration of medication.
  Or
- You can write a **personal statement** or **reflection** about your experience of how to report any immediate problems with the administration of medication.

REMEMBER TO:

- Provide a detailed account.
- Include details about how to report any immediate problems with the administration of medication.
- Ensure your evidence includes details of the reporting procedures you must follow.
- Think about **your work setting** and how to report any immediate problems with the administration of medication.

Learning Outcome 5: Administer and monitor individuals' medication

Assessment Criterion 5.4: Monitor the individual's condition throughout, recognise any adverse effects and take the appropriate action without delay

What does AC5.4 mean?

- The lead word **monitor** means that you must be able to **show through your work practices** how to observe and check the individual's condition throughout, recognise any adverse effects and take the appropriate action without delay.
- Your **observations of your work practices** must include you monitoring the individual's condition throughout.
- For the key word **condition** you can think about how to observe and check any changes in the individual's physical, mental or emotional condition.
- For the key words **appropriate action** you can think about the procedure you must follow in your work setting if you recognise any adverse effects in the individual.

Read the following **Real Work Setting** scenario and think about how it relates to your work setting and role:

Real Work Setting

Name: Andy

Job Role: Carer for adults who have mental health needs
(See page 204 for a description of the role)

Monitoring the individual's condition: After a short stay in hospital, Morag has been discharged and her medication has been changed. It has been noted by a few Carers and her brother, who visited her yesterday, that Morag seems very low in herself, tearful at times and very anxious when leaving her room. Although it is possible that her new medication is causing these adverse effects, it cannot yet be confirmed as she has only been taking this for a few days; so Andy and the team of Carers have been asked to monitor Morag's condition closely, record and report any changes observed immediately.

Evidencing AC5.4 to your assessor:

For AC5.4 you must evidence your skills in monitoring the individual's condition throughout, recognise any adverse effects and take the appropriate action without delay.

Assessment Method:

Direct Observation of your work practices

- You can **show** your assessor or an expert witness how to monitor the individual's condition throughout, recognise any adverse effects and take the appropriate action without delay.

REMEMBER TO:

- Make arrangements for **observation** of your **work practices.**
- Include **evidence** of you monitoring the individual's condition throughout.
- Ensure the evidence you provide includes recognising any adverse effects and taking the appropriate action without delay.
- Think about **your work setting** and how to monitor the individual's condition throughout, recognise any adverse effects and take the appropriate action without delay.

Derby Teaching Hospitals
NHS Foundation Trust
Library and Knowledge Centre

Learning Outcome 5: Administer and monitor individuals' medication

Assessment Criterion 5.5: Explain why it may be necessary to confirm that the individual actually takes the medication and does not pass the medication to others

What does AC5.5 mean?

- The lead word **explain** means that you must make clear the reasons why it may be necessary to confirm that the individual actually takes the medication and does not pass the medication to others.
- Your **account** must detail the reasons why.
- For the key word **confirm** you can think about the procedures you must follow in your work setting to ensure that the individual actually takes the medication and does not pass the medication to others.

Read the following **Real Work Setting** scenario and think about how it relates to your work setting and role:

Real Work Setting

Name: Andy

Job Role: Carer for adults who have mental health needs
(See page 204 for a description of the role)

Confirming that the individual actually takes the medication: One of Andy's less experienced colleagues has recently attended additional training in medication, as there were a number of areas for improvement identified in the observation undertaken of him while assisting individuals with the administering of medication. Andy begins by talking through with his colleague the importance of ensuring that individuals are observed taking their medication and that only after doing so is a record made that individuals have taken their medication. Andy goes on to explain the consequences for the individual, others, the Carer and the organisation if a Carer does not confirm that the individual actually takes the medication and does not pass the medication to others.

Evidencing AC5.5 to your assessor:

For AC5.5 you must evidence your knowledge of why it may be necessary to confirm that the individual actually takes the medication and does not pass the medication to others.

Assessment Methods:

Oral or **Written** Questioning or **Discussion** or a **Personal Statement** or **Reflection**

- You can **tell** your assessor about why it may be necessary to confirm that the individual actually takes the medication and does not pass the medication to others.
  Or
- You can **talk** to your assessor about why it may be necessary to confirm that the individual actually takes the medication and does not pass the medication to others.
  Or
- You can write a **personal statement** or **reflection** about why it may be necessary to confirm that the individual actually takes the medication and does not pass the medication to others.

REMEMBER TO:

- Provide an account and explain why.
- Include details about why it may be necessary to confirm that the individual actually takes the medication and does not pass the medication to others.
- Provide examples of how to do this and the reasons why.
- Think about **your work setting** and why it may be necessary to confirm that the individual actually takes the medication and does not pass the medication to others.

Learning Outcome 5: Administer and monitor individuals' medication

Assessment Criterion 5.6: Maintain the security of medication and related records throughout the process and return them to the correct place for storage

What does AC5.6 mean?

- The lead word **maintain** means that you must be able to show through your work practices how to keep secure medication and related records throughout the process and return them to the correct place for storage.
- Your observations of your work practices must include you maintaining the security of medication and related records throughout the process.
- For the key words **security of medication** you can think about the different ways of ensuring medication is kept secure while you administer it such as not leaving the medication cupboard or medicines fridge unlocked, keys for both only being held with authorised staff, storing medication administration records, medication plans and profiles safely and securely in a designated area after use.
- For the key words **correct place for storage** you can think about the different ways of storing different types of medication and where the medication administration records are stored in your work setting.

Read the following **Real Work Setting** scenario and think about how it relates to your work setting and role:

Real Work Setting

Name: Andy

Job Role: Carer for adults who have mental health needs
(See page 204 for a description of the role)

Maintaining the security of medication and related records throughout the process: Andy then continues to talk through with his less experienced colleague the importance of maintaining the security of medication and related records throughout the process and returning them to the correct place for storage, as well as the consequences of not doing so. Andy reinforces to his colleague that security in the administration of medication also relates to the records for individuals and includes the medication file, the medication administration record and individuals' medication plans and profiles, as all information contained on these is confidential.

Evidencing AC5.6 to your assessor:

For AC5.6 you must evidence your skills in maintaining the security of medication and related records throughout the process and return them to the correct place for storage.

Assessment Method:

Direct Observation of your work practices

- You can **show** your assessor how to maintain the security of medication and related records throughout the process and return them to the correct place for storage.

REMEMBER TO:

- Make arrangements for **observation** of your **work practices**.
- Include evidence of you maintaining the security of medication and related records throughout the process.
- Include evidence of you returning medication and related records to the correct place for storage.
- Think about **your work setting** and how to maintain the security of medication and related records throughout the process and return them to the correct place for storage.

Learning Outcome 5: Administer and monitor individuals' medication

Assessment Criterion 5.7: Describe how to dispose of out-of-date and part-used medications in accordance with legal and organisational requirements

What does AC5.7 mean?

- The lead word **describe** means that you must provide an **account** that **details** how to dispose of out-of-date and part-used medications in accordance with legal and organisational requirements.
- Your **account** must detail how to dispose of out-of-date and part-used medications.
- For the key words **out-of-date and part-used medications** you can think about how if a medication is not effective for an individual, or if the individual requests it in a different form, or if an individual refuses to take their medication you may have out-of-date and part-used medications.
- For the key words **legal and organisational requirements** you can think about the standards, regulations and work setting procedures in place that set out how to dispose of out-of-date and part-used medications.

Read the following **Real Work Setting** scenario and think about how it relates to your work setting and role:

Real Work Setting

Name: Andy

Job Role: Carer for adults who have mental health needs
(See page 204 for a description of the role)

Disposal of out-of-date and part-used medications: All Carers are encouraged to work with Seniors to keep their knowledge of how to dispose of out-of-date and part-used medications in accordance with legal and organisational requirements. Andy has recently observed a Senior make arrangements for the return of out-of-date and part-used medications. Andy found it interesting to find out more about the records that must be kept by his work setting and how these must detail the name of the person who returned them, the date, the quantity being returned, as well as the signature from a witness.

Evidencing AC5.7 to your assessor:

For AC5.7 you must evidence your knowledge of how to dispose of out-of-date and part-used medications in accordance with legal and organisational requirements.

Assessment Methods:

Oral or **Written** Questioning or **Discussion** or a **Personal Statement** or **Reflection**

- You can **tell** your assessor about how to dispose of out-of-date and part-used medications in accordance with legal and organisational requirements.
  Or
- You can **talk** to your assessor about how to dispose of out-of-date and part-used medications in accordance with legal and organisational requirements.
  Or
- You can write a **personal statement** or **reflection** about your experience of how to dispose of out-of-date and part-used medications in accordance with legal and organisational requirements.

REMEMBER TO:

- Provide a detailed account.
- Include details about how to dispose of out-of-date and part-used medications.
- Ensure your evidence includes details of how to do this in line with legal and organisational requirements.
- Think about **your work setting** and how to dispose of out-of-date and part-used medications in accordance with legal and organisational requirements.

HSC2002 Provide support for mobility

Learning Outcome 1: Understand the importance of mobility

Assessment Criterion 1.1: Define mobility

What does AC1.1 mean?

- The lead word **define** means that you must **make clear** the meaning of mobility.
- Your **definition** must make clear what mobility means.
- For the key word **mobility** you can think about how this includes an individual's ability to move or be assisted to move comfortably.

Read the following **Real Work Setting** scenario and think about how it relates to your work setting and role:

Real Work Setting

Name: Luke

Job Role: Care worker in a day service for adults who have physical disabilities

Luke has worked as a Care Worker for five years. His responsibilities include: supporting individuals with their independent living skills, budgeting, care planning and enabling individuals to access work and education opportunities available in both the day service and the community.

Mobility: Luke is attending a team meeting with some new Volunteers and has agreed to give a short presentation about the importance of mobility for the individuals that attend the day service. Luke begins by asking the team what their understanding of the term mobility is and then writes on the whiteboard the key words that are discussed: moving, helping with moving, independence, pain free, access to work and others.

Evidencing AC1.1 to your assessor:

For AC1.1 you must evidence your understanding of the meaning of mobility.

Assessment Methods:

Oral or **Written** Questioning or **Discussion** or a **Spidergram**

- You can **tell** your assessor about the meaning of mobility.
  Or
- You can **talk** to your assessor about the meaning of mobility.
  Or
- You can complete a **spidergram** of the meaning of mobility.

REMEMBER TO:

- Provide the meaning of mobility.
- Include details about what mobility involves.
- Think about **your work setting** and the meaning of mobility.

Learning Outcome 1: Understand the importance of mobility

Assessment Criterion 1.2: Explain how different health conditions may affect and be affected by mobility

What does AC1.2 mean?

- The lead word **explain** means that you must make clear how different health conditions may affect and be affected by mobility.
- Your **account** must make clear how.
- For the key words **different health conditions** you can think about how conditions such as arthritis, multiple sclerosis, cerebral palsy, partial or total paralysis can affect and be affected by mobility.
- For the key word **mobility** you can think about how different health conditions may affect and be affected by an individual's ability to move or be assisted to move comfortably.

Read the following **Real Work Setting** scenario and think about how it relates to your work setting and role:

Real Work Setting

Name: Luke
Job Role: Care worker in a day service for adults who have physical disabilities (See page 211 for a description of the role)
Health conditions and mobility: Luke then moves on to explain to the team how it is important that they are aware of individuals' health conditions, as these may affect mobility, and shares with the team that each individual has a plan of support in place and included in this are guidelines for how to support individuals to mobilise safely and comfortably. Luke provides examples of two individuals who use the service and whose health conditions affect and are affected by mobility. Individual A, Luke explains, has recently had a stroke and the weakness on the left side of his body needs to be taken into account when supporting him to move from one position to another. Luke explains that individual B has brittle bone disease and is prone to sustaining fractures; his mobility directly affects his health condition.

Evidencing AC1.2 to your assessor:

For AC1.2 you must evidence your understanding of how different health conditions may affect and be affected by mobility.

Assessment Methods:

Oral or **Written** Questioning or **Discussion** or a **Personal Statement** or **Reflection**

- You can **tell** your assessor about how different health conditions may affect and be affected by mobility.
  Or
- You can **talk** to your assessor about how different health conditions may affect and be affected by mobility.
  Or
- You can write a **personal statement** or **reflection** about your experience of how different health conditions may affect and be affected by mobility.

REMEMBER TO:

- Provide an account and explain how.
- Include details about how different health conditions may affect mobility.
- Include details about how different health conditions are affected by mobility.
- Think about **your work setting** and how different health conditions may affect and be affected by mobility.

Learning Outcome 1: Understand the importance of mobility

Assessment Criterion 1.3: Outline the effects that reduced mobility may have on an individual's well-being

What does AC1.3 mean?

- The lead word **outline** means that you must provide an **account** that includes brief **details** about the effects that reduced mobility may have on an individual's well-being.
- Your **account** must detail briefly the effects.
- For the key words **reduced mobility** you can think about how the ability to move around less, or less assistance to move around, can affect individuals' emotional, physical, cultural, religious, spiritual, political and social aspects of their lives and environment.
- For the key words **well-being** you can think about how reduced mobility may affect individuals' emotional, physical, cultural, religious, spiritual, political and social aspects of their lives and environment.

Read the following **Real Work Setting** scenario and think about how it relates to your work setting and role:

Real Work Setting

Name: Luke

Job Role: Care Worker in a day service for adults who have physical disabilities
(See page 211 for a description of the role)

The effects of reduced mobility on an individual's well-being: Luke asks the team to think about the effects that reduced mobility may have on an individual's well-being. Luke asks one half of the team to discuss how they think reduced mobility may impact on how well an individual feels emotionally, on their bodies physically and on how they experience and are viewed in their own cultures. Luke asks the other half of the team to consider and discuss how they think reduced mobility may impact on an individual's religion, aspects of their spirituality, their political beliefs and their ability to continue being socially active.

Evidencing AC1.3 to your assessor:

For AC1.3 you must evidence your understanding of the effects that reduced mobility may have on an individual's well-being.

Assessment Methods:

Oral or **Written** Questioning or **Discussion** or a **Personal Statement** or **Reflection**

- You can **tell** your assessor about the effects that reduced mobility may have on an individual's well-being.
  Or
- You can **talk** to your assessor about the effects that reduced mobility may have on an individual's well-being.
  Or
- You can write a **personal statement** or **reflection** about your experience of the effects that reduced mobility may have on an individual's well-being.

REMEMBER TO:

- Provide an account that includes brief details.
- Include brief details about the effects that reduced mobility may have on an individual's well-being.
- Ensure your evidence relates to the effects that reduced mobility may have.
- Ensure your evidence relates to the effects on an individual's well-being.
- Think about **your work setting** and the effects that reduced mobility may have on an individual's well-being.

Learning Outcome 1: Understand the importance of mobility

Assessment Criterion 1.4: Describe the benefits of maintaining and improving mobility

What does AC1.4 mean?

- The lead word **describe** means that you must provide an **account** that **details** the benefits of maintaining and improving mobility.
- Your **account** must detail different benefits.
- For the key word **maintaining** you can think about the benefits of retaining mobility for an individual and others involved in their lives.
- For the key word **improving** you can think about the benefits of developing or increasing mobility for an individual and others involved in their lives.

Read the following **Real Work Setting** scenario and think about how it relates to your work setting and role:

Real Work Setting

Name: Luke

Job Role: Care Worker in a day service for adults who have physical disabilities
(See page 211 for a description of the role)

The benefits of maintaining and improving mobility: Luke and the team discuss together the numerous benefits of maintaining and improving mobility not just for the individuals concerned, but also for all those involved in their lives. The team's discussion focuses on the benefits of how doing so can improve and sustain an individual in good physical health, can affect how an individual and others feel about themselves and their lives, can improve an individual's independent living skills and can mean less dependence on others for completion of daily tasks and activities.

Evidencing AC1.4 to your assessor:

For AC1.4 you must evidence your understanding of the benefits of maintaining and improving mobility.

Assessment Methods:

Oral or **Written** Questioning or **Discussion** or a **Personal Statement** or **Reflection**

- You can **tell** your assessor about the benefits of maintaining and improving mobility.
  Or
- You can **talk** to your assessor about the benefits of maintaining and improving mobility.
  Or
- You can write a **personal statement** or **reflection** about your experience of the benefits of maintaining and improving mobility.

REMEMBER TO:

- Provide a detailed account.
- Include details about the benefits.
- Include varied examples of the benefits of maintaining and improving mobility.
- Ensure your evidence is related to the benefits for both individuals and others involved in their lives.
- Think about your work setting and the benefits of maintaining and improving mobility.

Learning Outcome 2: Be able to prepare for mobility activities

Assessment Criterion 2.1: Agree mobility activities with the individuals and others

What does AC2.1 mean?

- The lead word **agree** means that you must be able to **show through your work practices** how to decide on mobility activities with the individuals and others.
- Your **observations of your work practices** must include you agreeing mobility activities.
- For the key words **mobility activities** you can think about how these may include exercises, physiotherapy, occupational therapy, household tasks and group activities such as moving from one position to another, stretching, relaxing, walking and swimming.
- For the key word **others** you can think about the different people with whom you may agree mobility activities such as the individual's family, friends, advocates, mobility specialists such as occupational or physiotherapist, line manager and others who are involved in their lives and are important to the individual's well-being.

Read the following **Real Work Setting** scenario and think about how it relates to your work setting and role:

Real Work Setting

Name: Lidia

Job Role: Live-in Carer to a young lady who has a physical impairment

Lidia has been working as a Live-in Carer for one year. Her responsibilities include: enabling Dianne to live an active and independent life, supporting Dianne with all aspects of her personal care, as well as with general household tasks and accessing her local community facilities.

Agreeing mobility activities: Dianne's plan of support involves the completion of gentle mobility exercises to keep her knees from feeling stiff and painful and to make her mobility easier. Today, her physiotherapist is visiting her at home and would like to observe her complete the knee mobility exercises. Lidia looks through the diagrams of Dianne's mobility exercises. Dianne explains that she does not think she will be able to complete these; Lidia reassures her, asks her to relax and adds that she can support her if she likes by talking through what each of these exercises involves with Lidia beforehand. Dianne agrees that she would like Lidia's support, so Lidia explains these with the help and agreement of the physiotherapist to Dianne step by step: Sitting in a chair, rest your left foot on another chair so your knee is slightly raised. Gently push your raised knee toward the floor using only your leg muscles. Hold for 5 to 10 seconds and then release. Repeat five times on each leg.

Evidencing AC2.1 to your assessor:

For AC2.1 you must evidence your skills of agreeing mobility activities with the individual and others.

Assessment Method:

Direct Observation of your work practices

- You can **show** your assessor how to agree mobility activities with the individual and others.

REMEMBER TO:

- Make arrangements for **observation** of your **work practices**.
- Include evidence of you agreeing mobility activities.
- Include evidence of different mobility activities.
- Include evidence of you agreeing mobility activities with the individual and others.
- Think about **your work setting** and how to agree mobility activities with the individual and others.

Learning Outcome 2: Be able to prepare for mobility activities

Assessment Criterion 2.2: Remove or minimise hazards in the environment before beginning a mobility activity

What does AC2.2 mean?

- The lead words **remove or minimise** mean that you must be able to **show through your work practices** how to eliminate or reduce hazards in the environment before beginning a mobility activity.
- Your **observations of your work practices** must include you removing or minimising hazards in the environment.
- For the key words **hazards in the environment** you can think about the actual dangers that can exist for harm to take place and that must be reduced or minimised before beginning a mobility activity such as faulty equipment, poorly maintained fixtures, objects or items on the floor, not knowing or finding out how to support individuals.
- For the key words **mobility activity** you can think about how to remove or minimise hazards in the environment before beginning exercises, physiotherapy, occupational therapy, household tasks and group activities such as moving from one position to another, stretching, relaxing, walking and swimming.

Read the following **Real Work Setting** scenario and think about how it relates to your work setting and role:

Real Work Setting

Name: Lidia

Job Role: Live-in Carer to a young lady who has a physical impairment
(See page 215 for a description of the role)

Removing or minimising hazards: Before beginning Dianne's mobility exercises, Lidia asks Dianne whether she would like her assistance with ensuring that the area where she is going to sit and complete her exercises is safe. Dianne explains that she would like assistance, so Lidia points out that the foot stool and magazine rack positioned in front of her chair may be unsafe as they may cause her to knock her leg or foot as she stretches it; Dianne and Lidia move these to one side. Lidia then asks Dianne whether the small table by her chair may also need moving further back as it is so close to her chair it will restrict her movements and may also cause her to injure herself; Lidia agrees and moves these to one side with Dianne's help.

Evidencing AC2.2 to your assessor:

For AC2.2 you must evidence your skills of how to remove or minimise hazards in the environment before beginning a mobility activity.

Assessment Method:

Direct Observation of your work practices

- You can **show** your assessor how to remove or minimise hazards in the environment before beginning a mobility activity.

REMEMBER TO:

- Make arrangements for **observation** of your **work practices**.
- Include evidence of you removing or minimising hazards in the environment.
- Include evidence of different hazards.
- Include evidence of you removing or minimising hazards before beginning a mobility activity.
- Think about **your work setting** and how to remove or minimise hazards in the environment before beginning a mobility activity.

Learning Outcome 2: Be able to prepare for mobility activities

Assessment Criterion 2.3: Check the suitability of an individual's clothing and footwear for safety and mobility

What does AC2.3 mean?

- The lead word **check** means that you must be able to **show through your work practices** how to examine the suitability of an individual's clothing and footwear for safety and mobility.
- Your **observations of your work practices** must include you checking the suitability of an individual's clothing and footwear.
- For the key word **suitability** you can think about the clothing and footwear that are appropriate for both safety and mobility.
- For the key word **clothing** you can think about how clothing must be suitable for the mobility activity being undertaken, not too loose or too tight, not ripped or too worn.
- For the key word **footwear** you can think about how footwear must be suitable for the mobility activity being undertaken, not too small or too big, not open or too high.

Read the following **Real Work Setting** scenario and think about how it relates to your work setting and role:

Real Work Setting

Name: Lidia

Job Role: Live-in Carer to a young lady who has a physical impairment
(See page 215 for a description of the role)

Checking the suitability of an individual's clothing and footwear: Lidia then asks Dianne whether she has decided what she will wear this afternoon for her knee mobility exercises. Dianne explains that she will change into her tracksuit bottoms as her jeans feel a little tight; Lidia agrees that this is a good idea and that the new pair she bought last week would be better, as they are not so loose as her other pair and would therefore enable her to stretch her legs comfortably. Lidia then discusses with Dianne the footwear that she will wear. Dianne says that she would like to wear her slippers but agrees with Lidia that although these may be comfortable they may keep on falling off when she is stretching her legs during her exercises and therefore that it may be better to wear something else that will stay securely on, such as her trainers.

Evidencing AC2.3 to your assessor:

For AC2.3 you must evidence your skills of how to check the suitability of an individual's clothing and footwear for safety and mobility.

Assessment Method:

Direct Observation of your work practices

- You can **show** your assessor how to check the suitability of an individual's clothing and footwear for safety and mobility.

REMEMBER TO:

- Make arrangements for **observation** of your **work practices**.
- Include evidence of you checking the suitability of an individual's clothing and footwear for safety and mobility.
- Include evidence of an individual's clothing and footwear.
- Include evidence of you checking their suitability in terms of both their safety and mobility.
- Think about **your work setting** and how to check the suitability of an individual's clothing and footwear for safety and mobility.

Learning Outcome 2: Be able to prepare for mobility activities

Assessment Criterion 2.4: Check the safety and cleanliness of mobility equipment and appliances

What does AC2.4 mean?

- The lead word **check** means that you must be able to **show through your work practices** how to examine the safety and cleanliness of mobility equipment and appliances.
- Your **observations of your work practices** must include you checking the safety and cleanliness.
- For the key word **safety** you can think about the checks that are necessary for ensuring that mobility equipment and appliances work and can be used safely without causing any injury or harm to the individual or others.
- For the key word **cleanliness** you can think about the checks that are necessary for ensuring that mobility equipment and appliances are clean both before and after their use.
- For the key words **mobility equipment and appliances** you can think about how these may include stairlifts, wheelchairs, sticks, walking frames and custom-made appliances such as light wheelchairs designed for playing sport activities, or adapted scooter aids, or specially designed standing frames.

Read the following **Real Work Setting** scenario and think about how it relates to your work setting and role:

Real Work Setting

Name: Lidia

Job Role: Live-in Carer to a young lady who has a physical impairment
(See page 215 for a description of the role)

Checking the safety and cleanliness of mobility equipment and appliances: Once Dianne has completed her knee mobility exercises and after a short rest she agrees to Lidia assisting her with checking the safety and cleanliness of her wheelchair and standing frame. Lidia checks when Dianne's annual wheelchair safety check is due and confirms that it is due in three months. Lidia then checks that the wheelchair's tyres are fully inflated and that they are not split or cracked, that the wheels and spokes are not bent, the brakes are working correctly and the footplates can be swung out and back again easily. Finally, Lidia checks that the wheelchair frame, seat, cushion and exterior fittings are clean. In terms of Dianne's standing frame, Lidia checks that it is clean and that all movable parts are working correctly and have not become loose.

Evidencing AC2.4 to your assessor:

For AC2.4 you must evidence your skills of how to check the safety and cleanliness of mobility equipment and appliances.

Assessment Method:

Direct Observation of your work practices

- You can **show** your assessor how to check the safety and cleanliness of mobility equipment and appliances.

REMEMBER TO:

- Make arrangements for **observation** of your **work practices**.
- Include evidence of you checking the safety and cleanliness of mobility equipment and appliances.
- Include evidence of mobility equipment and appliances.
- Think about your work setting and how to check the safety and cleanliness of mobility equipment and appliances.

Learning Outcome 3: Be able to support individuals to keep mobile

Assessment Criterion 3.1: Promote the active participation of the individual during a mobility activity

What does AC3.1 mean?

- The lead word **promote** means that you must be able to **show through your work practices** how to support or encourage the active participation of the individual during a mobility activity.
- Your **observations of your work practices** must include you promoting the active participation of the individual.
- For the key words **active participation** you can think about how you can support and encourage an individual to lead and get involved in a mobility activity.
- For the key words **mobility activity** you can think about how this may include exercises, physiotherapy, occupational therapy, household tasks and group activities such as moving from one position to another, stretching, relaxing, walking and swimming.

Read the following **Real Work Setting** scenario and think about how it relates to your work setting and role:

Real Work Setting

Name: Francesco

Job Role: Mental Health Worker in a drop-in service for adults who have mental health needs

Francesco has worked as a Mental Health Worker for eight years. His responsibilities include: providing individuals with advice, guidance and support in relation to budgeting, maintaining their tenancies and accessing a range of social, educational, work and mobility activities.

Promoting active participation: Francesco has agreed with Jordan to support him today with his walking exercises, using his new walking frame. In line with Jordan's support plan, Francesco begins by motivating Jordan to complete his walking exercises this morning by suggesting that he sets himself a personal target of completing these every morning before he has his cup of coffee and a biscuit at 11.00am. Jordan agrees that he does have more energy in the morning and also that he does enjoy his coffee and biscuit, so these can act as his reward for completing his walking exercises. Francesco also suggests that Jordan could try thinking about the benefits of doing these exercises and visualise how good he will feel after completing them every morning. Jordan thanks Francesco and feels that after their discussion he wants to try and use the waking frame with minimum assistance from him. Francesco agrees to stand close by him and assists Jordan to steady his frame only when asked to do so by him.

Evidencing AC3.1 to your assessor:

For AC3.1 you must evidence your skills of how to promote the active participation of the individual during a mobility activity.

Assessment Method:

Direct Observation of your work practices

- You can **show** your assessor how to promote the active participation of the individual during a mobility activity.

REMEMBER TO:

- Make arrangements for **observation** of your **work practices**.
- Include evidence of you promoting the active participation of the individual during a mobility activity.
- Include evidence of this occurring during a mobility activity.
- Think about **your work setting** and how to promote the active participation of the individual during a mobility activity.

Learning Outcome 3: Be able to support individuals to keep mobile

Assessment Criterion 3.2: Assist an individual to use mobility appliances correctly and safely

What does AC3.2 mean?

- The lead word **assist** means that you must be able to **show through your work practices** how to support and encourage an individual to use mobility appliances correctly and safely.
- Your **observations of your work practices** must include you assisting an individual to use mobility appliances.
- For the key words **mobility appliances** you can think about how these may include stairlifts, wheelchairs, sticks, walking frames and custom-made appliances such as light wheelchairs designed for playing sport activities, or adapted scooter aids, or specially designed standing frames.
- For the key words **correctly and safely** you can think about the guidelines and instructions that must be followed when using mobility appliances to ensure that they are being used appropriately and in a way that does not cause any danger or harm to the individual or others.

Read the following **Real Work Setting** scenario and think about how it relates to your work setting and role:

Real Work Setting

Name: Francesco

Job Role: Mental Health Worker in a drop-in service for adults who have mental health needs (See page 219 for a description of the role)

Using mobility appliances correctly and safely: Francesco meets with Ron this afternoon who has asked him for support with using his walker trolley to help carry around food and his rollator that he uses when he goes out. Francesco observes Ron use his walker trolley and suggests that he will find it safer and easier if he pushes rather than pulls the walker trolley after he places his meal on the tray. The rollator Ron uses consists of a frame with four large wheels, handlebars, a shopping basket and a built-in seat. Francesco suggests that Ron must use the handlebars when sitting down and getting up from using the seat, as this will help him to steady himself and avoid him losing his balance.

Evidencing AC3.2 to your assessor:

For AC3.2 you must evidence your skills of how to assist an individual to use mobility appliances correctly and safely.

Assessment Method:

Direct Observation of your work practices

- You can **show** your assessor how to assist an individual to use mobility appliances correctly and safely.

REMEMBER TO:

- Make arrangements for **observation** of your **work practices**.
- Include evidence of you assisting an individual to use mobility appliances.
- Include evidence of this being done in relation to the mobility appliances being used correctly and safely.
- Think about **your work setting** and how to assist an individual to use mobility appliances correctly and safely.

Learning Outcome 3: Be able to support individuals to keep mobile

Assessment Criterion 3.3: Give feedback and encouragement to the individual during mobility activities

What does AC3.3 mean?

- The lead words **give feedback and encouragement** mean that you must be able to **show through your work practices** how to support an individual during mobility activities and comment on the progress being made constructively.
- Your **observations of your work practices** must include you giving feedback and encouragement.
- For the key words **mobility activities** you can think about how you can give feedback and encouragement to the individual during mobility activities such as exercises, physiotherapy, occupational therapy, household tasks and group activities such as moving from one position to another, stretching, relaxing, walking and swimming.

Read the following **Real Work Setting** scenario and think about how it relates to your work setting and role:

Real Work Setting

Name: Francesco

Job Role: Mental Health Worker in a drop-in service for adults who have mental health needs
(See page 219 for a description of the role)

Giving feedback and encouragement: Francesco then observes Ron use his walker trolley again and praises him on pushing it rather than pulling it and also gently reminds him to always use both hands rather than one when pushing it, for safety reasons. Ron then shows Francesco how he can use the handlebars on his rollator when sitting down and getting up from using the seat; Ron finds this easy to do and comments on how much more steady he feels. Francesco praises him on the good progress he has already made with using both mobility appliances this afternoon and encourages him to continue to practise using them in the ways he has shown.

Evidencing AC3.3 to your assessor:

For AC3.3 you must evidence your skills of how to give feedback and encouragement to the individual during mobility activities.

Assessment Method:

Direct Observation of your work practices

- You can **show** your assessor how to give feedback and encouragement to the individual during mobility activities.

REMEMBER TO:

- Make arrangements for **observation** of your **work practices**.
- Include evidence of you giving feedback and encouragement to the individual.
- Include evidence of this being done during mobility activities.
- Think about **your work setting** and how to give feedback and encouragement to the individual during mobility activities.

Learning Outcome 4: Be able to observe, record and report on activities to support mobility

Assessment Criterion 4.1: Observe an individual to monitor changes and responses during a mobility activity

What does AC4.1 mean?

- The lead word **observe** means that you must be able to **show through your work practices** how to watch an individual closely to monitor changes and responses during a mobility activity.
- Your **observations of your work practices** must include you observing an individual.
- For the key word **changes** you can think about how to monitor the positive and negative differences in an individual during a mobility activity.
- For the key word **responses** you can think about how to monitor the positive and negative verbal and non-verbal signs in an individual during a mobility activity.
- For the key words **mobility activity** you can think about how you can observe an individual to monitor changes and responses during mobility activities such as exercises, physiotherapy, occupational therapy, household tasks and group activities such as moving from one position to another, stretching, relaxing, walking and swimming.

Read the following **Real Work Setting** scenario and think about how it relates to your work setting and role:

Real Work Setting

Name: Iris
Job Role: Carer in a residential care home for older people
Iris has been working as a Carer for seven years. Her responsibilities include: supporting individuals with personal care tasks; assisting individuals with restricted mobility to move to communal areas such as the dining room and television room, as well as to the privacy of their bedrooms at their request; and ensuring she supports individuals to maintain their privacy, dignity and independence at all times.
Monitoring changes and responses: Iris observes Alison, in line with her support plan, using two walking sticks when walking down the corridor from her room on the ground floor to the dining room. Iris observes Alison stopping more frequently than usual to place both walking sticks back on the floor when taking a step forward. Iris asks Alison if she is managing well and she shakes her head, saying that using them both is actually slowing her down even more. Iris also notes that Alison is frowning and looking a little upset.

Evidencing AC4.1 to your assessor:

For AC4.1 you must evidence your skills of how to observe an individual to monitor changes and responses during a mobility activity.

Assessment Method:

Direct Observation of your work practices

- You can **show** your assessor how to observe an individual to monitor changes and responses during a mobility activity.

REMEMBER TO:

- Make arrangements for **observation** of your **work practices**.
- Include evidence of you observing an individual.
- Include evidence of you monitoring changes and responses in an individual.
- Include evidence of this being done during a mobility activity.
- Think about **your work setting** and how to observe an individual to monitor changes and responses during a mobility activity.

Learning Outcome 4: Be able to observe, record and report on activities to support mobility

Assessment Criterion 4.2: Record observations of a mobility activity

What does AC4.2 mean?

- The lead word **record** means that you must be able to **show through your work practices** how to document observations of a mobility activity.
- Your **observations of your work practices** must include you recording your observations.
- For the key word **observations** you can think about how this involves recording the date, time and duration of the mobility activity, what the mobility activity involved, the aims agreed with the individual, whether the individual met the aims agreed, how and why, as well as any positive or negative changes and responses.
- For the key words **mobility activity** you can think about how you can record observations of a mobility activity such as exercises, physiotherapy, occupational therapy, household tasks and group activities such as moving from one position to another, stretching, relaxing, walking and swimming.

Read the following **Real Work Setting** scenario and think about how it relates to your work setting and role:

Real Work Setting

Name: Iris

Job Role: Carer in a residential care home for older people
(See page 222 for a description of the role)

Recording observations: Iris then documents in full on Alison's mobility plan the date, time and duration of her mobility activity that involved using two walking sticks when walking down the corridor from her room on the ground floor to the dining room. Iris also documents that Alison stopped walking on four occasions, as both walking sticks had tilted away from her slightly when walking and had lifted off the floor when she took a step forward. Iris records that at the end of the activity she asked Alison if she was managing well and that Alison responded by shaking her head and saying that using both walking sticks was actually slowing her down even more and that Alison was frowning and looking a little upset. Iris recorded her observations of Alison immediately after observing her and in private in the staff office.

Evidencing AC4.2 to your assessor:

For AC4.2 you must evidence your skills of how to record observations of a mobility activity.

Assessment Method:

Direct Observation of your work practices

- You can **show** your assessor how to record observations of a mobility activity.

REMEMBER TO:

- Make arrangements for **observation** of your **work practices**.
- Include evidence of you recording observations.
- Include evidence of a mobility activity.
- Think about **your work setting** and how to record observations of a mobility activity.

Learning Outcome 4: Be able to observe, record and report on activities to support mobility

Assessment Criterion 4.3: Report on progress and/or problems relating to the mobility activity including: choice of activities, equipment, appliances and the support provided

What does AC4.3 mean?

- The lead word **report** means that you must be able to **show through your work practices** how to give a spoken or written account of the progress and/or problems relating to the mobility activity including: choice of activities, equipment, appliances and the support provided.
- Your **observations of your work practices** must include you reporting on progress and/or problems relating to the mobility activity.
- For the key word **activities** you can think about how to report on progress and/or problems relating to mobility activities such as exercises, physiotherapy, occupational therapy, household tasks and group activities such as moving from one position to another, stretching, relaxing, walking and swimming.
- For the key words **equipment** and **appliances** you can think about how to report on progress and/or problems relating to mobility equipment and appliances such as stairlifts, wheelchairs, sticks, walking frames and custom-made appliances such as light wheelchairs designed for playing sport activities, or adapted scooter aids, or specially designed standing frames.
- For the key words **support provided** you can think about how to report on progress and/or problems relating to the assistance that is provided to an individual.

Read the following **Real Work Setting** scenario and think about how it relates to your work setting and role:

Real Work Setting

Name: Iris

Job Role: Carer in a residential care home for older people
(See page 222 for a description of the role)

Reporting on progress and/or problems: Iris then shares with her manager and the physiotherapist the progress and problems relating to the assistance that has been provided to Alison in terms of her walking exercises that involve her using two walking sticks unaided when walking from one area to another. Iris reports on the progress and problems concisely and accurately and in private in the staff office.

Evidencing AC4.3 to your assessor:

For AC4.3 you must evidence your skills of how to report on progress and/or problems relating to the mobility activity including: choice of activities, equipment, appliances and the support provided.

Assessment Method:

Direct Observation of your work practices

- You can **show** your assessor or an expert witness how to report on progress and/or problems relating to the mobility activity including: choice of activities, equipment, appliances and the support provided.

REMEMBER TO:

- Make arrangements for **observation** of your **work practices**.
- Include evidence of you reporting on progress and/or problems relating to the mobility activity.
- Ensure the evidence you provide is related to choice of activities, equipment, appliances and the support provided.
- Think about **your work setting** and how to report on progress and/or problems relating to the mobility activity including: choice of activities, equipment, appliances and the support provided.

HSC2013 Support care plan activities

Learning Outcome 1: Be able to prepare to implement care plan activities

Assessment Criterion 1.1: Identify sources of information about the individual and specific care plan activities

What does AC1.1 mean?

- The lead word **identify** means that you must be able to **show through your work practices** how to establish the sources of information about the individual and specific care plan activities.
- Your **observations of your work practices** must include you identifying both sources of information and specific care plan activities.
- For the key words **care plan** you can think about how individuals' day-to-day care and support requirements, needs and preferences are detailed. A care plan may be known by other names such as a support plan, individual plan, person-centred plan.
- For the key words **specific care plan activities** you can think about the different tasks that are developed to meet individuals' day-to-day care and support requirements, needs and preferences.

Read the following **Real Work Setting** scenario and think about how it relates to your work setting and role:

Real Work Setting

Name: Jeremy
Job Role: Personal Assistant for adults who have epilepsy
Jeremy has been working as a Personal Assistant for one year. His responsibilities include: supporting individuals with all aspects of daily living including personal care (dressing, undressing, using the toilet and washing), meal preparation and administering medication.
Sources of information and care plan activities: Jeremy is meeting with Harold for the first time at his home. Jeremy has read through Harold's care plan to familiarise himself with Harold's likes, dislikes, needs and preferences. Jeremy has also read through Harold's personal profile, which provides him with some information about his background, family and interests and hobbies. Areas where Harold requires support are also detailed, as well as activities that have been agreed with him and that his team of Personal Assistants will be required to support him with. Jeremy has been informed by his Co-ordinator that when he meets with Harold in his home he will find out more information from him and he will also be able to answer any questions he may have about how to support him with the specific care plan activities that are detailed in his care plan.

Evidencing AC1.1 to your assessor:

For AC1.1 you must evidence your skills of how to identify sources of information about the individual and specific care plan activities.

Assessment Method:

Direct Observation of your work practices

- You can **show** your assessor how to identify sources of information about the individual and specific care plan activities.

REMEMBER TO:

- Make arrangements for **observation** of your **work practices**.
- Include evidence of you identifying sources of information about the individual.
- Include evidence of you identifying specific care plan activities.
- Think about **your work setting** and how to identify sources of information about the individual and specific care plan activities.

AC 1.2

Learning Outcome 1: Be able to prepare to implement care plan activities

Assessment Criterion 1.2: Establish the individual's preferences about carrying out care plan activities

What does AC1.2 mean?

- The lead word **establish** means that you must be able to **show through your work practices** how to identify the individual's preferences about carrying out care plan activities.
- Your **observations of your work practices** must include you establishing the individual's preferences about carrying out care plan activities.
- For the key word **preferences** you can think about how an individual may choose how they may like to have their care plan activities carried out.
- For the key words **care plan activities** you can think how to establish the individual's preferences about how to carry out the tasks that are developed to meet the individual's day-to-day care and support requirements and needs.

Read the following **Real Work Setting** scenario and think about how it relates to your work setting and role:

Real Work Setting

Name: Jeremy

Job Role: Personal Assistant for adults who have epilepsy
(See page 225 for a description of the role)

Establish the individual's preferences: Jeremy meets with Harold in his home for the first time and begins by discussing with him the different care plan activities he will support him with this morning: including getting ready to go to work, preparing his breakfast, reminding him to take his medication and putting the rubbish out. In terms of supporting Harold to get ready to go to work, Jeremy asks him what he would like support with; Harold explains that he would like to have a shower this morning and would like Jeremy to support him with having a hair wash and a shave and to be around while he is in the shower, in case he has a seizure. In terms of preparing his breakfast and reminding him to take his medication, Harold explains that he doesn't require any support with these activities, as he has already had his breakfast and taken his medication earlier on this morning. In terms of putting the rubbish out, Harold asks Jeremy whether he can help him with this activity by lifting the bag out of the bin and putting it in the outside bin round the side of the house, as it is a little heavy for him to lift.

Evidencing AC1.2 to your assessor:

For AC1.2 you must evidence your skills of how to establish the individual's preferences about carrying out care plan activities.

Assessment Method:

Direct Observation of your work practices

- You can **show** your assessor how to establish the individual's preferences about carrying out care plan activities.

REMEMBER TO:

- Make arrangements for **observation** of your **work practices**.
- Include evidence of you establishing the individual's preferences.
- Ensure the evidence you provide is related to carrying out care plan activities.
- Think about **your work setting** and how to establish the individual's preferences about carrying out care plan activities.

Learning Outcome 1: Be able to prepare to implement care plan activities

Assessment Criterion 1.3: Confirm with others your understanding of the support required for care plan activities

What does AC1.3 mean?

- The lead word **confirm** means that you must be able to **show through your work practices** how to confirm with others your understanding of the support required for care plan activities.
- Your **observations of your work practices** must include you confirming with others your understanding.
- For the key word **others** you can think about how to confirm with the individual, the individual's advocate, family members, your line manager and other professionals your understanding of the support required for care plan activities.
- For the key words **care plan activities** you can think how to confirm with others your understanding of the support required for the tasks that are developed to meet the individual's day-to-day care and support requirements and needs.

Read the following **Real Work Setting** scenario and think about how it relates to your work setting and role:

Real Work Setting

Name: Jeremy

Job Role: Personal Assistant for adults who have epilepsy
(See page 225 for a description of the role)

Confirming with others: After Jeremy checks with Harold his understanding of how to support him with a shower this morning, Harold introduces Jeremy to his wife and then to his advocate who will be accompanying him when he travels to work on the train. Harold explains to his wife that Jeremy will be supporting him with a shower this morning for the first time and asks Jeremy to speak to his wife if he is unsure about any aspects of how to do this. Jeremy checks with Harold's wife where she usually stands to oversee him have a shower and how much help she gives him with having a hair wash and a shave. While Harold begins to get ready in the bathroom for his shower, Jeremy's advocate asks Jeremy whether he has put the rubbish out yet. Jeremy explains that he hasn't yet done so and confirms with him where the outside bin is and that he has correctly understood that he needs to put the rubbish bag from the kitchen into this bin.

Evidencing AC1.3 to your assessor:

For AC1.3 you must evidence your skills of how to confirm with others your understanding of the support required for care plan activities.

Assessment Method:

Direct Observation of your work practices

- You can **show** your assessor how to confirm with others your understanding of the support required for care plan activities.

REMEMBER TO:

- Make arrangements for **observation** of your **work practices**.
- Include evidence of you confirming with others your understanding.
- Ensure the evidence you provide is related to the support required for care plan activities.
- Think about **your work setting** and how to confirm with others your understanding of the support required for care plan activities.

Learning Outcome 2: Be able to support care plan activities

Assessment Criterion 2.1: Provide support for care plan activities in accordance with the care plan and with agreed ways of working

What does AC2.1 mean?

- The lead words **provide support** means that you must be able to **show through your work practices** how to provide assistance for care plan activities in accordance with the care plan and with agreed ways of working.
- Your **observations of your work practices** must include you providing support for care plan activities in accordance with the care plan and with agreed ways of working.
- For the key words **care plan activities** you can think about how you provide support for the tasks that are developed to meet the individual's day-to-day care and support requirements and needs.
- For the key words **care plan** you can think about how the support you provide for care plan activities must be in line with individuals' day-to-day care and support requirements, needs and preferences are detailed. A care plan may be known by other names such as a support plan, individual plan, person-centred plan.
- For the key words **agreed ways of working** you can think about how the support you provide for care plan activities must be in line with your work setting's policies and procedures, as well as the specific guidelines that are in place for the individuals that you provide care and support to.

Read the following **Real Work Setting** scenario and think about how it relates to your work setting and role:

Real Work Setting

Name: Femi
Job Role: Carer for older people living in the community
Femi has been working as a Carer for six years. Her responsibilities include: providing care and support to individuals with personal care tasks, the preparation of meals and drinks and general household tasks.
Providing support for care plan activities: Femi is visiting Katie this evening and, in line with Katie's care plan and her work setting's policies and procedures, supports her to have a hot drink, get undressed and ready for bed.

Evidencing AC2.1 to your assessor:

For AC2.1 you must evidence your skills of how to provide support for care plan activities in accordance with the care plan and with agreed ways of working.

Assessment Method:

Direct Observation of your work practices

- You can **show** your assessor how to provide support for care plan activities in accordance with the care plan and with agreed ways of working.

REMEMBER TO:

- Make arrangements for **observation** of your **work practices**.
- Include evidence of you providing support for care plan activities.
- Ensure the evidence you provide is in accordance with the individual's care plan.
- Ensure the evidence you provide is in accordance with agreed ways of working.
- Think about **your work setting** and how to provide support for care plan activities in accordance with the care plan and with agreed ways of working.

Learning Outcome 2: Be able to support care plan activities

Assessment Criterion 2.2: Encourage the active participation of an individual in care plan activities

What does AC2.2 mean?

- The lead word **encourage** means that you must be able to **show through your work practices** how to support and motivate the active participation of an individual in care plan activities.
- Your **observations of your work practices** must include you encouraging the active participation of an individual.
- For the key words **active participation** you can think about how you can encourage individuals to be fully involved in all aspects of their care plan activities.
- For the key words **care plan activities** you can think about how you can encourage the active participation of an individual in tasks that are developed to meet the individual's day-to-day care and support requirements and needs.

Read the following **Real Work Setting** scenario and think about how it relates to your work setting and role:

Real Work Setting

Name: Femi

Job Role: Carer for older people living in the community
(See page 228 for a description of the role)

Encourage the active participation of an individual: Femi asks Katie whether she would like to have a hot drink; Katie says that she would like one but does not know what to have. Femi provides Katie with a choice of her two favourite drinks, Ovaltine or tea. Katie says she thinks she would like to have some Ovaltine tonight. Once Katie finishes her hot drink, Femi supports her with getting undressed and encourages her to remove her slippers. Femi asks Katie what items of clothing she would like to remove next; Katie explains that she will remove her trousers first and then her cardigan and top. Femi begins by asking Katie whether she would like support with undoing the buttons on her trousers; Katie says that she does. After doing so, Femi asks Katie whether she can slip her own trousers down to her ankles. Katie does so and proceeds to remove them. Femi proceeds to prompt Katie to remove her cardigan and top and suggests it may be easier for her to do so if she slips them off over her head. Katie does so and thanks Femi for her help.

Evidencing AC2.2 to your assessor:

For AC2.2 you must evidence your skills of how to encourage the active participation of an individual in care plan activities.

Assessment Method:

Direct Observation of your work practices

- You can **show** your assessor how to encourage the active participation of an individual in care plan activities.

REMEMBER TO:

- Make arrangements for **observation** of your **work practices**.
- Include evidence of you encouraging the active participation of an individual.
- Ensure the evidence you provide is related to an individual's care plan activities.
- Think about **your work setting** and how to encourage the active participation of an individual in care plan activities.

Learning Outcome 2: Be able to support care plan activities

Assessment Criterion 2.3: Adapt actions to reflect the individual's needs or preferences during care plan activities

What does AC2.3 mean?

- The lead word **adapt** means that you must be able to **show through your work practices** how to adjust the actions to reflect the individual's needs or preferences during care plan activities.
- Your **observations of your work practices** must include you adapting actions to reflect the individual's needs or preferences during care plan activities.
- For the key words **the individual's needs or preferences** you can think about how you can adapt actions to reflect the individual's requirements or choices during care plan activities.
- For the key words **care plan activities** you can think about how you can adapt actions to reflect the individual's requirements or choices during tasks that are developed to meet the individual's day-to-day care and support requirements and needs.

Read the following **Real Work Setting** scenario and think about how it relates to your work setting and role:

Real Work Setting

Name: Femi

Job Role: Carer for older people living in the community
(See page 228 for a description of the role)

Adapt actions to reflect the individual's needs or preferences: As Katie is getting into bed she tells Femi that she is feeling a little hungry and asks Femi whether she can prepare a sandwich for her. Femi explains that she would be very happy to do so and asks her what she would like; Katie tells Femi that she has a little ham in the fridge and would like this on white bread and adds that she hopes she is not taking up too much of Femi's time. Femi explains that she isn't taking up her time and that she is very happy to help; Femi adds that supporting her with preparing meals and snacks is part of her job as a Carer.

Evidencing AC2.3 to your assessor:

For AC2.3 you must evidence your skills of how to adapt actions to reflect the individual's needs or preferences during care plan activities.

Assessment Method:

Direct Observation of your work practices

- You can **show** your assessor how to adapt actions to reflect the individual's needs or preferences during care plan activities.

REMEMBER TO:

- Make arrangements for **observation** of your **work practices**.
- Include evidence of you adapting actions.
- Ensure the evidence you provide is related to reflecting the individual's needs or preferences during care plan activities.
- Think about **your work setting** and how to adapt actions to reflect the individual's needs or preferences during care plan activities.

Learning Outcome 3: Be able to maintain records of care plan activities

Assessment Criterion 3.1: Record information about implementation of care plan activities, in line with agreed ways of working

What does AC3.1 mean?

- The lead word **record** means that you must be able to **show through your work practices** how to document information about implementation of care plan activities, in line with agreed ways of working.
- Your **observations of your work practices** must include you recording information about implementation of care plan activities.
- For the key word **information** you can think about the details you record about the implementation of care plan activities such as the date, time, your signature, the activity implemented, how it was implemented, the areas that worked well, the areas that didn't work well, as well as the support provided.
- For the key words **care plan activities** you can think about how you record information about the implementation of tasks that are developed to meet the individual's day-to-day care and support requirements and needs.
- For the key words **agreed ways of working** you can think about how to record information about implementation of care plan activities in line with your work setting's policies and procedures, as well as the specific guidelines that are in place for the individuals that you provide care and support to.

Read the following **Real Work Setting** scenario and think about how it relates to your work setting and role:

Real Work Setting

Name: Javier

Job Role: Support Worker for people who have learning difficulties

Javier has been working as a Support Worker for two years. His responsibilities include: supporting individuals to achieve their goals and aspirations, enabling individuals to access the community's services and facilities and participate in activities.

Record information about implementation of care plan activities: Javier supported Frank with going to the post office today. At the end of his shift, Javier records in Frank's daily record the date and time he accompanied Frank to the post office, details of the tasks Frank completed well, in addition to the extra support Frank required with checking his change. Javier then confirmed this information with Frank before signing the daily record.

Evidencing AC3.1 to your assessor:

For AC3.1 you must evidence your skills of how to record information about implementation of care plan activities, in line with agreed ways of working.

Assessment Method:

Direct Observation of your work practices

- You can **show** your assessor how to record information about implementation of care plan activities, in line with agreed ways of working.

REMEMBER TO:

- Make arrangements for observation of your work practices.
- Include evidence of you recording information about implementation of care plan activities.
- Ensure the evidence you provide is in line with agreed ways of working.
- Think about your work setting and how to record information about implementation of care plan activities, in line with agreed ways of working.

Learning Outcome 3: Be able to maintain records of care plan activities

Assessment Criterion 3.2: Record signs of discomfort, changes to an individual's needs or preferences, or other indications that care plan activities may need to be revised

What does AC3.2 mean?

- The lead word **record** means that you must be able to **show through your work practices** how to document signs of discomfort, changes to an individual's needs or preferences, or other indications that care plan activities may need to be revised.
- Your **observations of your work practices** must include you recording signs of discomfort, changes to an individual's needs or preferences, or other indications.
- For the key words **signs of discomfort** you can think about the visible indicators that an individual may be feeling uncomfortable, worried or embarrassed during care plan activities such as by frowning, shouting out, crying, withdrawing or avoiding eye contact.
- For the key words **changes to an individual's needs or preferences** you can think about how what an individual requires or chooses to do may alter during care plan activities such as going to bed later, having a shower instead of a bath, choosing to stay in rather than go out, or meeting up with friends in a different place or at a different time.
- For the key words **other indications** you can think about other factors that may alert you to an individual feeling uncomfortable, worried or embarrassed during care plan activities such as refusing to actively participate or a change in the way the individual interacts with you and others.

Read the following **Real Work Setting** scenario and think about how it relates to your work setting and role:

Real Work Setting

Name: Javier

Job Role: Support Worker for people who have learning difficulties
(See page 231 for a description of the role)

Recording signs of discomfort, changes to an individual's needs or preferences, or other indications: Javier also recorded that when supporting Frank with checking his change he noted that Frank looked embarrassed and kept on looking around to see if anyone else could see what they were doing.

Evidencing AC3.2 to your assessor:

For AC3.2 you must evidence your skills of how to record signs of discomfort, changes to an individual's needs or preferences, or other indications that care plan activities may need to be revised.

Assessment Method:

Direct Observation of your work practices

- You can **show** your assessor how to record signs of discomfort, changes to an individual's needs or preferences, or other indications that care plan activities may need to be revised.

REMEMBER TO:

- Make arrangements for **observation** of your **work practices**.
- Include evidence of you recording signs of discomfort, changes to an individual's needs or preferences, or other indications.
- Ensure the evidence you provide relates to care plan activities that may need to be revised.
- Think about **your work setting** and how to record signs of discomfort, changes to an individual's needs or preferences, or other indications that care plan activities may need to be revised.

Learning Outcome 4: Be able to contribute to reviewing activities in the care plan

Assessment Criterion 4.1: Describe your role and the roles of others in reviewing care plan activities

What does AC4.1 mean?

- The lead word **describe** means that you must provide an **account** that **details** your role and the roles of others in reviewing care plan activities.
- Your **account** must detail your role and the roles of others.
- For the key word **role** you can think about your duties and responsibilities, as well as the duties and responsibilities of others in reviewing care plan activities.
- For the key word **others** you can think about the role of the individual, the individual's family members, advocate, your line manager and other professionals in reviewing care plan activities.
- For the key words **care plan activities** you can think about your role and the roles of others in reviewing tasks that are developed to meet the individual's day-to-day care and support requirements and needs.

Read the following **Real Work Setting** scenario and think about how it relates to your work setting and role:

Real Work Setting

Name: Katrina

Job Role: Mental Health Support Worker

Katrina has been working as a Mental Health Support Worker for 11 years. Her responsibilities include: supporting individuals with daily living activities, assisting individuals with managing their continence, serving meals and drinks, changing beds and tidying rooms.

Reviewing care plan activities: Katrina is supporting Gemma to take an active part in reviewing the care plan activities that the team currently support her with. Katrina and Gemma will also involve Gemma's dietician, advocate and uncle in reviewing the implementation of her care plan activities over the last three months in order to establish their views and ideas.

Evidencing AC4.1 to your assessor:

For AC4.1 you must evidence your knowledge of your role and the roles of others in reviewing care plan activities.

Assessment Methods:

Oral or **Written** Questioning or **Discussion** or a **Personal Statement** or **Reflection**

- You can **tell** your assessor about your role and the roles of others in reviewing care plan activities.
  Or
- You can **talk** to your assessor about your role and the roles of others in reviewing care plan activities.
  Or
- You can write a **personal statement** or **reflection** about your experience of your role and the roles of others in reviewing care plan activities.

REMEMBER TO:

- Provide an **account** that includes **details**.
- Include details about your role and the roles of others.
- Ensure your evidence relates to reviewing care plan activities.
- Think about **your work setting** and your role and the roles of others in reviewing care plan activities.

Learning Outcome 4: Be able to contribute to reviewing activities in the care plan

Assessment Criterion 4.2: Seek feedback from the individual and others on how well specific care plan activities meet the individual's needs and preferences

What does AC4.2 mean?

- The lead words **seek feedback** mean that you must be able to **show through your work practices** how to obtain the comments and views from the individual and others on how well specific care plan activities meet the individual's needs and preferences.
- Your **observations of your work practices** must include you seeking feedback from the individual and others.
- For the key word **others** you can think about how to seek feedback from the individual's family members, advocate, your line manager and other professionals on how well specific care plan activities meet the individual's needs and preferences.
- For the key words **care plan activities** you can think about how to seek feedback from the individual and others on how well specific tasks meet the individual's day-to-day care and support requirements and needs.
- For the key words **the individual's needs and preferences** you can think about how to seek feedback from the individual and others on how well specific care plan activities meet what an individual requires or chooses to do.

Read the following **Real Work Setting** scenario and think about how it relates to your work setting and role:

Real Work Setting

Name: Katrina

Job Role: Mental Health Support Worker
(See page 233 for a description of the role)

Seeking feedback from the individual and others: Katrina discusses with Gemma and her dietician whether the nutrition plan they made has worked. The dietician confirms that Gemma has lost weight, as planned, and Gemma confirms that she has enjoyed eating a variety of healthy foods. Gemma's advocate explains how Gemma could not always go out when and where she wanted due to staff shortages and provides Katrina with a list of places where Gemma would like to go over the next three months. Gemma's uncle has fed back that he has noted Gemma seems more positive in herself and less dependent on him when going out.

Evidencing AC4.2 to your assessor:

For AC4.2 you must evidence your skills of how to seek feedback from the individual and others on how well specific care plan activities meet the individual's needs and preferences.

Assessment Method:

Direct Observation of your work practices

- You can **show** your assessor how to seek feedback from the individual and others on how well specific care plan activities meet the individual's needs and preferences.

REMEMBER TO:

- Make arrangements for **observation** of your **work practices**.
- Include evidence of you seeking feedback from the individual and others.
- Ensure the evidence you provide relates to how well specific care plan activities meet the individual's needs and preferences.
- Think about **your work setting** and how to seek feedback from the individual and others on how well specific care plan activities meet the individual's needs and preferences.

Learning Outcome 4: Be able to contribute to reviewing activities in the care plan

Assessment Criterion 4.3: Contribute to review of how well specific care plan activities meet the individual's needs and preferences

What does AC4.3 mean?

- The lead words **contribute to** mean that you must be able to **show through your work practices** how **to assist** in the review of how well specific care plan activities meet the individual's needs and preferences.
- Your **observations of your work practices** must include you contributing to the review.
- For the key words **care plan activities** you can think about how to contribute to the review of how well specific tasks meet the individual's day-to-day care and support requirements and needs.
- For the key words **the individual's needs and preferences** you can think about how to contribute to the review of how well specific care plan activities meet what an individual requires or chooses to do.

Read the following **Real Work Setting** scenario and think about how it relates to your work setting and role:

Real Work Setting

Name: Katrina

Job Role: Mental Health Support Worker
(See page 233 for a description of the role)

Contributing to the review of specific care plan activities: Katrina shares with Gemma and those others present how she too has noted that Gemma has lost weight, while still enjoying her meals. Katrina confirms she is aware that Gemma was not always able to go out when and where she wanted but how although this was at times due to unforeseen staff shortages, other times it was due to Gemma deciding that she didn't want to go out. Katrina adds that she is pleased that Gemma's uncle has noted that Gemma seems more positive in herself and less dependent on him when going out, as together both Gemma and herself have been working hard on building up Gemma's confidence when going out and motivating herself to complete activities for herself rather than depend on Katrina or her colleagues.

Evidencing AC4.3 to your assessor:

For AC4.3 you must evidence your skills of how to contribute to the review of how well specific care plan activities meet the individual's needs and preferences.

Assessment Method:

Direct Observation of your work practices

- You can **show** your assessor how to contribute to the review of how well specific care plan activities meet the individual's needs and preferences.

REMEMBER TO:

- Make arrangements for **observation** of your **work practices**.
- Include evidence of you contributing to the review.
- Ensure the evidence you provide relates to how well specific care plan activities meet the individual's needs and preferences.
- Think about **your work setting** and how to contribute to the review of how well specific care plan activities meet the individual's needs and preferences.

Learning Outcome 4: Be able to contribute to reviewing activities in the care plan

Assessment Criterion 4.4: Contribute to agreement on changes that may need to be made to the care plan

What does AC4.4 mean?

- The lead words **contribute to** mean that you must be able to **show through your work practices** how to **assist** in the agreement on changes that may need to be made to the care plan.
- Your **observations of your work practices** must include you contributing to agreement on changes.
- For the key word **changes** you can think about how to contribute to agreement on changes that may need to be made to an individual's care plan, in relation to the activity or the support required, or to meet the individual's needs and preferences.
- For the key words **the care plan** you can think about how to contribute to agreement on changes that may need to be made to an individual's day-to-day care and support requirements, needs and preferences. A care plan may be known by other names such as a support plan, individual plan, person-centred plan.

Read the following **Real Work Setting** scenario and think about how it relates to your work setting and role:

Real Work Setting

Name: Katrina

Job Role: Mental Health Support Worker
(See page 233 for a description of the role)

Contributing to agreement on changes: Katrina agrees with Gemma and the dietician to continue following the agreed nutrition plan and to review this in 12 weeks, time. Katrina agrees to support Gemma to try the list of new activities that she has told her advocate about and to work on Gemma maintaining her new-found confidence and motivation when going out and completing activities for herself. Katrina talks through and agrees with Gemma and her manager how to document these changes in Gemma's care plan.

Evidencing AC4.4 to your assessor:

For AC4.4 you must evidence your skills of how to contribute to agreement on changes that may need to be made to an individual's care plan.

Assessment Method:
Direct Observation of your work practices

- You can **show** your assessor how to contribute to agreement on changes that may need to be made to an individual's care plan.

REMEMBER TO:

- Make arrangements for **observation** of your **work practices**.
- Include evidence of you contributing to agreement on changes that may need to be made.
- Ensure the evidence you provide relates to an individual's care plan.
- Think about **your work setting** and how to contribute to agreement on changes that may need to be made to an individual's care plan.

HSC2014 Support individuals to eat and drink

Learning Outcome 1: Be able to support individuals to make choices about food and drink

Assessment Criterion 1.1: Establish with an individual the food and drink they wish to consume

What does AC1.1 mean?

- The lead word **establish** means that you must be able to **show through your work practices** how to identify and agree with an individual the food and drink they wish to consume.
- Your **observations of your work practices** must include you agreeing with an individual the food and drink they wish to consume.
- For the key word **consume** you can think about the different types of food and drink individuals may ingest.

Read the following **Real Work Setting** scenario and think about how it relates to your work setting and role:

Real Work Setting

Name: Betty

Job Role: Support Worker for people who have multiple sensory impairments

Betty has been working as a Support Worker for five years. Her responsibilities include: empowering individuals to live as independently as possible, providing practical support with daily living activities such as tidying, cleaning, washing, ironing, shopping, arranging appointments and socialising with family and friends.

Establishing with an individual the food and drink they wish to consume: Betty is supporting Lisa, who has a visual and hearing impairment, with making a shopping list as she plans to go food shopping this afternoon. Betty asks Lisa whether she wants to begin by thinking about the meals, snacks and drinks that she enjoys. After giving Lisa time to think about this, Betty then supports Lisa to think about the ingredients she will need for these and, at the same time, checks her cupboards to see whether she has these ingredients already, or whether she will need to buy them. Lisa then voice records her shopping list onto her mobile phone so that she can play this back at the supermarket.

Evidencing AC1.1 to your assessor:

For AC1.1 you must evidence your skills of how to establish with an individual the food and drink they wish to consume.

Assessment Method:

Direct Observation of your work practices

- You can **show** your assessor how to establish with an individual the food and drink they wish to consume.

REMEMBER TO:

- Make arrangements for **observation** of your **work practices**.
- Include evidence of you establishing with an individual the food and drink they wish to consume.
- Ensure the evidence you provide includes both food and drink that an individual wishes to consume.
- Think about **your work setting** and how to establish with an individual the food and drink they wish to consume.

Learning Outcome 1: Be able to support individuals to make choices about food and drink

Assessment Criterion 1.2: Encourage the individual to select suitable options for food and drink

What does AC1.2 mean?

- The lead word **encourage** means that you must be able to **show through your work practices** how to support and motivate the individual to select suitable options for food and drink.
- Your **observations of your work practices** must include you encouraging the individual.
- For the key words **suitable options** you can think about how to encourage the individual to choose a range of food and drink that takes account of their expressed wishes and preferences, general nutrition principles, specific dietary requirements, religious, cultural and personal beliefs and the resources available.

Read the following **Real Work Setting** scenario and think about how it relates to your work setting and role:

Real Work Setting

Name: Betty

Job Role: Support Worker for people who have multiple sensory impairments
(See page 237 for a description of the role)

Encouraging the individual to select suitable options: At the supermarket Betty accompanies Lisa to walk round the different aisles and think about the food and drink she is buying. Betty asks Lisa about her budget for the week's food shop and then informs her of the different options and prices of both frozen and fresh vegetables; Lisa decides to buy fresh vegetables but in smaller quantities so that she does not waste them and so that she increases her vegetable intake. Betty and Lisa then discuss the range of gluten-free cakes and biscuits that are available, including Lisa's favourite flavours and her budget available for these. Betty and Lisa then go to buy some fizzy drink; Betty explains to Lisa the sugar content in these drinks and, although Lisa knows that these are not good for her health, she decides to go ahead and buy two bottles of Pepsi but, instead of the usual 2-litre bottles, decides to buy the smaller 1- litre bottles in the hope that this will encourage her to consume less fizzy drink during the week.

Evidencing AC1.2 to your assessor:

For AC1.2 you must evidence your skills of how to encourage the individual to select suitable options for food and drink.

Assessment Method:

Direct Observation of your work practices

- You can **show** your assessor how to encourage the individual to select suitable options for food and drink.

REMEMBER TO:

- Make arrangements for **observation** of your **work practices**.
- Include evidence of you encouraging the individual to select suitable options for food and drink.
- Ensure the evidence you provide includes both food and drink.
- Think about **your work setting** and how to encourage the individual to select suitable options for food and drink.

Learning Outcome 1: Be able to support individuals to make choices about food and drink

Assessment Criterion 1.3: Describe ways to resolve any difficulties or dilemmas about the choice of food and drink

What does AC1.3 mean?

- The lead word **describe** means that you must provide an **account** that **details** ways to resolve any difficulties or dilemmas about the choice of food and drink.
- Your **account** must detail **different** ways to resolve any difficulties or dilemmas.
- For the key words **difficulties or dilemmas** you can think about how when supporting individuals to make choices about food and drink their preferences may contradict what has been agreed in their care or nutrition plan, or they may be undecided about the choices to make about food and drink.

Read the following **Real Work Setting** scenario and think about how it relates to your work setting and role:

Real Work Setting

Name: Betty

Job Role: Support Worker for people who have multiple sensory impairments
(See page 237 for a description of the role)

Ways to resolve any difficulties or dilemmas: A little later on, Lisa decides that she does not want to buy the smaller bottles of Pepsi as the 2-litre bottles will be cheaper. Lisa also decides that she is going to buy some chocolate biscuits that are not gluten-free, as she hasn't eaten any chocolate for a while. Betty says to Lisa that it is her choice and her money but that given the allergies and reactions she has to food containing gluten she would advise against buying some non-gluten-free chocolate biscuits and shows Lisa some other alternatives she may wish to buy. Lisa decides that for now she will buy the gluten-free biscuits as she does not want to become ill and, after discussion with Betty, decides to go ahead and buy one 2-litre and one 1-litre bottle of Pepsi as a compromise.

Evidencing AC1.3 to your assessor:

For AC1.3 you must evidence your knowledge of ways to resolve any difficulties or dilemmas about the choice of food and drink.

Assessment Methods:

Oral or **Written** Questioning or **Discussion** or a **Personal Statement** or **Reflection**

- You can **tell** your assessor about ways to resolve any difficulties or dilemmas about the choice of food and drink.
  Or
- You can **talk** to your assessor about ways to resolve any difficulties or dilemmas about the choice of food and drink.
  Or
- You can write a **personal statement** or **reflection** about your experience of ways to resolve any difficulties or dilemmas about the choice of food and drink.

REMEMBER TO:

- Provide an **account** that includes **details**.
- Include details about ways to resolve any difficulties or dilemmas about the choice of food and drink.
- Include evidence of different ways.
- Ensure your evidence relates to an individual's choice of food and drink.
- Think about **your work setting** and ways to resolve any difficulties or dilemmas about the choice of food and drink.

Learning Outcome 1: Be able to support individuals to make choices about food and drink

Assessment Criterion 1.4: Describe how and when to seek additional guidance about an individual's choice of food and drink

What does AC1.4 mean?

- The lead word **describe** means that you must provide an **account** that **details** how and when to seek additional guidance about an individual's choice of food and drink.
- Your **account** must detail both how and when.
- For the key words **additional guidance** you can think about the process you must follow, as well as the occasions when you must seek more information, advice and support about an individual's choice of food and drink.

Read the following **Real Work Setting** scenario and think about how it relates to your work setting and role:

Real Work Setting

Name: Betty

Job Role: Support Worker for people who have multiple sensory impairments
(See page 237 for a description of the role)

How and when to seek additional guidance: On Betty's return to the office she requests to meet with her manager in private to discuss Lisa's choice of food and drink when out shopping today. Betty explains the support she provided to Lisa to make her own choices about suitable options for food and drink, and the outcome of this. Betty then explores with her manager other ways that Lisa could be encouraged to buy less fizzy drink and gluten-free food including visiting a health food shop, researching the effects of consuming large quantities of fizzy drink and arranging another appointment with Lisa's dietician.

Evidencing AC1.4 to your assessor:

For AC1.4 you must evidence your knowledge of how and when to seek additional guidance about an individual's choice of food and drink.

Assessment Methods:

Oral or **Written** Questioning or **Discussion** or a **Personal Statement** or **Reflection**

- You can **tell** your assessor about how and when to seek additional guidance about an individual's choice of food and drink.
  Or
- You can **talk** to your assessor about how and when to seek additional guidance about an individual's choice of food and drink.
  Or
- You can write a **personal statement** or **reflection** about your experience of how and when to seek additional guidance about an individual's choice of food and drink.

REMEMBER TO:

- Provide an **account** that includes **details**.
- Include details about both how and when to seek additional guidance.
- Ensure your evidence relates to an individual's choice of food and drink.
- Think about **your work setting** and how and when to seek additional guidance about an individual's choice of food and drink.

Learning Outcome 2: Be able to prepare to provide support for eating and drinking

Assessment Criterion 2.1: Identify the level and type of support an individual requires when eating and drinking

What does AC2.1 mean?

- The lead word **identify** means that you must be able to **show through your work practices** how to establish the level and type of support an individual requires when eating and drinking.
- Your **observations of your work practices** must include you identifying the level and type of support an individual requires.
- For the key word **level** you can think about whether an individual requires low level of support such as a prompt to eat slowly, or high level of support such as physically assisting an individual when eating and drinking.
- For the key word **type** you can think about whether an individual requires actual physical guidance or physical prompts with some aspects of verbal prompting only with eating and drinking.

Read the following **Real Work Setting** scenario and think about how it relates to your work setting and role:

Real Work Setting

Name: Norbert

Job Role: Care Assistant for older people

Norbert has been working as a Care Assistant for one year. His responsibilities include delivering individualised plans of care, assisting individuals with their mobility, continence, physical care, eating and drinking.

Identifying the level and type of support: Norbert is supporting Aziz with his breakfast this morning and references Aziz's care plan and guidelines to check the level and type of support he requires when eating and drinking. Norbert confirms that Aziz requires low-level support and only verbal prompts when eating and drinking, with respect to eating and drinking slowly, holding his utensils and wiping his mouth clean. Aziz's guidelines also suggest that Aziz responds better to verbal prompting when you are not sitting or standing too close to him.

Evidencing AC2.1 to your assessor:

For AC2.1 you must evidence your skills of how to identify the level and type of support an individual requires when eating and drinking.

Assessment Method:

Direct Observation of your work practices

- You can **show** your assessor how to identify the level and type of support an individual requires when eating and drinking.

REMEMBER TO:

- Make arrangements for **observation** of your **work practices**.
- Include evidence of you identifying both the level and type of support an individual requires.
- Ensure the evidence you provide relates to eating and drinking.
- Think about **your work setting** and how to identify the level and type of support an individual requires when eating and drinking.

Learning Outcome 2: Be able to prepare to provide support for eating and drinking

Assessment Criterion 2.2: Demonstrate effective hand washing and use of protective clothing when handling food and drink

What does AC2.2 mean?

- The lead word **demonstrate** means that you must be able to **show through your work practices** how to show effective hand washing and use of protective clothing when handling food and drink.
- Your **observations of your work practices** must include you using effective hand washing and protective clothing.
- For the key words **hand washing** you can think about your work setting's hand-washing policy, as well as all the preparations that must be made before and after washing your hands when handling food and drink.
- For the key words **protective clothing** you can think about the procedures to follow to ensure that protective clothing such as aprons, gloves, hair nets are correctly put on, taken off and disposed of when handling food and drink.

Read the following **Real Work Setting** scenario and think about how it relates to your work setting and role:

Real Work Setting

Name: Norbert

Job Role: Care Assistant for older people
(See page 241 for a description of the role)

Effective hand washing and use of protective clothing: Norbert then prepares himself to support Aziz with his breakfast. Aziz removes his watch, rolls his sleeves up to his elbows, ensures he runs the water so that it is neither too hot nor too cold before then following the steps outlined in the World Health Organization's diagrams for washing his hands thoroughly. Aziz demonstrates that he washes his hands thoroughly and ensures that all areas of his hands are washed effectively. Norbert then puts on a polythene pair of blue disposable gloves and a pink-coloured plastic disposable apron as he will be supporting Aziz with eating and drinking.

Evidencing AC2.2 to your assessor:

For AC2.2 you must evidence your skills of effective hand washing and use of protective clothing when handling food and drink.

Assessment Method:

Direct Observation of your work practices

- You can **show** your assessor how to use effective hand washing and protective clothing when handling food and drink.

REMEMBER TO:

- Make arrangements for **observation** of your **work practices**.
- Include evidence of you using effective hand washing and protective clothing.
- Ensure the evidence you provide relates to when handling food and drink.
- Think about **your work setting** and how to demonstrate effective hand washing and use of protective clothing when handling food and drink.

Learning Outcome 2: Be able to prepare to provide support for eating and drinking

Assessment Criterion 2.3: Support the individual to prepare to eat and drink in a way that meets their personal needs and preferences

What does AC2.3 mean?

- The lead word **support** means that you must be able to **show through your work practices** how to assist the individual to prepare to eat and drink in a way that meets their personal needs and preferences.
- Your **observations of your work practices** must include you supporting the individual to prepare to eat and drink.
- For the key word **prepare** you can think about how this may include supporting an individual to choose where to eat, choosing with whom to eat, protecting clothes from potential spills and taking up a comfortable position.
- For the key words **personal needs and preferences** you can think about how to support an individual to prepare to eat and drink in accordance with their requirements and wishes.

Read the following **Real Work Setting** scenario and think about how it relates to your work setting and role:

Real Work Setting

Name: Norbert

Job Role: Care Assistant for older people
(See page 241 for a description of the role)

Supporting the individual to prepare to eat and drink: Norbert then confirms with Aziz that he is ready for his breakfast and asks him whether he would like to have it in his room or downstairs in the dining room; Aziz decides to eat in his room this morning. Norbert then asks Aziz whether he would like to have his breakfast sitting by his window or in bed; Aziz replies that he would like to sit by his window and have it on his table as it is a sunny morning and he can look out onto the garden. Norbert asks Aziz whether he would like a serviette across his lap to protect his dressing gown from any food or drink that may spill; Aziz tells Norbert that this is a very good idea and asks Norbert whether he can help him with this.

Evidencing AC2.3 to your assessor:

For AC2.3 you must evidence your skills of supporting the individual to prepare to eat and drink in a way that meets their personal needs and preferences.

Assessment Method:

Direct Observation of your work practices

- You can **show** your assessor how to support the individual to prepare to eat and drink in a way that meets their personal needs and preferences.

REMEMBER TO:

- Make arrangements for **observation** of your **work practices**.
- Include evidence of you supporting the individual to prepare to eat and drink.
- Ensure the support you provide takes into account the individual's personal needs and preferences.
- Think about **your work setting** and how to support the individual to prepare to eat and drink in a way that meets their personal needs and preferences.

Learning Outcome 2: Be able to prepare to provide support for eating and drinking

Assessment Criterion 2.4: Provide suitable utensils to assist the individual to eat and drink

What does AC2.4 mean?

- The lead word **provide** means that you must be able to **show through your work practices** how to supply suitable utensils to assist the individual to eat and drink.
- Your **observations of your work practices** must include you providing suitable utensils.
- For the key words **suitable utensils** you can think about how this may include adapted knives, forks, spoons and cups that are necessary for the individual to eat and drink, such as lightweight cutlery for individuals who have weakness in the arms or shoulders, weighted cutlery for individuals who have tremors, foam tubing that can be placed over utensils' handles for individuals who have pain or stiffness in their hands, a handle strap for individuals who are unable to grasp, angled cutlery for individuals who have restricted movement in their arms, wrists or shoulders, plastic-coated cutlery for individuals who have a strong bite reflex, cups with large handles for individuals who have a reduced grip and cups with lids for individuals who have tremors.

Read the following **Real Work Setting** scenario and think about how it relates to your work setting and role:

Real Work Setting

Name: Norbert

Job Role: Care Assistant for older people
(See page 241 for a description of the role)

Providing suitable utensils: Norbert then places in front of Aziz on his table his weighted knife and fork and a covered spoon. Aziz asks Norbert whether it is necessary for him to use these utensils. Norbert explains to Aziz that his weighted knife and fork are useful in terms of helping with the tremors he experiences in his hands, as these allow him to hold them independently and that the added weight helps with reducing the severity of his tremors. The covered spoon, Norbert explains, is also designed for individuals with tremors as the lid reduces spillages that may occur with hand tremors. Norbert then shows Aziz his cup and asks him whether he would like to use his cup with a lid, or the spill-resistant insert in his mug to help reduce spillage of his tea; Aziz tells Norbert that he prefers to have his tea in his favourite mug so will use the insert instead.

Evidencing AC2.4 to your assessor:

For AC2.4 you must evidence your skills of providing suitable utensils to assist the individual to eat and drink.

Assessment Method:

Direct Observation of your work practices

- You can **show** your assessor how to provide suitable utensils to assist the individual to eat and drink.

REMEMBER TO:

- Make arrangements for **observation** of your **work practices**.
- Include evidence of you providing suitable utensils.
- Ensure the evidence you provide relates to assisting the individual to eat and drink.
- Think about **your work setting** and how to provide suitable utensils to assist the individual to eat and drink.

Learning Outcome 3: Be able to provide support for eating and drinking

Assessment Criterion 3.1: Describe factors that help promote an individual's dignity, comfort and enjoyment while eating and drinking

What does AC3.1 mean?

- The lead word **describe** means that you must provide an **account** that **details** factors that help promote an individual's dignity, comfort and enjoyment while eating and drinking.
- Your **account** must detail **different** factors.
- For the key word **dignity** you can think about the factors that help promote an individual's self-respect and worthiness while eating and drinking.
- For the key word **comfort** you can think about the factors that help promote an individual to feel relaxed and free from pain when eating and drinking.
- For the key word **enjoyment** you can think about the factors that help promote an individual to feel that they like and take pleasure in eating and drinking.

Read the following **Real Work Setting** scenario and think about how it relates to your work setting and role:

Real Work Setting

Name: Sally
Job Role: Support Worker for people who have learning disabilities
Sally has been working as a Support Worker for four years. Her responsibilities include: assisting individuals with personal care tasks, eating and drinking, as well as with accessing a wide range of activities both at home and in the community.
Factors that help promote an individual's dignity, comfort and enjoyment: Sally discusses with the new Volunteer shadowing her today how it is very important that when individuals eat and drink they feel dignified, relaxed, happy and comfortable. Sally tells the new Volunteer that she will observe her today supporting Annette with her lunch. Sally tells the new Volunteer how Annette likes a large serviette to be placed across her lap to protect her clothes and some hand wipes placed on the table, should she need to wipe her hands or mouth. Annette also enjoys sitting with others when eating and drinking and having a cushion round her back to ensure she is sitting upright and comfortably.

Evidencing AC3.1 to your assessor:

For AC3.1 you must evidence your knowledge of the factors that help promote an individual's dignity, comfort and enjoyment while eating and drinking.

Assessment Methods:

Oral or **Written** Questioning or **Discussion** or a **Personal Statement** or **Reflection**

- You can **tell** your assessor about the factors that help promote an individual's dignity, comfort and enjoyment while eating and drinking.
  Or
- You can **talk** to your assessor about the factors that help promote an individual's dignity, comfort and enjoyment while eating and drinking.
  Or
- You can write a **personal statement** or **reflection** about your experience of the factors that help promote an individual's dignity, comfort and enjoyment while eating and drinking.

REMEMBER TO:

- Provide an **account** that includes **details**.
- Include details about different factors.
- Ensure your evidence relates to promoting an individual's dignity, comfort and enjoyment while eating and drinking.
- Think about **your work setting** and the factors that help promote an individual's dignity, comfort and enjoyment while eating and drinking.

Learning Outcome 3: Be able to provide support for eating and drinking

Assessment Criterion 3.2: Support the individual to consume manageable amounts of food and drink at their own pace

What does AC3.2 mean?

- The lead word **support** means that you must be able to **show through your work practices** how to assist the individual to consume manageable amounts of food and drink at their own pace.
- Your **observations of your work practices** must include you supporting the individual to consume manageable amounts of food and drink.
- For the key words **manageable amounts** you can think about how to support the individual to eat and drink easily and safely.
- For the key words **at their own pace** you can think about how to support an individual to eat and drink at a speed that is comfortable for them.

Read the following **Real Work Setting** scenario and think about how it relates to your work setting and role:

Real Work Setting

Name: Sally

Job Role: Support Worker for people who have learning disabilities
(See page 245 for a description of the role)

Support the individual to consume manageable amounts of food and drink: Sally supports Annette with her lunch and asks the new Volunteer to observe how she enables Annette to eat and drink at her own pace. Sally begins by asking Annette what she would like to drink; Annette responds by saying that she would like a cup of tea with her lunch. Sally makes Annette a cup of tea and then places this in front of her, telling her that it is hot; Annette thanks Sally and says that she will drink this after her meal. Annette tells Sally that she would like to begin eating her fish and chips. Sally places a small amount of fish and a chip on Annette's fork and then puts the fork on the plate in front of her and waits for Annette to pick this up and eat the food on it. Once she has done so, Annette places another small amount of fish and a chip on Annette's fork and then puts the fork on the plate in front of her and again waits for Annette to pick this up.

Evidencing AC3.2 to your assessor:

For AC3.2 you must evidence your skills of supporting the individual to consume manageable amounts of food and drink at their own pace.

Assessment Method:

Direct Observation of your work practices

- You can **show** your assessor how to support the individual to consume manageable amounts of food and drink at their own pace.

REMEMBER TO:

- Make arrangements for **observation** of your **work practices**.
- Include evidence of you supporting the individual to consume manageable amounts of food and drink.
- Include evidence of you supporting the individual to consume manageable amounts of food and drink at their own pace.
- Think about **your work setting** and how to support the individual to consume manageable amounts of food and drink at their own pace.

Learning Outcome 3: Be able to provide support for eating and drinking

Assessment Criterion 3.3: Provide encouragement to the individual to eat and drink

What does AC3.3 mean?

- The lead word **provide** means that you must be able to **show through your work practices** how to support and encourage the individual to eat and drink.
- Your **observations of your work practices** must include you providing encouragement to the individual.
- For the key word **encouragement** you can think about the different ways of supporting and motivating an individual to eat and drink, such as by saying how nice the food looks and smells, by explaining the benefits of eating and drinking to the individual, by physically prompting the individual to pick up their utensils to eat and drink, or by providing the individual with different options of food and drink.

Read the following **Real Work Setting** scenario and think about how it relates to your work setting and role:

Real Work Setting

Name: Sally

Job Role: Support Worker for people who have learning disabilities
(See page 245 for a description of the role)

Provide encouragement to the individual to eat and drink: Halfway through her meal Annette tells Sally that she doesn't want to eat any more. Sally asks Annette why she doesn't want to eat any more and Annette says that she feels full. Sally asks Annette whether she wants to think about if she could eat at least another two mouthfuls, as she didn't feel like eating her breakfast this morning, and places a small amount of food on her fork for Annette to pick up when she is ready. Annette does so and says to Sally that she will eat one more mouthful; Sally praises Annette on the efforts she has made. Annette then tells Sally that she can't drink her tea because it has gone cold. Sally offers to make Annette another fresh hot cup of tea; Annette thanks Sally and then a little later, once it has cooled down a little, drinks it slowly.

Evidencing AC3.3 to your assessor:

For AC3.3 you must evidence your skills of providing encouragement to the individual to eat and drink.

Assessment Method:

Direct Observation of your work practices

- You can **show** your assessor how to provide encouragement to the individual to eat and drink.

REMEMBER TO:

- Make arrangements for **observation** of your **work practices**.
- Include evidence of you providing encouragement to the individual to eat and drink.
- Ensure your evidence relates to eating and drinking.
- Think about **your work setting** and how to provide encouragement to the individual to eat and drink.

Derby Teaching Hospitals
NHS Foundation Trust
Library and Knowledge Centre

Learning Outcome 3: Be able to provide support for eating and drinking

Assessment Criterion 3.4: Support the individual to clean themselves if food or drink is spilt

What does AC3.4 mean?

- The lead word **support** means that you must be able to **show through your work practices** how to assist the individual to clean themselves if food or drink is spilt.
- Your **observations of your work practices** must include you supporting the individual to clean themselves.
- For the key words **clean themselves** you can think about how to support the individual to clean their hands, mouth, face or clothes if food or drink is spilt.

Read the following **Real Work Setting** scenario and think about how it relates to your work setting and role:

Real Work Setting

Name: Sally

Job Role: Support Worker for people who have learning disabilities
(See page 245 for a description of the role)

Support the individual to clean themselves: After Annette has drunk her cup of tea Sally asks Annette how she feels. Annette tells Sally that she really enjoyed her lunch but that her hands feel sticky. Sally suggests that Annette uses the hand wipes to clean her hands; Annette does so and shows Sally that she has spilt some of her tea on her blouse. Sally asks Annette whether she would like to change her blouse for a clean one; Annette tells Sally that this is a good idea and asks Sally whether she can walk down to her room with her. On her way down to her room, Annette says that her mouth and left hand still feel a little sticky; Sally suggests that Annette may like to wash her hands and face.

Evidencing AC3.4 to your assessor:

For AC3.4 you must evidence your skills of supporting the individual to clean themselves if food or drink is spilt.

Assessment Method:

Direct Observation of your work practices

- You can **show** your assessor how to support the individual to clean themselves if food or drink is spilt.

REMEMBER TO:

- Make arrangements for **observation** of your **work practices**.
- Include evidence of you supporting the individual to clean themselves.
- Include evidence of you supporting the individual if food or drink is spilt.
- Think about **your work setting** and how to support the individual to clean themselves if food or drink is spilt.

Learning Outcome 3: Be able to provide support for eating and drinking

Assessment Criterion 3.5: Adapt support in response to an individual's feedback or observed reactions while eating and drinking

What does AC3.5 mean?

- The lead word **adapt** means that you must be able to **show through your work practices** how to change the support you provide in response to an individual's feedback or observed reactions while eating and drinking.
- Your **observations of your work practices** must include you adapting the support you provide.
- For the key word **feedback** you can think about how to change the support you provide in response to an individual's comments and views while eating and drinking.
- For the key words **observed reactions** you can think about how to change the support you provide in response to how an individual reacts while eating and drinking.

Read the following **Real Work Setting** scenario and think about how it relates to your work setting and role:

Real Work Setting

Name: Sally

Job Role: Support Worker for people who have learning disabilities
(See page 245 for a description of the role)

Adapting support in response to an individual's feedback or observed reactions: A little later on, Sally records in Annette's daily record the support she provided to her today with eating and drinking at lunchtime, including the amount of food and drink Annette consumed. Sally also documented in full Annette's body language when she was eating and drinking; although Annette said that she had enjoyed her meal she did not appear to be doing so while eating it, as she swallowed her food quickly after each mouthful and looked anxious while eating. Sally also documented that the presence of the new Volunteer may have made Annette anxious and therefore asked the Volunteer to leave and noted that Annette seemed to relax a little more.

Evidencing AC3.5 to your assessor:

For AC3.5 you must evidence your skills of adapting support in response to an individual's feedback or observed reactions while eating and drinking.

Assessment Method:

Direct Observation of your work practices

- You can **show** your assessor or an expert witness how to adapt support in response to an individual's feedback or observed reactions while eating and drinking.

REMEMBER TO:

- Make arrangements for **observation** of your **work practices**.
- Include evidence of you adapting support.
- Include evidence of you doing this in response to an individual's feedback or observed reactions while eating and drinking.
- Ensure your evidence relates to eating and drinking.
- Think about **your work setting** and how to adapt support in response to an individual's feedback or observed reactions while eating and drinking.

Learning Outcome 4: Be able to clear away after food and drink

Assessment Criterion 4.1: Explain why it is important to be sure that an individual has chosen to finish eating and drinking before clearing away

What does AC4.1 mean?

- The lead word **explain** means that you must **make clear** the reasons why it is important to be sure that an individual has chosen to finish eating and drinking before clearing away.
- Your **account** must make clear the reasons why.
- For the key words **clearing away** you can think about the reasons why it is important to be sure that an individual has chosen to finish eating and drinking before clearing away the individual's eating and drinking utensils, plate, cup, left-over food and drink.

Read the following **Real Work Setting** scenario and think about how it relates to your work setting and role:

Real Work Setting

Name: Chen
Job Role: Personal Assistant to a young disabled woman
Chen has been working as a Personal Assistant for three years. Her responsibilities include: supporting the individual with all aspects of daily living including assistance with personal care activities, eating and drinking, moving and positioning and general household tasks.
The importance of being sure that an individual has chosen to finish eating and drinking before clearing away: Chen asks Gillian whether she has finished eating and drinking before clearing away her food tray. Gillian tells Chen that she gets annoyed by the fact that each of her Personal Assistants keep on asking her the same question after she finishes her meals and feels that this is patronising. Chen explains to Gillian why the team of Personal Assistants want to be sure that she has chosen to finish eating and drinking before clearing away her tray.

Evidencing AC4.1 to your assessor:

For AC4.1 you must evidence your understanding of why it is important to be sure that an individual has chosen to finish eating and drinking before clearing away.

Assessment Methods:

Oral or **Written** Questioning or **Discussion** or a **Personal Statement** or **Reflection**

- You can **tell** your assessor about why it is important to be sure that an individual has chosen to finish eating and drinking before clearing away.
  Or
- You can **talk** to your assessor about why it is important to be sure that an individual has chosen to finish eating and drinking before clearing away.
  Or
- You can write a **personal statement** or **reflection** about your experience of why it is important to be sure that an individual has chosen to finish eating and drinking before clearing away.

REMEMBER TO:

- Provide an account and explain why it is important.
- Include the reasons why it is important to be sure that an individual has chosen to finish eating and drinking before clearing away.
- Include examples of why it is important.
- Think about **your work setting** and why it is important to be sure that an individual has chosen to finish eating and drinking before clearing away.

Learning Outcome 4: Be able to clear away after food and drink

Assessment Criterion 4.2: Confirm that the individual has finished eating and drinking

What does AC4.2 mean?

- The lead word **confirm** means that you must be able to **show through your work practices** how to establish that the individual has finished eating and drinking.
- Your **observations of your work practices** must include you confirming that the individual has finished eating and drinking.
- For the key word **confirm** you can think about the ways to establish with different individuals that they have finished eating and drinking, such as by asking the individual, by observing their body language, or by using visual signs or symbols.

Read the following **Real Work Setting** scenario and think about how it relates to your work setting and role:

Real Work Setting

Name: Chen

Job Role: Personal Assistant to a young disabled woman
(See page 250 for a description of the role)

Confirming that the individual has finished eating and drinking: Chen gives Gillian some time alone before returning to her room and asking her whether she is all right; Gillian confirms she is feeling all right and asks Chen to remove her food tray. As Chen does so, Gillian reaches out for her cup and then withdraws her hand quickly. Chen observes that there is a little juice still left in her cup and, without making any eye contact with Gillian, asks her whether she would like to finish it; Gillian confirms she would like to finish drinking her juice, drinks it and then hands the empty cup back to Chen and says that she has also definitely finished her meal, although she hasn't eaten all of it. Chen thanks Gillian and removes her tray.

Evidencing AC4.2 to your assessor:

For AC4.2 you must evidence your skills of how to confirm that the individual has finished eating and drinking.

Assessment Method:

Direct Observation of your work practices

- You can **show** your assessor how to confirm that the individual has finished eating and drinking.

REMEMBER TO:

- Make arrangements for **observation** of your **work practices**.
- Include evidence of you confirming that the individual has finished eating and drinking.
- Ensure your evidence relates to both eating and drinking.
- Think about **your work setting** and how to confirm that the individual has finished eating and drinking.

Learning Outcome 4: Be able to clear away after food and drink

Assessment Criterion 4.3: Clear away used crockery and utensils in a way that promotes active participation

What does AC4.3 mean?

- The lead words **clear away** mean that you must be able to **show through your work practices** how to remove used crockery and utensils in a way that promotes active participation.
- Your **observations of your work practices** must include you clearing away used crockery and utensils.
- For the key words **active participation** you can think about how you can support and encourage an individual to lead and get involved in clearing away used crockery and utensils after finishing eating and drinking.

Read the following **Real Work Setting** scenario and think about how it relates to your work setting and role:

Real Work Setting

Name: Chen

Job Role: Personal Assistant to a young disabled woman
(See page 250 for a description of the role)

Active participation and clearing away used crockery and utensils: Gillian asks Chen whether she would like any help with clearing away her used crockery and utensils. Chen thanks Gillian for her offer of help and explains that she can help with rinsing these through before placing them in the dishwasher if she likes; Gillian does so and then decides that she will also wipe clean her food tray and the worktop before placing all the used crockery and utensils in the dishwasher.

Evidencing AC4.3 to your assessor:

For AC4.3 you must evidence your skills of how to clear away used crockery and utensils in a way that promotes active participation.

Assessment Method:

Direct Observation of your work practices

- You can **show** your assessor how to clear away used crockery and utensils in a way that promotes active participation.

REMEMBER TO:

- Make arrangements for **observation** of your **work practices**.
- Include evidence of you clearing away used crockery and utensils in a way that promotes active participation.
- Ensure your evidence relates to promoting active participation.
- Think about **your work setting** and how to clear away used crockery and utensils in a way that promotes active participation.

Learning Outcome 4: Be able to clear away after food and drink

Assessment Criterion 4.4: Support the individual to make themselves clean and tidy after eating or drinking

What does AC4.4 mean?

- The lead word **support** means that you must be able to **show through your work practices** how to support the individual to make themselves clean and tidy after eating or drinking.
- Your **observations of your work practices** must include you supporting the individual to make themselves clean and tidy.
- For the key words **make themselves clean and tidy** you can think about how to support the individual to clean their hands, mouth, face or change their clothes after eating and drinking.

Read the following **Real Work Setting** scenario and think about how it relates to your work setting and role:

Real Work Setting

Name: Chen

Job Role: Personal Assistant to a young disabled woman
(See page 250 for a description of the role)

Supporting the individual to make themselves clean and tidy: After loading the dishwasher, Gillian asks Chen whether she can help her to make herself clean and tidy. Chen goes with Gillian to her room and assists her to transfer from her wheelchair onto her chair in front of her sink and begins by passing her a new bottle of liquid soap from her cupboard, as there is none on her sink. Gillian washes and dries her hands thoroughly and then brushes her teeth and washes her face. Chen then asks Gillian whether she would like any support with changing her top; Gillian explains that she can do this herself but would like to wear the top she has recently washed, which is still in the laundry area; Chen brings this to her and agrees to iron it, while Gillian tidies up the sink area in her room and makes her bed.

Evidencing AC4.4 to your assessor:

For AC4.4 you must evidence your skills of supporting the individual to make themselves clean and tidy after eating or drinking.

Assessment Method:

Direct Observation of your work practices

- You can **show** your assessor how to support the individual to make themselves clean and tidy after eating or drinking.

REMEMBER TO:

- Make arrangements for **observation** of your **work practices**.
- Include evidence of you supporting the individual to make themselves clean and tidy.
- Include evidence of you supporting the individual after eating or drinking.
- Think about **your work setting** and how to support the individual to make themselves clean and tidy after eating or drinking.

Learning Outcome 5: Be able to monitor eating and drinking and the support provided

Assessment Criterion 5.1: Explain the importance of monitoring the food and drink an individual consumes and any difficulties they encounter

What does AC5.1 mean?

- The lead word **explain** means that you must **make clear** the importance of monitoring the food and drink an individual consumes and any difficulties they encounter.
- Your **account** must make clear the importance of monitoring an individual's food and drink and any difficulties.
- For the key word **monitoring** you can think about the importance of observing and checking over a period of time the food and drink an individual consumes and any difficulties they encounter.
- For the key word **difficulties** you can think about the importance of monitoring the problems an individual may encounter when consuming food and drink, such as not consuming enough, or consuming too much food and drink, or having difficulties with swallowing or eating some types of food and drink, or having allergies to some types of food and drink.

Read the following **Real Work Setting** scenario and think about how it relates to your work setting and role:

Real Work Setting

Name: Simon
Job Role: Support Worker for people who have learning difficulties and complex needs
Simon has been working as a Support Worker for ten years. His responsibilities include supporting individuals to lead active and fulfilling lives.
The importance of monitoring the food and drink an individual consumes and any difficulties they encounter: Simon has put together a short information guide for the team, which explains the importance of monitoring the food and drink an individual consumes and any difficulties they encounter, as well as the consequences of not doing so.

Evidencing AC5.1 to your assessor:

For AC5.1 you must evidence your understanding of the importance of monitoring the food and drink an individual consumes and any difficulties they encounter.

Assessment Methods:

Oral or **Written** Questioning or **Discussion** or a **Personal Statement** or **Reflection**

- You can **tell** your assessor about the importance of monitoring the food and drink an individual consumes and any difficulties they encounter.
  Or
- You can **talk** to your assessor about the importance of monitoring the food and drink an individual consumes and any difficulties they encounter.
  Or
- You can write a **personal statement** or **reflection** about your experience of the importance of monitoring the food and drink an individual consumes and any difficulties they encounter.

REMEMBER TO:

- Provide an account and explain the importance.
- Include the reasons why it is important to monitor the food and drink an individual consumes.
- Include the reasons why it is important to monitor any difficulties the individual encounters.
- Include examples of why it is important.
- Think about **your work setting** and the importance of monitoring the food and drink an individual consumes and any difficulties they encounter.

Learning Outcome 5: Be able to monitor eating and drinking and the support provided

Assessment Criterion 5.2: Carry out and record agreed monitoring processes

What does AC5.2 mean?

- The lead words **carry out and record** mean that you must be able to **show through your work practices** how to implement and document agreed monitoring processes for monitoring the food and drink an individual consumes and any difficulties they encounter.
- Your **observations of your work practices** must include you carrying out and recording agreed monitoring processes.
- For the key words **agreed monitoring processes** you can think about how to monitor the food and drink an individual consumes and any difficulties they encounter in line with your work setting's policies and procedures, as well as the specific guidelines that are in place for the individuals that you provide care and support to.

Read the following **Real Work Setting** scenario and think about how it relates to your work setting and role:

Real Work Setting

Name: Simon

Job Role: Support Worker for people who have learning difficulties and complex needs
(See page 254 for a description of the role)

Carry out and record agreed monitoring processes: A key part of Simon's information guide for the team includes a digitally recorded demonstration of the monitoring processes in place for carrying out and recording an individual's food and drink intake, output and difficulties encountered; this includes who to seek further information and advice from, the actions to take should any difficulties arise, the information to record, as well as the correct way of documenting the information obtained, the forms to use and where these are kept.

Evidencing AC5.2 to your assessor:

For AC5.2 you must evidence your skills of how to carry out and record agreed monitoring processes.

Assessment Method:

Direct Observation of your work practices

- You can **show** your assessor how to carry out and record agreed monitoring processes.

REMEMBER TO:

- Make arrangements for **observation** of your **work practices**.
- Include evidence of you carrying out and recording.
- Include evidence of you doing this in line with agreed monitoring processes.
- Think about **your work** setting and how to carry out and record agreed monitoring processes.

Learning Outcome 5: Be able to monitor eating and drinking and the support provided

Assessment Criterion 5.3: Report on the support provided for eating and drinking in accordance with agreed ways of working

What does AC5.3 mean?

- The lead word **report** means that you must be able to **show through your work practices** how to give a verbal or written account of the support provided for eating and drinking, in accordance with agreed ways of working.
- Your **observations of your work practices** must include you reporting on the support provided for eating and drinking.
- For the key word **support** you can think about how to report on the type and level of support provided for eating and drinking, such as whether an individual requires a low level of support such as a prompt to eat slowly, or high level of support such as physically assisting an individual when eating and drinking, and whether an individual requires actual physical guidance or physical prompts with some aspects, or verbal prompting only with eating and drinking.
- For the key words **agreed ways of working** you can think about how to report on the support provided for eating and drinking in line with your work setting's policies and procedures, as well as the specific guidelines that are in place for the individuals that you provide care and support to.

Read the following **Real Work Setting** scenario and think about how it relates to your work setting and role:

Real Work Setting

Name: Simon
Job Role: Support Worker for people who have learning difficulties and complex needs (See page 254 for a description of the role)
Reporting on the support provided for eating and drinking: Simon's information guide for the team also considers the types and levels of support provided to individuals with eating and drinking. It details how to report on aspects of the support provided for eating and drinking, including how to identify and report any changes that are observed in individuals, in accordance with the work setting's policies and procedures and individuals' specific and agreed guidelines.

Evidencing AC5.3 to your assessor:

For AC5.3 you must evidence your skills of how to report on the support provided for eating and drinking in accordance with agreed ways of working.

Assessment Method:

Direct Observation of your work practices

- You can **show** your assessor how to report on the support provided for eating and drinking in accordance with agreed ways of working.

REMEMBER TO:

- Make arrangements for **observation** of your **work practices**.
- Include evidence of you reporting on the support provided for eating and drinking.
- Include evidence of you doing this in accordance with agreed ways of working.
- Think about **your work setting** and how to report on the support provided for eating and drinking in accordance with agreed ways of working.

HSC2015 Support individuals to meet personal care needs

Learning Outcome 1: Be able to work with individuals to identify their needs and preferences in relation to personal care

Assessment Criterion 1.1: Encourage an individual to communicate their needs, preferences and personal beliefs affecting their personal care

What does AC1.1 mean?

- The lead word **encourage** means that you must be able to **show through your work practices** how to support and motivate an individual to communicate their needs, preferences and personal beliefs affecting their personal care.
- Your **observations of your work practices** must include you encouraging an individual.
- For the key word **communicate** you can think about the different ways of encouraging an individual to express their needs, preferences and personal beliefs affecting their personal care, such as verbally, through their body language, their use of an advocate or interpreter, or through their use of a communication aid such as a Dynavox.
- For the key words **needs, preferences and personal beliefs** you can think about how you can encourage an individual to communicate their special requirements, wishes and expectations affecting their personal, care such as choice of toilet facilities, or personal hygiene routines to follow, or how to maintain their personal appearance.
- For the key words **personal care** you can think about how you can encourage an individual to communicate their special requirements, wishes and expectations affecting their use of toilet facilities, such as using a commode or the toilet, their personal hygiene routines such as washing, showering or bathing, and attending to their personal appearance such as grooming or shaving.

Read the following **Real Work Setting** scenario and think about how it relates to your work setting and role:

Real Work Setting

Name: Eva
Job Role: Carer to young adults who have physical disabilities
Eva has been working as a Carer for two years. Her responsibilities include: supporting individuals with all aspects of their personal care and enabling individuals to participate in a range of daily activities.
Encouraging an individual to communicate their needs, preferences and personal beliefs: Eva is meeting with Jennie this afternoon to talk to her and her advocate about Jennie's needs, preferences and personal beliefs affecting her personal care.

Evidencing AC1.1 to your assessor:

For AC1.1 you must evidence your skills of how to encourage an individual to communicate their needs, preferences and personal beliefs affecting their personal care.

Assessment Method:

Direct Observation of your work practices

- You can **show** your assessor or an expert witness how to encourage an individual to communicate their needs, preferences and personal beliefs affecting their personal care.

REMEMBER TO:

- Make arrangements for **observation** of your **work practices**.
- Include evidence of you encouraging an individual.
- Ensure your evidence relates to an individual communicating their needs, preferences and personal beliefs.
- Include evidence of how these can affect an individual's personal care.
- Think about **your work setting** and how to encourage an individual to communicate their needs, preferences and personal beliefs affecting their personal care.

Learning Outcome 1: Be able to work with individuals to identify their needs and preferences in relation to personal care

Assessment Criterion 1.2: Establish the level and type of support an individual needs for personal care

What does AC1.2 mean?

- The lead word **establish** means that you must be able to **show through your work practices** how to confirm the level and type of support an individual needs for personal care.
- Your **observations of your work practices** must include you establishing the level and type of support an individual needs.
- For the key word **level** you can think about how to establish whether an individual requires a low level of support such as a prompt to use the toilet or to have a shower, or a high level of support such as physically assisting an individual with using the toilet or having a shower.
- For the key word **type** you can think about how to establish whether an individual requires actual physical guidance or physical prompts with some aspects, or verbal prompting only with using the toilet, maintaining their personal hygiene, or attending to their personal appearance.
- For the key words **personal care** you can think about how to establish the level and type of support an individual needs for their use of toilet facilities, such as using a commode or the toilet, their personal hygiene routines such as washing, showering or bathing, and attending to their personal appearance such as grooming or shaving.

Read the following **Real Work Setting** scenario and think about how it relates to your work setting and role:

Real Work Setting

Name: Eva

Job Role: Carer to young adults who have physical disabilities
(See page 257 for a description of the role)

Establishing the level and type of support an individual needs for personal care: Eva then discusses with Jennie and her advocate the level and type of support Jenny would like. All agree that Jennie would like to be as independent as possible regarding her personal care and would like the Carers to use only verbal prompts when she uses the toilet, has a shower or bath, and puts on and removes her make-up.

Evidencing AC1.2 to your assessor:

For AC1.2 you must evidence your skills of how to establish the level and type of support an individual needs for personal care.

Assessment Method:
Direct Observation of your work practices

- You can **show** your assessor or an expert witness how to establish the level and type of support an individual needs for personal care.

REMEMBER TO:

- Make arrangements for **observation** of your **work practices**.
- Include evidence of you establishing the level and type of support an individual needs.
- Ensure your evidence relates to an individual's personal care.
- Think about **your work setting** and how to establish the level and type of support an individual needs for personal care.

Learning Outcome 1: Be able to work with individuals to identify their needs and preferences in relation to personal care

Assessment Criterion 1.3: Agree with the individual how privacy will be maintained during personal care

What does AC1.3 mean?

- The lead word **agree** means that you must be able to **show through your work practices** how to decide with the individual how privacy will be maintained during personal care.
- Your **observations of your work practices** must include you agreeing with the individual how privacy will be maintained.
- For the key word **privacy** you can think about how to agree with the individual how intimacy will be maintained during personal care, such as by using a towel to cover the individual up, or avoiding direct eye contact with the individual.
- For the key words **personal care** you can think about how to agree with the individual how privacy will be maintained for their use of toilet facilities such as using a commode or the toilet, their personal hygiene routines such as washing, showering or bathing, and attending to their personal appearance such as grooming or shaving.

Read the following **Real Work Setting** scenario and think about how it relates to your work setting and role:

Real Work Setting

Name: Eva

Job Role: Carer to young adults who have physical disabilities
(See page 257 for a description of the role)

Agree with the individual how privacy will be maintained: Eva then discusses with Jennie and her advocate how Jennie would like the Carers to maintain her privacy during personal care. Jennie indicates through her advocate that she would like Eva to be discreet when she asks her whether she needs to use the toilet and to remain outside the toilet when she is prompting her to wash her hands afterwards. All agree that while Jennie is having a shower Eva will remain at all times behind the shower door and when she is having a bath she will stand outside the bathroom door. Jennie likes to put on and remove her make-up in her room and discusses with Eva how she can maintain her privacy while doing this; Jennie suggests that she will feel more comfortable if Eva stands not too close to her and prompts her gently to apply make-up evenly or remove it completely, when required only.

Evidencing AC1.3 to your assessor:

For AC1.3 you must evidence your skills of how to agree with the individual how privacy will be maintained during personal care.

Assessment Method:

Direct Observation of your work practices

- You can **show** your assessor or an expert witness how to agree with the individual how privacy will be maintained during personal care.

REMEMBER TO:

- Make arrangements for **observation** of your **work practices**.
- Include evidence of you agreeing with the individual how privacy will be maintained.
- Ensure your evidence relates to an individual's privacy during personal care.
- Think about **your work setting** and how to agree with the individual how privacy will be maintained during personal care.

Learning Outcome 2: Be able to provide support for personal care safely

Assessment Criterion 2.1: Support the individual to understand the reasons for hygiene and safety precautions

What does AC2.1 mean?

- The lead word **support** means that you must be able to **show through your work practices** how to assist the individual to understand the reasons for hygiene and safety precautions.
- Your **observations of your work practices** must include you supporting the individual to understand the reasons.
- For the key word **reasons** you can think about why the individual must understand the importance of hygiene and safety precautions, such as to promote their well-being and to avoid risks of danger, harm and injury to themselves and others.
- For the key words **hygiene and safety precautions** you can think about how to support the individual to understand the reasons for taking precautions regarding, for example, maintaining cleanliness and avoiding risks of danger, harm and injury to themselves and others.

Read the following **Real Work Setting** scenario and think about how it relates to your work setting and role:

Real Work Setting

Name: Yanis
Job Role: Live-in Carer for an individual who has dementia
Yanis has been working as a Live-in Carer for five years. His responsibilities include: supporting the individual with daily activities such as personal care, preparing meals, cleaning and running errands. Yanis also provides the individual with companionship.
Support the individual to understand the reasons for hygiene and safety precautions: Yanis ensures he reassures John both before and during personal care about the reasons for hygiene and safety precautions. Prior to washing his hands and putting on an apron and gloves, Yanis explains to John why he must do this and reassures him that this is so that he can protect him from any infections and ensure he is maintaining John's physical and emotional well-being. As John does frequently forget information that is spoken to him, Yanis ensures that he repeats the reasons for hygiene and safety precautions for personal care in a reassuring way during personal care. In terms of safety precautions, Yanis explains to John that he will be supporting him with using the bath lift when getting in and out of the bath and with getting dressed in his room to prevent any falls that could cause injury and harm to both himself and others.

Evidencing AC2.1 to your assessor:

For AC2.1 you must evidence your skills of how to support the individual to understand the reasons for hygiene and safety precautions.

Assessment Method:

Direct Observation of your work practices

- You can **show** your assessor or an expert witness how to support the individual to understand the reasons for hygiene and safety precautions.

REMEMBER TO:

- Make arrangements for **observation** of **your work practices**.
- Include evidence of you supporting the individual.
- Ensure your evidence relates to an individual understanding the reasons for hygiene and safety precautions.
- Think about **your work setting** and how to support the individual to understand the reasons for hygiene and safety precautions.

Learning Outcome 2: Be able to provide support for personal care safely

Assessment Criterion 2.2: Use protective equipment, protective clothing and hygiene techniques to minimise the risk of infection

What does AC2.2 mean?

- The lead word **use** means that you must be able to **show through your work practices** how to apply protective equipment, wear protective clothing and follow hygiene techniques to minimise the risk of infection.
- Your **observations of your work practices** must include you applying protective equipment, wearing protective clothing and following hygiene techniques.
- For the key words **protective equipment** you can think about how equipment such as aprons and gloves can minimise the risk of infection during personal care.
- For the key words **protective clothing** you can think about how clothing such as a uniform and enclosed shoes can minimise the risk of infection during personal care.
- For the key words **hygiene techniques** you can think about how following hygiene techniques such as washing your hands, changing aprons and gloves and cleaning equipment can minimise the risk of infection.

Read the following **Real Work Setting** scenario and think about how it relates to your work setting and role:

Real Work Setting

Name: Yanis

Job Role: Live-in Carer for an individual who has dementia
(See page 260 for a description of the role)

Use protective equipment, protective clothing and hygiene techniques: Yanis is supporting John this morning to have a bath and then breakfast. Prior to John having a bath, Yanis observes John walk towards the downstairs toilet and then stop. Yanis opens the door to the toilet and asks John whether he wants to use the toilet; John walks in and uses the toilet. John then goes upstairs to the bathroom and Yanis follows him, explaining that he would like to support him with his bath this morning. John looks at the bath and then nods at Yanis. Yanis ensures he is wearing an apron, gloves and enclosed shoes prior to operating the bath lift. After John has had his bath Yanis makes sure he cleans it and the surrounding area in the bathroom and then removes and disposes of his used apron and gloves carefully in the bathroom.

Evidencing AC2.2 to your assessor:

For AC2.2 you must evidence your skills of how to use protective equipment, protective clothing and hygiene techniques to minimise the risk of infection.

Assessment Method:

Direct Observation of your work practices

- You can **show** your assessor how to use protective equipment, protective clothing and hygiene techniques to minimise the risk of infection.

REMEMBER TO:

- Make arrangements for **observation** of **your work practices.**
- Include evidence of you using protective equipment.
- Include evidence of you using protective clothing.
- Include evidence of you using hygiene techniques.
- Ensure your evidence relates to minimising the risk of infection.
- Think about **your work setting** and how to use protective equipment, protective clothing and hygiene techniques to minimise the risk of infection.

Learning Outcome 2: Be able to provide support for personal care safely

Assessment Criterion 2.3: Explain how to report concerns about the safety and hygiene of equipment or facilities used for personal care

What does AC2.3 mean?

- The lead word **explain** means that you must **make clear** how to report concerns about the safety and hygiene of equipment or facilities used for personal care.
- Your **account** must make clear how to report concerns.
- For the key word **concerns** you can think about the process to follow in your work setting for reporting a worry or anxiety you may have about the safety and hygiene of equipment or facilities used for personal care, such as the toilet leaking, or the commode not being emptied regularly.
- For the key words **safety and hygiene** you can think about how to report concerns about equipment or facilities used for personal care in relation to causing danger, risk or injury through not being maintained, repaired or cleaned.

Read the following **Real Work Setting** scenario and think about how it relates to your work setting and role:

Real Work Setting

Name: Yanis

Job Role: Live-in Carer for an individual who has dementia
(See page 260 for a description of the role)

Reporting concerns about the safety and hygiene of equipment or facilities used for personal care: Yanis reports to both his manager and John's brother his concerns that the vinyl floor covering in the bathroom would benefit from being replaced as it is looking quite dirty and a little worn round the edges, which is unhygienic and unsafe. Yanis also explains that the bath lift is due for its annual maintenance check tomorrow and that as far as he is aware an appointment to have this done has not been booked in, which means that he will be unable to use the bath lift with John until it has been completed, for safety reasons.

Evidencing AC2.3 to your assessor:

For AC2.3 you must evidence your understanding of how to report concerns about the safety and hygiene of equipment or facilities used for personal care.

Assessment Methods:

Oral or **Written** Questioning or **Discussion** or a **Personal Statement** or **Reflection**

- You can **tell** your assessor about how to report concerns about the safety and hygiene of equipment or facilities used for personal care.
  Or
- You can **talk** to your assessor about how to report concerns about the safety and hygiene of equipment or facilities used for personal care.
  Or
- You can write a **personal statement** or **reflection** about your experience of how to report concerns about the safety and hygiene of equipment or facilities used for personal care.

REMEMBER TO:

- Provide an account and explain how.
- Include details about how to report concerns.
- Ensure your evidence relates to reporting concerns about the safety and hygiene of equipment or facilities used for personal care.
- Think about **your work setting** and how to report concerns about the safety and hygiene of equipment or facilities used for personal care.

Learning Outcome 2: Be able to provide support for personal care safely

Assessment Criterion 2.4: Describe ways to ensure the individual can summon help when alone during personal care

What does AC2.4 mean?

- The lead word **describe** means that you must provide an **account** that **details** the ways to ensure the individual can summon help when alone during personal care.
- Your **account** must detail **different** ways.
- For the key words **summon help** you can think about the different ways the individual can request assistance when alone during personal care such as calling out, making a vocal sound, or using the call bell.

Read the following **Real Work Setting** scenario and think about how it relates to your work setting and role:

Real Work Setting

Name: Yanis

Job Role: Live-in Carer for an individual who has dementia
(See page 260 for a description of the role)

Summoning help when alone during personal care: Yanis supports John with getting dressed in his room and then leaves John alone to brush his teeth and comb his hair, in line with his care plan. Yanis shows John the call bell and places this over his armchair, in case he requires any assistance, and tells John that he will be waiting outside his room. A little while later, John uses the call bell and Yanis responds to this immediately by entering into John's room and asking him if he is all right. John shows Yanis that his comb has fallen onto the floor in one corner of his en-suite toilet. John reaches down to retrieve it and cleans it before returning it to John for him to comb his hair.

Evidencing AC2.4 to your assessor:

For AC2.4 you must evidence your knowledge of ways to ensure the individual can summon help when alone during personal care.

Assessment Methods:

Oral or **Written** Questioning or **Discussion** or a **Personal Statement** or **Reflection**

- You can **tell** your assessor about ways to ensure the individual can summon help when alone during personal care.
  Or
- You can **talk** to your assessor about ways to ensure the individual can summon help when alone during personal care.
  Or
- You can write a **personal statement** or **reflection** about your experience of ways to ensure the individual can summon help when alone during personal care.

REMEMBER TO:

- Provide a detailed account.
- Include details about different ways.
- Include varied examples of ways to ensure the individual can summon help.
- Ensure your evidence is related to summoning help when the individual is alone during personal care.
- Think about **your work setting** and the ways to ensure the individual can summon help when alone during personal care.

Learning Outcome 2: Be able to provide support for personal care safely

Assessment Criterion 2.5: Ensure safe disposal of waste materials

What does AC2.5 mean?

- The lead word **ensure** means that you must be able to **show through your work practices** how to make certain that you dispose of waste materials safely.
- Your **observations of your work practices** must include you ensuring the safe disposal of waste materials.
- For the key words **safe disposal** you can think about how to ensure you dispose of waste materials safely such as by flushing the toilet immediately after it has been used, cleaning the commode after it has been emptied, and disposing of waste containing body fluids in the bin allocated for this type of waste.
- For the key words **waste materials** you can think about the different types of waste that need to be disposed of safely during personal care, such as bodily fluids, protective equipment worn such as aprons and gloves, or empty packaging from used materials such as toothpaste, shampoo or shower gel.

Read the following **Real Work Setting** scenario and think about how it relates to your work setting and role:

Real Work Setting

Name: Yanis

Job Role: Live-in Carer for an individual who has dementia
(See page 260 for a description of the role)

Ensuring the safe disposal of waste materials: Once John finishes combing his hair, Yanis asks John whether he could assist him with ensuring his en-suite toilet facilities are clean; John smiles, nods and sits down on his bed. Yanis puts on another apron and pair of gloves; flushes the toilet, disposes of the empty toothpaste container in the waste bin in the en-suite and then gently removes his apron and gloves before disposing of these in the enclosed waste bin too. Yanis then puts on another pair of gloves, removes the bin liner and disposes of this in the bin outside, along with his used gloves. Yanis then washes his hands thoroughly using the recommended hand-washing technique.

Evidencing AC2.5 to your assessor:

For AC2.5 you must evidence your skills of how to ensure the safe disposal of waste materials.

Assessment Method:

Direct Observation of your work practices

- You can **show** your assessor or an expert witness how to ensure the safe disposal of waste materials.

REMEMBER TO:

- Make arrangements for **observation** of **your work practices.**
- Include evidence of you ensuring the safe disposal of waste materials.
- Ensure your evidence relates to the safe disposal of personal care waste materials.
- Think about **your work setting** and how to ensure the safe disposal of waste materials.

Learning Outcome 3: Be able to support individuals to use the toilet

Assessment Criterion 3.1: Provide support for the individual to use toilet facilities in ways that respect dignity

What does AC3.1 mean?

- The lead words **provide support** mean that you must be able to **show through your work practices** how to provide assistance for the individual to use toilet facilities in ways that respect their dignity.
- Your **observations of your work practices** must include you providing support for the individual.
- For the key words **toilet facilities** you can think about how to assist individuals to use the toilet or commode or bedpan or urinal in ways that respect their dignity such as by asking the individual what toilet facilities they would like to use, or finding out about the level and type of support the individual would like you to provide when using the urinal.
- For the key word **dignity** you can think about how to provide support for the individual to use toilet facilities in ways that maintains the individual's self-respect and pride such as by avoiding direct eye contact with the individual, or closing the door while the individual is using the toilet facilities.

Read the following **Real Work Setting** scenario and think about how it relates to your work setting and role:

Real Work Setting

Name: Charlene

Job Role: Support Worker to adults who have mental health needs

Charlene has been working as a Support Worker to adults who have mental health needs for two-and-a-half years. Charlene's responsibilities include: supporting individuals with their personal care, assisting individuals with daily tasks and supporting individuals to access and use services and facilities available in their local communities.

Provide support for the individual to use toilet facilities in ways that respect dignity: During Charlene's shift this morning she will support three individuals with their personal care. When providing assistance to Manny, Charlene asks the individual whether he would like to use the urinal or toilet as she knows that he likes to be provided with the choice of both. When assisting Emma, Charlene asks her what toilet facilities she would prefer to use; and when assisting Sasha, Charlene confirms with her whether she would like her to remain in the room when she is using the commode.

Evidencing AC3.1 to your assessor:

For AC3.1 you must evidence your skills of how to provide support for the individual to use toilet facilities in ways that respect dignity.

Assessment Method:

Direct Observation of your work practices

- You can **show** your assessor or an expert witness how to provide support for the individual to use toilet facilities in ways that respect dignity.

REMEMBER TO:

- Make arrangements for **observation** of **your work practices.**
- Include evidence of you providing support for the individual to use toilet facilities.
- Include evidence of you providing support for the individual in ways that respect dignity.
- Think about **your work setting** and how to provide support for the individual to use toilet facilities in ways that respect dignity.

Learning Outcome 3: Be able to support individuals to use the toilet

Assessment Criterion 3.2: Support the individual to make themselves clean and tidy after using toilet facilities

What does AC3.2 mean?

- The lead word **support** means that you must be able to **show through your work practices** how to assist the individual to make themselves clean and tidy after using toilet facilities.
- Your **observations of your work practices** must include you supporting the individual.
- For the key words **clean and tidy** you can think about how to support the individual to cleanse themselves and be well-groomed after using toilet facilities, such as by using running water, toilet paper or wipes, rearranging or changing their clothes.
- For the key words **toilet facilities** you can think about how to support the individual to make themselves clean and tidy after using toilet facilities, such as the toilet, commode, bedpan or urinal.

Read the following **Real Work Setting** scenario and think about how it relates to your work setting and role:

Real Work Setting

Name: Charlene

Job Role: Support Worker to adults who have mental health needs
(See page 265 for a description of the role)

Support the individual to make themselves clean and tidy after using toilet facilities: When Sasha indicates to Charlene that she has finished using the commode, Charlene agrees with Sasha to enter back into her room to support her to wipe herself clean using the wipes that have been placed close by Sasha's commode. Charlene then supports Sasha to wash her hands and then to change her skirt for another one. Sasha thanks Charlene for all her support and finishes by saying to Charlene that she thinks she is going to apply a little perfume.

Evidencing AC3.2 to your assessor:

For AC3.2 you must evidence your skills of how to support the individual to make themselves clean and tidy after using toilet facilities.

Assessment Method:

Direct Observation of your work practices

- You can **show** your assessor or an expert witness how to support the individual to make themselves clean and tidy after using toilet facilities.

REMEMBER TO:

- Make arrangements for **observation** of **your work practices.**
- Include evidence of you supporting the individual to make themselves clean and tidy.
- Include evidence of the individual making themselves clean and tidy after using toilet facilities.
- Think about **your work setting** and how to support the individual to make themselves clean and tidy after using toilet facilities.

Learning Outcome 4: Be able to support individuals to maintain personal hygiene

Assessment Criterion 4.1: Ensure room and water temperatures meet individual needs and preferences for washing, bathing and mouth care

What does AC4.1 mean?

- The lead word **ensure** means that you must be able to **show through your work practices** how to make certain room and water temperatures meet individual needs and preferences for washing, bathing and mouth care.
- Your **observations of your work practices** must include you ensuring room and water temperatures meet individual needs and preferences.
- For the key words **individual needs and preferences** you can think about how to ensure you take into account individuals' requirements and wishes for room and water temperatures for washing, bathing and mouth care, such as by asking the individual whether the room they are in is comfortable for them, or by asking the individual to test whether the temperature of the water is all right before getting into the shower, or by asking the individual whether they would like to rinse their mouth after brushing their teeth with cold or warm water.

Read the following **Real Work Setting** scenario and think about how it relates to your work setting and role:

Real Work Setting

Name: Maria

Job Role: Residential Carer for older people

Maria has been working as a Residential Carer for ten years. Her responsibilities include: supporting individuals with personal care tasks, eating and drinking, as well as participating in daily household tasks and activities.

Ensure room and water temperatures meet individual needs and preferences: Maria is working with Sarah, another Residential Carer, in supporting Elisha to have a bath this morning in accordance with Elisha's care plan. Elisha likes the bathroom to feel warm but not too hot when she is having a bath. Maria ensures she regulates the temperature on the radiator in the bathroom so it feels warm and then asks Elisha to go in and see if the temperature is comfortable for her before they start to run her bath water. Elisha confirms that it is at the right temperature, just as she likes it to be. While running Elisha's bath and later while supporting Elisha to brush her teeth, Maria asks Elisha to check the temperature of the water.

Evidencing AC4.1 to your assessor:

For AC4.1 you must evidence your skills of how to ensure room and water temperatures meet individual needs and preferences for washing, bathing and mouth care.

Assessment Method:

Direct Observation of your work practices

- You can **show** your assessor or an expert witness how to ensure room and water temperatures meet individual needs and preferences for washing, bathing and mouth care.

REMEMBER TO:

- Make arrangements for **observation** of **your work practices**.
- Include evidence of you ensuring room and water temperatures meet individual needs and preferences.
- Ensure your evidence is related to washing, bathing and mouth care.
- Think about **your work setting** and how to ensure room and water temperatures meet individual needs and preferences for washing, bathing and mouth care.

Learning Outcome 4: Be able to support individuals to maintain personal hygiene

Assessment Criterion 4.2: Ensure toiletries, materials and equipment are within reach of the individual

What does AC4.2 mean?

- The lead word **ensure** means that you must be able to **show through your work practices** how to make certain toiletries, materials and equipment are within reach of the individual.
- Your **observations of your work practices** must include you ensuring toiletries, materials and equipment are within reach of the individual.
- For the key word **toiletries** you can think about how to ensure that an individual's shower gel, soap or shampoo are within reach such as by using holders in which to place these, or by placing these near the individual, or by passing these to the individual when they request them.
- For the key word **materials** you can think about how to ensure that an individual's sponge, flannel or towel are within easy reach, such as by placing these near the individual or by passing these to the individual when they request them.
- For the key word **equipment** you can think about how to ensure that an individual's shower chair or bath seat or call bell is within reach of the individual, such as by placing these near the individual or positioning at the right height for the individual.

Read the following **Real Work Setting** scenario and think about how it relates to your work setting and role:

Real Work Setting

Name: Maria

Job Role: Residential Carer for older people
(See page 267 for a description of the role)

Ensure toiletries, materials and equipment are within reach of the individual: Maria and her colleague Sarah promote Elisha's independence while having a bath this morning by ensuring that they place the holder across the bath and place all of Elisha's toiletries in it. In this way, Elisha is able to reach for her toiletries as and when she wants them.

Evidencing AC4.2 to your assessor:

For AC4.2 you must evidence your skills of how to ensure toiletries, materials and equipment are within reach of the individual.

Assessment Method:

Direct Observation of your work practices

- You can **show** your assessor or an expert witness how to ensure toiletries, materials and equipment are within reach of the individual.

REMEMBER TO:

- Make arrangements for **observation** of your **work practices**.
- Include evidence of you ensuring toiletries, materials and equipment are within reach of the individual.
- Ensure your evidence is related to toiletries, materials and equipment.
- Think about **your work setting** and how to ensure toiletries, materials and equipment are within reach of the individual.

Learning Outcome 4: Be able to support individuals to maintain personal hygiene

Assessment Criterion 4.3: Provide support to carry out personal hygiene activities in ways that maintain comfort, respect dignity and promote active participation

What does AC4.3 mean?

- The lead words **provide support** mean that you must be able to **show through your work practices** how to provide assistance to carry out personal hygiene activities in ways that maintain comfort, respect, dignity and promote active participation.
- Your **observations of your work practices** must include you providing support to carry out personal hygiene activities.
- For the key word **comfort** you can think about how to provide support in ways that enable the individual to feel at ease and that do not cause the individual any pain or distress, such as by supporting the individual with carrying out personal hygiene activities in a gentle and relaxed manner.
- For the key word **respect** you can think about how to provide support in ways that enable the individual to have their feelings, wishes and rights recognised such as by taking into account an individual's needs and beliefs while carrying out personal hygiene activities.
- For the key word **dignity** you can think about how to provide support in ways that maintain the individual's self-respect and pride, such as by avoiding eye contact with the individual during personal hygiene activities.
- For the key words **active participation** you can think about how to provide support in ways that encourage individuals to be fully involved in all aspects of their personal hygiene, such as by agreeing with the individual the support required to carry out personal hygiene activities.

Read the following **Real Work Setting** scenario and think about how it relates to your work setting and role:

Real Work Setting

Name: Maria

Job Role: Residential Carer for older people
(See page 267 for a description of the role)

Providing support to carry out personal hygiene activities: Maria and Sarah support Elisha with personal hygiene activities and always make sure that they both use ways that maintain her comfort and dignity, respect her and promote her active participation.

Evidencing AC4.3 to your assessor:

For AC4.3 you must evidence your skills of how to provide support to carry out personal hygiene activities in ways that maintain comfort, respect dignity and promote active participation.

Assessment Method:

Direct Observation of your work practices

- You can **show** your assessor or an expert witness how to provide support to carry out personal hygiene activities in ways that maintain comfort, respect dignity and promote active participation.

REMEMBER TO:

- Make arrangements for **observation** of your **work practices**.
- Include evidence of you providing support to carry out personal hygiene activities.
- Include evidence of you using ways that maintain comfort, respect dignity and promote active participation.
- Think about **your work setting** and how to provide support to carry out personal hygiene activities in ways that maintain comfort, respect dignity and promote active participation.

Learning Outcome 5: Be able to support individuals to manage their personal appearance

Assessment Criterion 5.1: Provide support to enable the individual to manage their personal appearance in ways that respect dignity and promote active participation

What does AC5.1 mean?

- The lead words **provide support** mean that you must be able to **show through your work practices** how to provide assistance to enable the individual to manage their personal appearance in ways that respect dignity and promote active participation.
- Your **observations of your work practices** must include you providing support to enable the individual to manage their personal appearance.
- For the key words **manage their personal appearance** you can think about how to provide support to enable the individual to take care of their hair, nails, shaving, skin, use of cosmetics and use of prostheses or orthoses in ways that respect dignity and promote active participation, such as by confirming with them how they like to have cosmetics applied, or by asking them when they want to use their prosthetic limb.
- For the key word **dignity** you can think about how to provide support in ways that maintain the individual's self-respect and pride, such as by avoiding asking the individual too many questions while supporting them.
- For the key words **active participation** you can think about how to provide support in ways that encourage individuals to be fully involved in all aspects of managing their personal appearance, such as by agreeing with the individual the support required.

Read the following **Real Work Setting** scenario and think about how it relates to your work setting and role:

Real Work Setting

Name: Tim
Job Role: Personal Assistant to a young man who has autism
Tim has been working as a Personal Assistant for five years. His responsibilities include: providing support with all aspects of daily living to enable Alan to lead a fulfilling and active life.
Providing support to enable the individual to manage their personal appearance: Alan is very aware of his personal appearance and likes Tim to help him with ensuring he takes good care of his hair, nails and skin and often asks him for advice.

Evidencing AC5.1 to your assessor:

For AC5.1 you must evidence your skills of how to provide support to enable the individual to manage their personal appearance in ways that respect dignity and promote active participation.

Assessment Method:

Direct Observation of your work practices

- You can **show** your assessor or an expert witness how to provide support to enable the individual to manage their personal appearance in ways that respect dignity and promote active participation.

REMEMBER TO:

- Make arrangements for **observation** of your **work practices**.
- Include evidence of you providing support to enable the individual to manage their personal appearance.
- Include evidence of you using ways that respect dignity and promote active participation.
- Think about **your work setting** and how to provide support to enable the individual to manage their personal appearance in ways that respect dignity and promote active participation.

Learning Outcome 5: Be able to support individuals to manage their personal appearance

Assessment Criterion 5.2: Encourage the individual to keep their clothing and personal care items clean, safe and secure

What does AC5.2 mean?

- The lead word **encourage** means that you must be able to **show through your work practices** how to support and motivate the individual to keep their clothing and personal care items clean, safe and secure.
- Your **observations of your work practices** must include you encouraging an individual.
- For the key words **clothing and personal care items** you can think about the different ways of encouraging an individual to keep their clothes, toiletries and items including hairbrush, toothbrush, shaver, prostheses and orthoses clean, safe and secure, such as by cleaning these regularly after use and returning them to their designated areas after use.

Read the following **Real Work Setting** scenario and think about how it relates to your work setting and role:

Real Work Setting

Name: Tim

Job Role: Personal Assistant to a young man who has autism
(See page 270 for a description of the role)

Encouraging the individual to keep their clothing and personal care items clean, safe and secure: As part of the support that Tim provides to Alan, he also supports and motivates Alan to keep his clothes and personal care items clean, safe and secure. After Alan uses his hair gel, Tim encourages him to wipe the container clean and then return this to his bathroom cabinet. Similarly, after Alan has trimmed his nails and moisturised his skin, Tim encourages him to return his nail-grooming kit to his bathroom cabinet and his moisturiser to his bedside table, again after wiping both clean.

Evidencing AC5.2 to your assessor:

For AC5.2 you must evidence your skills of how to encourage the individual to keep their clothing and personal care items clean, safe and secure.

Assessment Method:

Direct Observation of your work practices

- You can **show** your assessor or an expert witness how to encourage the individual to keep their clothing and personal care items clean, safe and secure.

REMEMBER TO:

- Make arrangements for **observation** of your **work practices.**
- Include evidence of you encouraging the individual.
- Ensure your evidence relates to keeping an individual's clothing and personal care items clean, safe and secure.
- Think about **your work setting** and how to encourage an individual to keep their clothing and personal care items clean, safe and secure.

Learning Outcome 6: Be able to monitor and report on support for personal care

Assessment Criterion 6.1: Seek feedback from the individual and others on how well support for personal care meets the individual's needs and preferences

What does AC6.1 mean?

- The lead words **seek feedback** mean that you must be able to **show through your work practices** how to obtain comments and views from the individual and others on how well support for personal care meets the individual's needs and preferences.
- Your **observations of your work practices** must include you seeking feedback from the individual and others.
- For the key word **others** you can think about how to seek feedback from the individual's family members, friends, advocates, specialists, healthcare professionals, your line manager and others who are important to the individual's well-being.
- For the key words **personal care** you can think about how to seek feedback from the individual and others on how well support for use of toilet facilities, personal hygiene routines and with attending to their personal appearance meets the individual's needs and preferences.
- For the key words **the individual's needs and preferences** you can think about how to seek feedback from the individual and others on how well the support meets what an individual requires or chooses to do.

Read the following **Real Work Setting** scenario and think about how it relates to your work setting and role:

Real Work Setting

Name: Chao-xing
Job Role: Reablement Officer for individuals living in their own home
Chao-xing has been working as a Reablement Officer for eight years. Her responsibilities include: providing assistance to individuals with personal care in line with their support plans, including dressing, undressing, washing and toileting and enabling individuals to maintain and develop their independent living skills.
Seeking feedback from the individual and others: Chao-xing is meeting with Zara, the individual she supports, her parents and the occupational therapist to find out from them how well the support provided to Zara for personal care over the last month meets her individual requirements and her wishes for how she prefers this to be done.

Evidencing AC6.1 to your assessor:

For AC6.1 you must evidence your skills of how to seek feedback from the individual and others on how well support for personal care meets the individual's needs and preferences.

Assessment Method:

Direct Observation of your work practices

- You can **show** your assessor or an expert witness how to seek feedback from the individual and others on how well support for personal care meets the individual's needs and preferences.

REMEMBER TO:

- Make arrangements for **observation** of your **work practices**.
- Include evidence of you seeking feedback from the individual and others.
- Ensure your evidence relates to how well support for personal care meets the individual's needs and preferences.
- Think about **your work setting** and how to seek feedback from the individual and others on how well support for personal care meets the individual's needs and preferences.

Learning Outcome 6: Be able to monitor and report on support for personal care

Assessment Criterion 6.2: Monitor personal care functions and activities in agreed ways

What does AC6.2 mean?

- The lead word **monitor** means that you must be able to **show through your work practices** how to observe and check personal care functions and activities in agreed ways.
- Your **observations of your work practices** must include you monitoring personal care functions and activities.
- For the key words **personal care functions** you can think about how to monitor in agreed ways individuals' bodily functions such as by using recording charts, or observing the regularity and types of individuals' bodily functions.
- For the key words **personal care activities** you can think about how to monitor in agreed ways the support for use of toilet facilities, personal hygiene routines and with attending to individuals' personal appearance by recording the support provided to individuals, or by asking individuals and others involved in their lives.
- For the key words **agreed ways** you can think about how to monitor personal care functions and activities in line with your work setting's policies and procedures, as well as the specific guidelines that are in place for the individuals that you support.

Read the following **Real Work Setting** scenario and think about how it relates to your work setting and role:

Real Work Setting

Name: Chao-xing

Job Role: Reablement Officer for individuals living in their own home
(See page 272 for a description of the role)

Monitoring personal care functions and activities in agreed ways: Chao-xing has discussed with Zara, the individual she supports, the information that has been collected in relation to Zara's bodily functions and both agree that there are no longer any problems with these. Chao-xing and Zara have agreed to discuss with Zara's parents and the occupational therapist the support provided to Zara with personal care activities over the last month, as both feel that Zara is becoming more independent and that she would like to ensure that her parents, who also assist her with personal care activities, understand this.

Evidencing AC6.2 to your assessor:

For AC6.2 you must evidence your skills of how to monitor personal care functions and activities in agreed ways.

Assessment Method:

Direct Observation of your work practices

- You can **show** your assessor or an expert witness how to monitor personal care functions and activities in agreed ways.
- You can also use as a **supporting piece of work product evidence** monitoring records you have completed in relation to an individual's personal care functions and activities.

REMEMBER TO:

- Make arrangements for **observation** of your **work practices.**
- Include evidence of you monitoring personal care functions and activities.
- Ensure your evidence relates to monitoring in agreed ways.
- Think about **your work setting** and how to monitor personal care functions and activities in agreed ways.

Learning Outcome 6: Be able to monitor and report on support for personal care

Assessment Criterion 6.3: Record and report on an individual's personal care in agreed ways

What does AC6.3 mean?

- The lead words **record and report** mean that you must be able to **show through your work practices** how to document and share information on an individual's personal care in agreed ways.
- Your **observations of your work practices** must include you recording and reporting on an individual's personal care.
- For the key words **record and report** you can think about the information to document and share with others in agreed ways on an individual's personal care, such as the regularity and types of individuals' bodily functions, or the support provided to individuals with activities such as using toilet facilities, maintaining personal hygiene, as well as individuals' personal appearance.
- For the key words **agreed ways** you can think about how to record and report on an individual's personal care in line with your work setting's policies and procedures, as well as the specific guidelines that are in place for the individuals that you support.

Read the following **Real Work Setting** scenario and think about how it relates to your work setting and role:

Real Work Setting

Name: Chao-xing

Job Role: Reablement Officer for individuals living in their own home
(See page 272 for a description of the role)

Recording and reporting on an individual's personal care: Chao-xing has agreed with Zara and her parents the monitoring charts to use, should Zara experience problems again with her bodily functions; all agree that the monitoring charts completed to date have collated the necessary information and have been completed fully and accurately. The entries made by different people on Zara's daily support records do not include sufficient details about the progress Zara has made in becoming more independent, so Chao-xing reinforces to Zara's parents and the occupational therapist how the support provided for personal care activities needs to be more consistently recorded by everyone.

Evidencing AC6.3 to your assessor:

For AC6.3 you must evidence your skills of how to record and report on an individual's personal care in agreed ways.

Assessment Method:

Direct Observation of your work practices

- You can **show** your assessor or an expert witness how to record and report on an individual's personal care in agreed ways.

REMEMBER TO:

- Make arrangements for **observation** of your **work practices**.
- Include evidence of you recording and reporting on an individual's personal care.
- Ensure your evidence is in line with agreed ways.
- Think about **your work setting** and how to record and report on an individual's personal care in agreed ways.

HSC2028 Move and position individuals in accordance with their plan of care

Learning Outcome 1: Understand anatomy and physiology in relation to moving and positioning individuals

Assessment Criterion 1.1: Outline the anatomy and physiology of the human body in relation to the importance of correct moving and positioning of individuals

What does AC1.1 mean?

- The lead word **outline** means that you must provide an **account** that includes brief **details** about the anatomy and physiology of the human body in relation to the importance of correct moving and positioning of individuals.
- Your **account** must detail briefly the anatomy and physiology of the human body.
- For the key words **anatomy and physiology** you can think about the body parts that are visible to the human eye such as back, upper and lower limbs, as well as the function of body parts that are not visible such as bones, joints and ligaments, and how this relates to the correct moving and positioning of individuals.
- For the key words **correct moving and positioning** of individuals you can think about how this involves following the correct techniques, such as ensuring your back is straight and your knees are slightly bent when moving and positioning an individual, avoiding dragging an individual in order to prevent their ligaments from being sprained, or causing an individual's limb to fracture by moving them incorrectly or suddenly.

Read the following **Real Work Setting** scenario and think about how it relates to your work setting and role:

Real Work Setting

Name: Aasim

Job Role: Home Carer for older people

Aasim has been working as a Home Carer for six years. His responsibilities include: providing support to individuals with daily activities and enabling individuals to maintain their independent living skills.

The anatomy and physiology of the human body: Aasim is attending a training session on moving and positioning individuals and finds it useful to further his understanding of the body's musculoskeletal system.

Evidencing AC1.1 to your assessor:

For AC1.1 you must evidence your understanding of the anatomy and physiology of the human body in relation to the importance of correct moving and positioning of individuals.

Assessment Methods:

Oral or **Written** Questioning or **Discussion** or a **Personal Statement**

- You can **tell** your assessor about the anatomy and physiology of the human body in relation to the importance of correct moving and positioning of individuals.

  Or
- You can **talk** to your assessor about the anatomy and physiology of the human body in relation to the importance of correct moving and positioning of individuals.

  Or
- You can write a **personal statement** about anatomy and physiology of the human body in relation to the importance of correct moving and positioning of individuals.

REMEMBER TO:

- Provide an **account** that includes brief **details**.
- Include brief details about the anatomy and physiology of the human body.
- Ensure your evidence relates to the importance of correct moving and positioning of individuals.
- Think about **your work setting** and the anatomy and physiology of the human body in relation to the importance of correct moving and positioning of individuals.

Learning Outcome 1: Understand anatomy and physiology in relation to moving and positioning individuals

Assessment Criterion 1.2: Describe the impact of specific conditions on the correct movement and positioning of an individual

What does AC1.2 mean?

- The lead word **describe** means that you must provide an **account** that **details** the impact of specific conditions on the correct movement and positioning of an individual.
- Your **account** must detail the impact of specific conditions.
- For the key words **specific conditions** you can think about individuals who may be paralysed, have brittle bone disease, be blind or have dementia and how this may affect their correct moving and positioning, such as by not being able to be moved in certain ways, or by feeling anxious when being moved or positioned, or not being able to understand instructions.
- For the key words **correct movement and positioning of individuals** you can think about how specific conditions may impact on following the correct techniques when moving and positioning individuals, such as having to use specifically designed equipment, or requiring assistance from two or three people to correctly move and position an individual.

Read the following **Real Work Setting** scenario and think about how it relates to your work setting and role:

Real Work Setting

Name: Aasim

Job Role: Home Carer for older people
(See page 275 for a description of the role)

The impact of specific conditions: Aasim also learns more about how it is important to follow individuals' care plans and the guidelines in place when moving and positioning them, as there are specific conditions that impact on the correct movement and positioning of individuals and therefore it is important to be aware of them. For example, during the training session the participants discussed a case scenario of an older individual who had recently had a stroke and how this affected the way his team of Carers supported him to move from one position to another when assisting him with his personal care.

Evidencing AC1.2 to your assessor:

For AC1.2 you must evidence your understanding of the impact of specific conditions on the correct movement and positioning of an individual.

Assessment Methods:

Oral or **Written** Questioning or **Discussion** or a **Personal Statement** or **Reflection**

- You can **tell** your assessor about the impact of specific conditions on the correct movement and positioning of an individual.

  Or
- You can **talk** to your assessor about the impact of specific conditions on the correct movement and positioning of an individual.

  Or
- You can write a **personal statement** or **reflection** about the impact of specific conditions on the correct movement and positioning of an individual.

REMEMBER TO:

- Provide an **account** that includes **details**.
- Include details about the impact of specific conditions.
- Ensure your evidence relates to the correct movement and positioning of individuals.
- Think about **your work setting** and the impact of specific conditions on the correct movement and positioning of an individual.

Learning Outcome 2: Understand legislation and agreed ways of working when moving and positioning individuals

Assessment Criterion 2.1: Describe how legislation and agreed ways of working affect working practices related to moving and positioning individuals

What does AC2.1 mean?

- The lead word **describe** means that you must provide an **account** that **details** how legislation and agreed ways of working affect working practices related to moving and positioning individuals.
- Your **account** must detail how.
- For the key word **legislation** you can think about how laws such as the Manual Handling Operations Regulations 1992 (amended 2002), the Lifting Operations and Lifting Equipment Regulations (LOLER) 1998 and the Provision and Use of Work Equipment Regulations (PUWER) 1998 affect working practices related to moving and positioning individuals.
- For the key words **agreed ways of working** you can think about how your work setting's policies and procedures, as well as the specific guidelines that are in place for the individuals that you provide care and support to, affect working practices related to moving and positioning individuals, such as by specifying techniques to use, the equipment to use, or how the individual must be supported.

Read the following **Real Work Setting** scenario and think about how it relates to your work setting and role:

Real Work Setting

Name: Megan
Job Role: Community Carer for young adults
Megan has been working as a Community Carer for twelve years. Her responsibilities include: supporting adults with personal care and daily living, including moving and positioning individuals and enabling them to access a range of activities.
How legislation and agreed ways of working affect working practices: Megan is working with a Volunteer today and, as part of her induction, discusses with her the guidelines that are in place to move and position three different individuals who will be trampolining this afternoon. Megan also discusses with her the legislation and work setting's policies and procedures that also affect how individuals are moved and positioned.

Evidencing AC2.1 to your assessor:

For AC2.1 you must evidence your understanding of how legislation and agreed ways of working affect working practices related to moving and positioning individuals.

Assessment Methods:

Oral or **Written** Questioning or **Discussion** or a **Personal Statement** or **Reflection**

- You can **tell** your assessor about how legislation and agreed ways of working affect working practices related to moving and positioning individuals.
  Or
- You can **talk** to your assessor about how legislation and agreed ways of working affect working practices related to moving and positioning individuals.
  Or
- You can write a **personal statement** or **reflection** about your experience of how legislation and agreed ways of working affect working practices related to moving and positioning individuals.

REMEMBER TO:

- Provide an **account** that includes **details**.
- Include details about how legislation and agreed ways of working affect working practices.
- Ensure your evidence relates to moving and positioning of individuals.
- Think about **your work setting** and how legislation and agreed ways of working affect working practices related to moving and positioning individuals.

Learning Outcome 2: Understand legislation and agreed ways of working when moving and positioning individuals

Assessment Criterion 2.2: Describe what health and safety factors need to be taken into account when moving and positioning individuals and any equipment used to do this

What does AC2.2 mean?

- The lead word **describe** means that you must provide an **account** that **details** the health and safety factors that need to be taken into account when moving and positioning individuals and any equipment used to do this.
- Your **account** must detail the health and safety factors and the equipment.
- For the key words **health and safety factors** you can think about how aspects such as the individual's needs, the staffing required, the equipment to be used and the environment must be risk assessed when moving and positioning individuals.
- For the key word **equipment** you can think about the items that are available to move and position individuals such as hoists, bath lifts, slide sheets, transfer boards, handling belts and lifting cushions.

Read the following **Real Work Setting** scenario and think about how it relates to your work setting and role:

Real Work Setting

Name: Megan

Job Role: Community Carer for young adults
(See page 277 for a description of the role)

Health and safety factors: Megan then talks through each individual's guidelines with the Volunteer, detailing the equipment that is used with each individual in line with their support plans and the health and safety factors that need to be taken into account when assisting individuals to get on and off the trampoline, as well as to move and position themselves on the trampoline from sitting and standing positions.

Evidencing AC2.2 to your assessor:

For AC2.2 you must evidence your understanding of what health and safety factors need to be taken into account when moving and positioning individuals and any equipment used to do this.

Assessment Methods:

Oral or **Written** Questioning or **Discussion** or a **Personal Statement** or **Reflection**

- You can **tell** your assessor about what health and safety factors need to be taken into account when moving and positioning individuals and any equipment used to do this.
  Or
- You can **talk** to your assessor about what health and safety factors need to be taken into account when moving and positioning individuals and any equipment used to do this.
  Or
- You can write a **personal statement** or **reflection** about your experience of what health and safety factors need to be taken into account when moving and positioning individuals and any equipment used to do this.

REMEMBER TO:

- Provide an **account** that includes **details**.
- Include details about what health and safety factors need to be taken into account when moving and positioning individuals.
- Include details about equipment used when moving and positioning individuals.
- Think about **your work setting** and what health and safety factors need to be taken into account when moving and positioning individuals and any equipment used to do this.

Learning Outcome 3: Be able to minimise risk before moving and positioning individuals

Assessment Criterion 3.1: Access up-to-date copies of risk assessment documentation

What does AC3.1 mean?

- The lead word **access** means that you must be able to **show through your work practices** how to obtain up-to-date copies of risk assessment documentation.
- Your **observations of your work practices** must include you accessing up-to-date copies of risk assessment documentation.
- For the key words **risk assessment documentation** you can think about how you can access up-to-date copies of individuals' risk assessments and care plans, as well as specific guidelines in place to move and position different individuals.

Read the following **Real Work Setting** scenario and think about how it relates to your work setting and role:

Real Work Setting

Name: Jakob

Job Role: Home Carer for adults who have autism

Jakob has been working as a Home Carer for two years. His responsibilities include: supporting individuals with daily tasks as specified in their support plans, including moving and positioning individuals, attending college and work placements, developing independent living skills and working alongside others to build positive working relationships.

Accessing up-to-date copies of risk assessment documentation: Jakob is supporting Frederiko this morning to transfer from his wheelchair to the seat in the taxi that will be taking him to college. In line with Jakob's work setting's policies and procedures, Jakob goes to Frederiko's moving and handling file, which is situated in the locked cabinet in Frederiko's room, and reads through the moving and positioning section in his care plan, as well as the current risk assessment guidelines for this particular transfer.

Evidencing AC3.1 to your assessor:

For AC3.1 you must evidence your skills of how to access up-to-date copies of risk assessment documentation.

Assessment Method:

Direct Observation of your work practices

- You can **show** your assessor how to access up-to-date copies of risk assessment documentation.

REMEMBER TO:

- Make arrangements for **observation** of your **work practices**.
- Include evidence of you accessing up-to-date copies of risk assessment documentation.
- Ensure your evidence relates to before moving and positioning individuals.
- Think about **your work setting** and how to access up-to-date copies of risk assessment documentation.

Learning Outcome 3: Be able to minimise risk before moving and positioning individuals

Assessment Criterion 3.2: Carry out preparatory checks using the individual's care plan and the moving and handling risk assessment

What does AC3.2 mean?

- The lead words **carry out** mean that you must be able to **show through your work practices** how to implement preparatory checks using the individual's care plan and the moving and handling risk assessment.
- Your **observations of your work practices** must include you carrying out preparatory checks.
- For the key words **the individual's care plan** you can think about how you can carry out preparatory checks using an individual's moving and handling requirements, needs and preferences detailed in their plan of care and support. A care plan may be known by other names such as a support plan, individual plan person-centred plan.
- For the key words **the moving and handling risk assessment** you can think about how you can carry out preparatory checks using the information detailed in an individual's moving and handling risk assessment, such as the type of equipment to use for different tasks, how to use the equipment, the number of Carers needed to carry out the task, as well as any other relevant information specific to the individual: for example, the individual feeling anxious when moved and positioned, or experiencing pain when moved and positioned, or the actions to take if an individual has an epileptic seizure when moved and positioned.

Read the following **Real Work Setting** scenario and think about how it relates to your work setting and role:

Real Work Setting

Name: Jakob
Job Role: Home Carer for adults who have autism (See page 279 for a description of the role)
Carrying out preparatory checks: After reading through the moving and positioning section in Frederiko's care plan, as well as the risk assessment guidelines for moving and positioning him from his wheelchair to the seat in the taxi, Jakob checks that Frederiko wants to wear his moving and handling belt and feels comfortable to make the transfer with minimum assistance from him today; Frederiko confirms that he is feeling well and has already used the belt earlier on this morning.

Evidencing AC3.2 to your assessor:

For AC3.2 you must evidence your skills of how to carry out preparatory checks using the individual's care plan and the moving and handling risk assessment.

Assessment Method:
Direct Observation of your work practices

- You can **show** your assessor how to carry out preparatory checks using the individual's care plan and the moving and handling risk assessment.

REMEMBER TO:

- Make arrangements for **observation** of your **work practices**.
- Include evidence of you carrying out preparatory checks.
- Include evidence of you using the individual's care plan and the moving and handling risk assessment.
- Ensure your evidence relates to before moving and positioning individuals.
- Think about **your work setting** and how to carry out preparatory checks using the individual's care plan and the moving and handling risk assessment.

Learning Outcome 3: Be able to minimise risk before moving and positioning individuals

Assessment Criterion 3.3: Identify any immediate risks to the individual

What does AC3.3 mean?

- The lead word **identify** means that you must be able to **show through your work practices** how to recognise any immediate risks to the individual.
- Your **observations of your work practices** must include you identifying any immediate risks to the individual.
- For the key words **immediate risks** you can think about how you can recognise any sudden likelihood of danger or harm to individuals before moving and positioning, such as not having the right type or the correct size of equipment available, or the individual telling you that they are feeling unwell.

Read the following **Real Work Setting** scenario and think about how it relates to your work setting and role:

Real Work Setting

Name: Jakob

Job Role: Home Carer for adults who have autism
(See page 279 for a description of the role)

Identifying any immediate risks to the individual: Jakob has noted before supporting Frederiko to transfer from his wheelchair to the taxi that Frederiko's shoe laces are untied, he is not wearing his wheelchair belt and that he is holding a heavy rucksack. Jakob thinks that all of these are potential risks, as Frederiko's untied shoe laces could lead to him tripping over his laces, not wearing a wheelchair belt could lead to him slipping out of his wheelchair as he rides over the front door step, and holding a heavy rucksack means that Fredriko is unable to use his hands to steady himself as he transfers onto the taxi seat.

Evidencing AC3.3 to your assessor:

For AC3.3 you must evidence your skills of how to identify any immediate risks to the individual.

Assessment Method:

Direct Observation of your work practices

- You can **show** your assessor how to identify any immediate risks to the individual.
- You can also use as a **supporting piece of work product evidence** the immediate risks to the individual you have identified and documented in the individual's risk assessment documentation.

REMEMBER TO:

- Make arrangements for **observation** of your **work practices**.
- Include evidence of you identifying any immediate risks to the individual.
- Ensure your evidence relates to before moving and positioning individuals.
- Think about **your work** setting and how to identify any immediate risks to the individual.

Learning Outcome 3: Be able to minimise risk before moving and positioning individuals

Assessment Criterion 3.4: Describe actions to take in relation to identified risks

What does AC3.4 mean?

- The lead word **describe** means that you must provide an **account** that **details** the actions to take in relation to identified risks.
- Your **account** must detail the actions to take.
- For the key words **actions to take** you can think about how to record and report the risks you have identified before moving and positioning individuals, in line with your work setting's policies and procedures, the individual's care plan and moving and handling risk assessment.
- For the key words **identified risks** you can think about the actions to take when you recognise any sudden likelihood of danger or harm to individuals before moving and positioning, such as a worn floor covering or damaged or missing moving and handling equipment.

Read the following **Real Work Setting** scenario and think about how it relates to your work setting and role:

Real Work Setting

Name: Jakob

Job Role: Home Carer for adults who have autism
(See page 279 for a description of the role)

Actions to take in relation to identified risks: In accordance with Frederiko's care plan, Jakob asks Frederiko whether he can speak to him about getting prepared for transferring from his wheelchair into the taxi; Frederiko agrees and Jakob begins by showing him his care plan and his moving and handling risk assessment guidelines. Jakob then moves on to explain to Frederiko how it is his role to support him to move and position safely, before detailing to him the three areas of risk he has identified: his untied shoe laces could lead to him tripping, not wearing a wheelchair belt could lead to him slipping out of his wheelchair as he rides over the front door step, and holding a heavy rucksack means that he is unable to use his hands to steady himself as he transfers onto the taxi seat.

Evidencing AC3.4 to your assessor:

For AC3.4 you must evidence your knowledge of actions to take in relation to identified risks.

Assessment Methods:

Oral or **Written** Questioning or **Discussion** or a **Personal Statement** or **Reflection**

- You can **tell** your assessor about actions to take in relation to identified risks.
  Or
- You can **talk** to your assessor about actions to take in relation to identified risks.
  Or
- You can write a **personal statement** or **reflection** about your experience of actions to take in relation to identified risks.

REMEMBER TO:

- Provide an **account** that includes **details**.
- Include details about actions to take in relation to identified risks.
- Include details about different risks you have identified.
- Ensure your evidence relates to actions to take in relation to identified risks before moving and positioning individuals.
- Think about **your work setting** and the actions to take in relation to identified risks.

Learning Outcome 3: Be able to minimise risk before moving and positioning individuals

Assessment Criterion 3.5: Describe what action should be taken if the individual's wishes conflict with their plan of care in relation to health and safety and their risk assessment

What does AC3.5 mean?

- The lead word **describe** means that you must provide an **account** that **details** what action should be taken if the individual's wishes conflict with their plan of care in relation to health and safety and their risk assessment.
- Your **account** must detail what action should be taken if the individual's wishes conflict with their plan of care.
- For the key words **what action should be taken** you can think about how to record and report if the individual's wishes conflict with their plan of care in relation to health and safety and their risk assessment, in line with your work setting's policies and procedures, the individual's care plan and moving and handling risk assessment.
- For the key word **conflict** you can think about the actions to take before moving and positioning if the individual's wishes conflict with their plan of care in relation to health and safety and their risk assessment, such as choosing not to use the agreed moving and handling equipment, or requesting to not be moved and positioned with the agreed numbers of Carers.

Read the following **Real Work Setting** scenario and think about how it relates to your work setting and role:

Real Work Setting

Name: Jakob

Job Role: Home Carer for adults who have autism
(See page 279 for a description of the role)

The actions to take if the individual's wishes conflict with their plan of care: Frederiko tells Jakob that the taxi has arrived and that he will get into it by himself as this will be quicker. Jakob phones the office for advice and records the conflict that has arisen.

Evidencing AC3.5 to your assessor:

For AC3.5 you must evidence your knowledge of actions to take if the individual's wishes conflict with their plan of care in relation to health and safety and their risk assessment.

Assessment Methods:

Oral or **Written** Questioning or **Discussion** or a **Personal Statement** or **Reflection**

- You can **tell** your assessor about the actions to take if the individual's wishes conflict.
  Or
- You can **talk** to your assessor about the actions to take if the individual's wishes conflict.
  Or
- You can write a **personal statement** or **reflection** about your experience of the actions to take if the individual's wishes conflict.

REMEMBER TO:

- Provide an **account** that includes **details**.
- Include details about actions to take if the individual's wishes conflict with their plan of care.
- Ensure your evidence relates to actions to take in relation to identified risks before moving and positioning individuals.
- Think about **your work setting** and the actions to take if the individual's wishes conflict with their plan of care in relation to health and safety and their risk assessment.

Learning Outcome 3: Be able to minimise risk before moving and positioning individuals

Assessment Criterion 3.6: Prepare the immediate environment ensuring adequate space for the move in agreement with all concerned and that potential hazards are removed

What does AC3.6 mean?

- The lead word **prepare** means that you must be able to **show through your work practices** how to make the immediate environment ready by ensuring adequate space for the move, in agreement with all concerned and that potential hazards are removed.
- Your **observations of your work practices** must include you preparing the immediate environment.
- For the key words **adequate space** you can think about how to ensure in agreement with all concerned that there is sufficient room, for example by checking that the move can be carried out safely in the space available.
- For the key words **potential hazards** you can think about how to ensure in agreement with all concerned that items that have the potential to cause danger and harm, such as a wheelchair's footplates or a small piece of furniture, are removed before carrying out the move.

Read the following **Real Work Setting** scenario and think about how it relates to your work setting and role:

Real Work Setting

Name: Jakob

Job Role: Home Carer for adults who have autism
(See page 279 for a description of the role)

Preparing the immediate environment: After speaking with the office, Jakob has been advised to ensure the transfer is as safe as possible; he asks the taxi driver to park in the centre of the drive so that the taxi door can be fully opened. Jakob asks Frederiko whether he would like him to place his heavy rucksack on the back seat of the taxi; Frederiko passes him the rucksack and agrees that this is a good idea and also asks Jakob whether he wouldn't mind picking up his shoes and placing these on the back seat, too, as he plans to slip these off before getting into the taxi.

Evidencing AC3.6 to your assessor:

For AC3.6 you must evidence your skills of how to prepare the immediate environment ensuring adequate space for the move in agreement with all concerned and that potential hazards are removed.

Assessment Method:

Direct Observation of your work practices

- You can **show** your assessor how to prepare the immediate environment ensuring adequate space for the move in agreement with all concerned and that potential hazards are removed.

REMEMBER TO:

- Make arrangements for **observation** of your **work practices**.
- Include evidence of you preparing the immediate environment.
- Include evidence of you ensuring adequate space for the move in agreement with all concerned.
- Include evidence of you ensuring that potential hazards are removed.
- Ensure your evidence relates to before moving and positioning individuals.
- Think about **your work setting** and how to prepare the immediate environment ensuring adequate space for the move in agreement with all concerned and that potential hazards are removed.

Learning Outcome 3: Be able to minimise risk before moving and positioning individuals

Assessment Criterion 3.7: Apply standard precautions for infection prevention and control

What does AC3.7 mean?

- The lead word **apply** means that you must be able to **show through your work practices** how to use standard precautions for infection prevention and control.
- Your **observations of your work practices** must include you applying standard precautions.
- For the key words **standard precautions** you can think about how to use universal safety measures for infection prevention and control before moving and positioning individuals, such as by using the recommended hand-washing technique when washing your hands, checking moving and handling equipment is clean, and wearing personal protective equipment such as an apron and disposable gloves.

Read the following **Real Work Setting** scenario and think about how it relates to your work setting and role:

Real Work Setting

Name: Jakob

Job Role: Home Carer for adults who have autism
(See page 279 for a description of the role)

Standard precautions for infection prevention and control: When Jakob arrives at college with Frederiko, Frederiko asks Jakob whether he could support him with accessing the toilet as he is beginning to feel a little tired. After signing in to the visitors book, Jakob supports Frederiko to go to the downstairs toilet and agrees with him and one of the college staff to use his moving and handling belt to transfer from his wheelchair to the toilet; Jakob checks that it is clean and safe to use. Jakob and his colleague ensure that they wash their hands prior to putting on a pair of disposable gloves and then on the count of three, after checking that Frederiko is ready to move, assist Frederiko to stand and move across to the toilet. When Frederiko finishes using the toilet, both assist him again to transfer back onto his wheelchair. After removing his moving and handling belt, they gently remove their gloves, dispose of these in the clinical waste bin and then wash their hands thoroughly using the recommended hand-washing technique.

Evidencing AC3.7 to your assessor:

For AC3.7 you must evidence your skills of how to apply standard precautions for infection prevention and control.

Assessment Method:

Direct Observation of your work practices

- You can **show** your assessor how to apply standard precautions for infection prevention and control.

REMEMBER TO:

- Make arrangements for **observation** of your **work practices**.
- Include evidence of you applying standard precautions.
- Ensure your evidence relates to infection prevention and control.
- Ensure your evidence relates to applying standard precautions before moving and positioning individuals.
- Think about **your work setting** and how to apply standard precautions for infection prevention and control.

Learning Outcome 4: Be able to prepare individuals before moving and positioning

Assessment Criterion 4.1: Demonstrate effective communication with the individual to ensure that they understand the details and reasons for the action/activity being undertaken and agree the level of support required

What does AC4.1 mean?

- The lead word **demonstrate** means that you must be able to **show through your work practices** how to effectively communicate with the individual to ensure that they understand the details and reasons for the action/activity being undertaken and agree the level of support required.
- Your **observations of your work practices** must include you demonstrating effective communication with the individual.
- For the key words **effective communication** you can think about the different methods to use when communicating with individuals, such as by discussing the move with them, or showing them visual aids of the equipment and move to be undertaken.
- For the key words **action/activity** you can think about how this may include moving, repositioning or transferring the individual from a sitting to a standing position after using the toilet, or from a lying to a sitting position for eating and drinking.
- For the key words **the level of support** you can think about how to agree with individuals whether they require a low level of support such as a prompt to move and position themselves, or a high level of support such as physical assistance with moving and positioning.

Read the following **Real Work Setting** scenario and think about how it relates to your work setting and role:

Real Work Setting

Name: Isabella
Job Role: Residential Worker for adults who have complex needs
Isabella has been working as a Residential Worker for four years. Her responsibilities include: providing support to individuals with daily activities and enabling individuals to participate in a range of social activities.
Demonstrating effective communication: Isabella supports Mark to position himself in an upright position in his armchair, as he is leaning over to the right. Isabella begins by explaining to Mark that she can physically support him to sit more comfortably by assisting him to sit in a more central position in his chair.

Evidencing AC4.1 to your assessor:

For AC4.1 you must evidence your skills of how to demonstrate effective communication with the individual to ensure that they understand the details and reasons for the action/activity being undertaken and agree the level of support required.

Assessment Method:

Direct Observation of your work practices

- You can **show** your assessor how to demonstrate effective communication with the individual.

REMEMBER TO:

- Make arrangements for **observation** of your **work practices**.
- Include evidence of you demonstrating effective communication with the individual.
- Ensure your evidence relates to understanding the details and reasons for the action/activity being undertaken and agreeing the level of support required.
- Think about **your work setting** and how to demonstrate effective communication with the individual to ensure that they understand the details and reasons for the action/activity being undertaken and agree the level of support required.

Learning Outcome 4: Be able to prepare individuals before moving and positioning

Assessment Criterion 4.2: Obtain valid consent for the planned activity

What does AC4.2 mean?

- The lead word **obtain** means that you must be able to **show through your work practices** how to gain valid consent for the planned activity.
- Your **observations of your work practices** must include you obtaining valid consent.
- For the key words **valid consent** you can think about how this must be in line with the agreed UK country definition and how this involves agreement to an activity being voluntary and informed, and the person agreeing having the ability to use and understand information to make a decision, and communicate any decision made.
- For the key words **planned activity** you can think about how this may include moving, repositioning or transferring the individual, such as from a sitting to a standing position after using the toilet, or from a lying to a sitting position for eating and drinking.

Read the following **Real Work Setting** scenario and think about how it relates to your work setting and role:

Real Work Setting

Name: Isabella

Job Role: Residential Worker for adults who have complex needs
(See page 286 for a description of the role)

Obtaining valid consent for the planned activity: Mark looks at Isabella and looks straight ahead. Isabella moves a little closer to Mark, gently taps Mark on the hand and when he makes eye contact with her she explains to him that she can assist him with positioning himself in an upright position in his armchair, as he is leaning over to the right and his side must be feeling uncomfortable. Isabella then explains to Mark again that she can physically support him to sit more comfortably by assisting him to sit in a more central position in his chair and gently taps him on his back. Mark looks at Isabella and blinks twice; Isabella checks with him that he agrees that she can physically assist him to sit in a more upright position; again, Mark looks at Isabella and blinks twice. Isabella is satisfied that she has obtained Mark's valid consent, as agreed in his care plan.

Evidencing AC4.2 to your assessor:

For AC4.2 you must evidence your skills of how to obtain valid consent for the planned activity.

Assessment Method:

Direct Observation of your work practices

- You can **show** your assessor how to obtain valid consent for the planned activity.

REMEMBER TO:

- Make arrangements for **observation** of your **work practices**.
- Include evidence of you obtaining valid consent.
- Include evidence of a planned activity.
- Ensure your evidence relates to preparing to move and position individuals.
- Think about **your work setting** and how to obtain valid consent for the planned activity.

Learning Outcome 5: Be able to move and position an individual

Assessment Criterion 5.1: Follow the care plan to ensure that the individual is positioned using the agreed technique and in a way that will avoid causing undue pain or discomfort

What does AC5.1 mean?

- The lead word **follow** means that you must be able to **show through your work practices** how to use the care plan to ensure that the individual is positioned using the agreed technique and in a way that will avoid causing undue pain or discomfort.
- Your **observations of your work practices** must include you following the care plan.
- For the key words **using the agreed technique** you can think about how the individual is positioned in line with their care plan, the specific moving and positioning guidelines that may be in place for them, as well as with your work setting's policies and procedures, such as by specifying the correct techniques to use, the equipment and/or aids that must be used, and how the individual must be supported in line with their needs and preferences.
- For the key words **undue pain or discomfort** you can think about how this involves positioning the individual in a way that ensures their comfort and safety, such as by avoiding dragging the individual, placing too much pressure on an individual's limb, moving them too quickly or without the correct size or piece of equipment that has been specified in their care plan.

Read the following **Real Work Setting** scenario and think about how it relates to your work setting and role:

Real Work Setting

Name: Huy
Job Role: Day Centre Worker for adults
Huy has been working as a Day Centre Worker for one year. His responsibilities include supporting adults with a range of activities and personal care tasks, including moving and positioning.
Following the care plan: Huy reads through An's care plan to check how to move and position An safely from his chair onto a beanbag.

Evidencing AC5.1 to your assessor:

For AC5.1 you must evidence your skills of how to follow the care plan to ensure that the individual is positioned using the agreed technique and in a way that will avoid causing undue pain or discomfort.

Assessment Method:

Direct Observation of your work practices

- You can **show** your assessor how to follow the care plan to ensure that the individual is positioned using the agreed technique and in a way that will avoid causing undue pain or discomfort.

REMEMBER TO:

- Make arrangements for **observation** of your **work practices**.
- Include evidence of you following the care plan when positioning the individual.
- Include evidence of using the agreed technique and avoiding causing undue pain or discomfort.
- Ensure your evidence relates to moving and positioning an individual.
- Think about **your work setting** and how to follow the care plan to ensure that the individual is positioned using the agreed technique and in a way that will avoid causing undue pain or discomfort.

Learning Outcome 5: Be able to move and position an individual

Assessment Criterion 5.2: Demonstrate effective communication with any others involved in the manoeuvre

What does AC5.2 mean?

- The lead word **demonstrate** means that you must be able to **show through your work practices** how to effectively communicate with any others involved in the manoeuvre.
- Your **observations of your work practices** must include you demonstrating effective communication with others.
- For the key words **effective communication** you can think about the different methods to use when communicating with others involved in the manoeuvre, such as by agreeing with others who is going to lead the manoeuvre, where to stand and position yourself, and when and how to undertake the manoeuvre such as on the count of three.
- For the key word **others** you can think about how this may include a colleague, your line manager, the individual's family, the individual's advocate or another professional.

Read the following **Real Work Setting** scenario and think about how it relates to your work setting and role:

Real Work Setting

Name: Huy

Job Role: Day Centre Worker for adults
(See page 288 for a description of the role)

Demonstrating effective communication: After reading through An's care plan to check how to move and position An safely from his chair onto a beanbag, Huy asks the Senior on duty whether he can assist him with hoisting An from his chair onto the beanbag on the floor, in preparation for his relaxation session this afternoon. Huy discusses the move with the Senior and agrees that he will take the lead in operating the hoist and putting the sling on An and that the Senior will support An while in the hoist.

Evidencing AC5.2 to your assessor:

For AC5.2 you must evidence your skills of how to demonstrate effective communication with any others involved in the manoeuvre.

Assessment Method:

Direct Observation of your work practices

- You can **show** your assessor how to demonstrate effective communication with any others involved in the manoeuvre.

REMEMBER TO:

- Make arrangements for **observation** of your **work practices**.
- Include evidence of you demonstrating effective communication with any others involved in the manoeuvre.
- Ensure your evidence relates to moving and positioning an individual.
- Think about **your work setting** and how to demonstrate effective communication with any others involved in the manoeuvre.

Learning Outcome 5: Be able to move and position an individual

Assessment Criterion 5.3: Describe the aids and equipment that may be used for moving and positioning

What does AC5.3 mean?

- The lead word **describe** means that you must provide an **account** that **details** the aids and equipment that may be used for moving and positioning.
- Your **account** must detail the aids and equipment.
- For the key words **aids and equipment** you can think about the items that may be used to move and position individuals such as ceiling, standing and mobile hoists, bath lifts, slide sheets, transfer boards, hand rails, walking aids, handling belts and lifting cushions.

Read the following **Real Work Setting** scenario and think about how it relates to your work setting and role:

Real Work Setting

Name: Huy

Job Role: Day Centre Worker for adults
(See page 288 for a description of the role)

Demonstrating effective communication: Huy and the Senior then discuss the various aids and equipment they will use with An today to move and position him from his chair onto the beanbag on the floor, in preparation for his relaxation session this afternoon. Huy then shows An the ceiling hoist and sling that they will be using to hoist him onto the beanbag on the floor. An asks Huy whether he can complete his walking exercises prior to the relaxation session; so Huy and the Senior discuss the most suitable walking aid that An could use for walking on the carpeted floor in the hallway and reference his care plan to ensure they make the correct choice.

Evidencing AC5.3 to your assessor:

For AC5.3 you must evidence your knowledge of the aids and equipment that may be used for moving and positioning individuals.

Assessment Methods:

Oral or **Written** Questioning or **Discussion** or a **Personal Statement** or **Reflection**

- You can **tell** your assessor about the aids and equipment that may be used for moving and positioning individuals.
  Or
- You can **talk** to your assessor about the aids and equipment that may be used for moving and positioning individuals.
  Or
- You can write a **personal statement** or **reflection** about your experience of the aids and equipment that may be used for moving and positioning individuals.

REMEMBER TO:

- Provide an **account** that includes **details**.
- Include details about the aids and equipment that may be used.
- Ensure your evidence relates to moving and positioning individuals.
- Think about **your work setting** and the aids and equipment that may be used for moving and positioning individuals.

Learning Outcome 5: Be able to move and position an individual

Assessment Criterion 5.4: Use equipment to maintain the individual in the appropriate position

What does AC5.4 mean?

- The lead word **use** means that you must be able to **show through your work practices** how to operate equipment to maintain the individual in the appropriate position.
- Your **observations of your work practices** must include you using equipment.
- For the key word **equipment** you can think about the items that may be used to maintain the individual in the appropriate position, such as cushion supports, armchair-shaped supports, 'V' pillows, wedge-shaped beanbags and inflatable supports, adjustable back rests, pillow lifts, mattress inclinators and foot boards.

Read the following **Real Work Setting** scenario and think about how it relates to your work setting and role:

Real Work Setting

Name: Huy

Job Role: Day Centre Worker for adults
(See page 288 for a description of the role)

Use equipment to maintain the individual in the appropriate position: After An has completed his walking exercises, Huy and the Senior hoist him onto the floor mat as agreed and in line with his care plan. Once safely onto the floor, Huy moves An's wedge-shaped beanbag close to An so that he can maintain a comfortable sitting position. Huy also shows An the posture wedge for him to use when lying on his front on the floor mat during his relaxation exercises.

Evidencing AC5.4 to your assessor:

For AC5.4 you must evidence your skills of how to use equipment to maintain the individual in the appropriate position.

Assessment Method:

Direct Observation of your work practices

- You can **show** your assessor how to use equipment to maintain the individual in the appropriate position.

REMEMBER TO:

- Make arrangements for **observation** of your **work practices**.
- Include evidence of you using equipment to maintain the individual in the appropriate position.
- Ensure your evidence relates to moving and positioning an individual.
- Think about **your work setting** and how to use equipment to maintain the individual in the appropriate position.

Learning Outcome 5: Be able to move and position an individual

Assessment Criterion 5.5: Encourage the individual's active participation in the manoeuvre

What does AC5.5 mean?

- The lead word **encourage** means that you must be able to **show through your work practices** how to support and motivate the individual's active participation in the manoeuvre.
- Your **observations of your work practices** must include you encouraging the individual's active participation.
- For the key words **active participation** you can think about how to encourage individuals to be fully involved in all aspects of the moving and positioning manoeuvre, such as by agreeing with the individual what the manoeuvre will involve, or discussing with the individual their role in the manoeuvre.

Read the following **Real Work Setting** scenario and think about how it relates to your work setting and role:

Real Work Setting

Name: Huy
Job Role: Day Centre Worker for adults (See page 288 for a description of the role)
Encourage the individual's active participation in the manoeuvre: During the relaxation session, Huy supports An with using the posture wedge for lying on his front. Huy talks through with An how he is going to roll over from lying on his back onto his front and suggests that An decides which side he would like to roll onto. An decides he wishes to roll onto his right side; Huy encourages An to bring his left leg and then his left arm across his body so that he can roll onto his right side. Once An achieves this, Huy talks him through how he needs to place his left hand onto the wedge and then steady himself with his right hand as he pushes upwards so that he can lie on his front on the wedge.

Evidencing AC5.5 to your assessor:

For AC5.5 you must evidence your skills of how to encourage the individual's active participation in the manoeuvre.

Assessment Method:

Direct Observation of your work practices

- You can **show** your assessor how to encourage the individual's active participation in the manoeuvre.

REMEMBER TO:

- Make arrangements for **observation** of your **work practices**.
- Include evidence of you encouraging the individual's active participation.
- Ensure your evidence relates to the manoeuvre.
- Think about **your work setting** and how to encourage the individual's active participation in the manoeuvre.

Learning Outcome 5: Be able to move and position an individual

Assessment Criterion 5.6: Monitor the individual throughout the activity so that the procedure can be stopped if there is any adverse reaction

What does AC5.6 mean?

- The lead word **monitor** means that you must be able to **show through your work practices** how to observe and check the individual throughout the activity so that the procedure can be stopped if there is any adverse reaction.
- Your **observations of your work practices** must include you monitoring the individual throughout the activity.
- For the key word **activity** you can think about how this may include moving, repositioning or transferring the individual, such as from a sitting to a standing position to go for a walk, or from a lying to a sitting position for getting up in the morning.
- For the key words **adverse reaction** you can think about how this may include an individual feeling unwell, in pain, anxious, or choosing to not continue with the activity.

Read the following **Real Work Setting** scenario and think about how it relates to your work setting and role:

Real Work Setting

Name: Huy

Job Role: Day Centre Worker for adults
(See page 288 for a description of the role)

Monitoring the individual throughout the activity: During the relaxation session, Huy monitors An lying on his front on the posture wedge by checking with An every five minutes that he is comfortable and by observing that An's hands remain free on the wedge and that his body does not slide off the wedge.

Evidencing AC5.6 to your assessor:

For AC5.6 you must evidence your skills of how to monitor the individual throughout the activity so that the procedure can be stopped if there is any adverse reaction.

Assessment Method:

Direct Observation of your work practices

- You can **show** your assessor how to monitor the individual throughout the activity so that the procedure can be stopped if there is any adverse reaction.

REMEMBER TO:

- Make arrangements for **observation** of your **work practices**.
- Include evidence of you monitoring the individual throughout the activity.
- Ensure your evidence relates to the procedure being stopped if there is any adverse reaction.
- Think about **your work setting** and how to monitor the individual throughout the activity so that the procedure can be stopped if there is any adverse reaction.

Learning Outcome 5: Be able to move and position an individual

Assessment Criterion 5.7: Demonstrate how to report and record the activity, noting when the next positioning manoeuvre is due

What does AC5.7 mean?

- The lead word **demonstrate** means that you must be able to **show through your work practices** how to report and record the activity, noting when the next positioning manoeuvre is due.
- Your **observations of your work practices** must include you demonstrating how to report and record the activity.
- For the key words **report and record** you can think about how to verbally report and record in writing the activity, noting when the next positioning manoeuvre is due in line with your work setting's policies and procedures.
- For the key word **activity** you can think about how this may include moving, repositioning or transferring the individual, such as from a sitting to a standing position to go for a walk, or from one side to another when in a lying position.

Read the following **Real Work Setting** scenario and think about how it relates to your work setting and role:

Real Work Setting

Name: Huy

Job Role: Day Centre Worker for adults
(See page 288 for a description of the role)

Reporting and recording the activity: At the end of the relaxation session, Huy discusses with An the progress he has made with getting onto his wedge and lying on his front during the relaxation session and documents this in Huy's activity record sheet and in his moving and positioning chart. Huy and An then share, as agreed, An's progress with the rest of the participants in the group. Huy also records in An's moving and positioning chart that this evening An is to be encouraged to spend some time lying on his back with a pillow wedge for support.

Evidencing AC5.7 to your assessor:

For AC5.7 you must evidence your skills of how to report and record the activity, noting when the next positioning manoeuvre is due.

Assessment Method:

Direct Observation of your work practices

- You can **show** your assessor how to report and record the activity, noting when the next positioning manoeuvre is due.

REMEMBER TO:

- Make arrangements for **observation** of your **work practices**.
- Include evidence of how you report and record the activity.
- Include evidence of you noting when the next positioning manoeuvre is due.
- Think about **your work setting** and how to report and record the activity, noting when the next positioning manoeuvre is due.

Learning Outcome 6: Know when to seek advice from and/or involve others when moving and positioning an individual

Assessment Criterion 6.1: Describe when advice and/or assistance should be sought to move or handle an individual safely

What does AC6.1 mean?

- The lead word **describe** means that you must provide an **account** that **details** when advice and/or assistance should be sought to move or handle an individual safely.
- Your **account** must detail when advice and/or assistance should be sought.
- For the key words **advice and/or assistance** you can think about the occasions when information, guidance and/or support should be sought to move and handle an individual safely, such as when an individual has a specific condition that affects their moving and positioning, or when using a new piece of equipment, or when an individual becomes unwell or distressed.

Read the following **Real Work Setting** scenario and think about how it relates to your work setting and role:

Real Work Setting

Name: Louise
Job Role: Support Worker for deaf and hard of hearing adults
Louise has been working as a Support Worker for three years. Her responsibilities include: supporting individuals to run their own home, access and take part in a variety of social and leisure activities, plan and achieve the goals agreed with individuals as part of their support plans.
When advice and/or assistance should be sought to move or handle an individual safely: Louise is supporting Frank to begin his transfer from his wheelchair to a chair when the transfer board they are using suddenly appears to be giving way. Louise shouts out to her colleague for assistance and together they support Frank to gently slide back onto his wheelchair to avoid him falling and then together examine the transfer board that appears to be showing some signs of weakness across its centre. Both agree that they will remove the transfer board from use and record and report this to the manager.

Evidencing AC6.1 to your assessor:

For AC6.1 you must evidence your knowledge of when advice and/or assistance should be sought to move or handle an individual safely.

Assessment Methods:

Oral or **Written** Questioning or **Discussion** or a **Personal Statement** or **Reflection.**

- You can **tell** your assessor about when advice and/or assistance should be sought to move or handle an individual safely.
  Or
- You can **talk** to your assessor about when advice and/or assistance should be sought to move or handle an individual safely.
  Or
- You can write a **personal statement** or **reflection** about your experience of when advice and/or assistance should be sought to move or handle an individual safely.

REMEMBER TO:

- Provide an **account** that includes **details.**
- Include details about when advice and/or assistance should be sought.
- Ensure your evidence relates to moving or handling an individual safely.
- Think about **your work setting** and when advice and/or assistance should be sought to move or handle an individual safely.

Learning Outcome 6: Know when to seek advice from and/or involve others when moving and positioning an individual

Assessment Criterion 6.2: Describe what sources of information are available about moving and positioning individuals

What does AC6.2 mean?

- The lead word **describe** means that you must provide an **account** that **details** what sources of information are available about moving and positioning individuals.
- Your **account** must detail sources of information that are available about moving and positioning individuals.
- For the key words **sources of information** you can think about how these may include documents, people and organisations available within and outside your work setting, such as individuals' care plans and moving and handling guidelines, experienced or senior colleagues, your line manager, professionals such as occupational therapists, physiotherapists, manual handling advisers, and organisations such as the National Back Exchange or the Chartered Society for Physiotherapists.

Read the following **Real Work Setting** scenario and think about how it relates to your work setting and role:

Real Work Setting

Name: Louise

Job Role: Support Worker for deaf and hard of hearing adults
(See page 295 for a description of the role)

Sources of information available about moving and positioning individuals: At the team meeting held at the end of the week, Louise raises the problem that occurred with the transfer board she used when transferring Frank from his wheelchair to a chair; the manager explains to Louise and the team the outcome of this and shows the team the new transfer board that has arrived and will be used with Frank. The team then discuss other sources of information that are available about moving and positioning individuals, including all the documentation available in the work setting for each individual and other professionals and organisations that can be accessed by the team.

Evidencing AC6.2 to your assessor:

For AC6.2 you must evidence your knowledge of sources of information that are available about moving and positioning individuals.

Assessment Methods:

Oral or **Written** Questioning or **Discussion** or a **Personal Statement** or **Reflection**

- You can **tell** your assessor about what sources of information are available about moving and positioning individuals.
  Or
- You can **talk** to your assessor about what sources of information are available about moving and positioning individuals.
  Or
- You can write a **personal statement** or **reflection** about your experience of what sources of information are available about moving and positioning individuals.

REMEMBER TO:

- Provide an **account** that includes **details.**
- Include details about sources of information.
- Ensure your evidence relates to moving and positioning individuals.
- Think about **your work setting** and what sources of information are available about moving and positioning individuals.

LD206C Support individuals to maintain personal hygiene

Learning Outcome 1: Understand the importance of good personal hygiene

Assessment Criterion 1.1: Explain why personal hygiene is important

What does AC1.1 mean?

- The lead word **explain** means that you must **make clear** the reasons why personal hygiene is important.
- Your **account** must detail the reasons why.
- For the key words **personal hygiene** you can think about the reasons why it is important to care for your body and keep it clean and healthy.

Read the following **Real Work Setting** scenario and think about how it relates to your work setting and role:

Real Work Setting

Name: Amali
Job Role: Home Carer
Amali has been working as a Home Carer for six years. His responsibilities include: supporting individuals with getting dressed and undressed, eating and drinking, personal care including using and cleansing toileting facilities, cooking, food shopping, clothes washing, ironing and other household tasks.
The importance of maintaining personal hygiene: Amali is supporting Don to get washed and dressed, but Don tells Amali that he would rather not get washed this morning. Amali asks him why he does not want to and Don tells him that he is just feeling lazy. Amali reads through Don's file and shares with him how it is documented on his daily records that he also chose to not have a wash yesterday and the day before. Amali explains to Don that it is his choice to refuse to have a wash but agrees with Don to discuss with him over a cup of tea the importance of maintaining personal hygiene. Amali discusses with Don the reasons why it is important for Don, his family and the Home Carers who support him for Don to maintain his personal hygiene.

Evidencing AC1.1 to your assessor:

For AC1.1 you must evidence your understanding of why personal hygiene is important.

Assessment Methods:

Oral or **Written** Questioning or **Discussion** or a **Personal Statement** or **Reflection**

- You can **tell** your assessor about why personal hygiene is important.
  Or
- You can **talk** to your assessor about why personal hygiene is important.
  Or
- You can write a **personal statement** or **reflection** about your experience of why personal hygiene is important.

REMEMBER TO:

- Provide an **account** and **explain why** personal hygiene is important.
- Include **details** about different reasons why.
- Include **examples** of why personal hygiene is important.
- Think about **your work setting** and why personal hygiene is important.

Learning Outcome 1: Understand the importance of good personal hygiene

Assessment Criterion 1.2: Describe the effects of poor personal hygiene on health and well-being

What does AC1.2 mean?

- The lead word **describe** means that you must provide an **account** that **details** the effects of poor personal hygiene on health and well-being.
- Your **account** must detail the effects of poor personal hygiene on health and well-being.
- For the key words **poor personal hygiene** you can think about the effects of not caring for your body and keeping it clean and healthy.
- For the key words **health and well-being** you can think about the effects on you and others of not caring for your body and keeping it clean and healthy in terms of your physical, emotional, mental and social health and well-being such as skin and parts of the body becoming irritated and sore, offensive body odour that may lead to others not wanting to socialise with you, and feeling unwell and low in mood.

Read the following **Real Work Setting** scenario and think about how it relates to your work setting and role:

Real Work Setting

Name: Amali

Job Role: Home Carer
(See page 297 for a description of the role)

The effects of poor personal hygiene: During Amali's discussion with Don, they also talk about the effects of poor personal hygiene on Don's physical, emotional, mental and social health and well-being. After much discussion, Don says to Amali that he thinks he will have a shower and a hair wash this morning, as perhaps not doing so is part of the reason why he is feeling lazy and a little depressed.

Evidencing AC1.2 to your assessor:

For AC1.2 you must evidence your understanding of the effects of poor personal hygiene on health and well-being.

Assessment Methods:

Oral or **Written** Questioning or **Discussion** or a **Personal Statement** or **Reflection**

- You can **tell** your assessor about the effects of poor personal hygiene on health and well-being.
  Or
- You can **talk** to your assessor about the effects of poor personal hygiene on health and well-being.
  Or
- You can write a **personal statement** or **reflection** about your experience of the effects of poor personal hygiene on health and well-being.

REMEMBER TO:

- Provide a detailed **account**.
- Include **details** and **examples** of the effects of poor personal hygiene on health and well-being.
- Ensure your evidence relates to the effects of poor personal hygiene on different aspects of health and well-being.
- Think about **your work setting** and the effects of poor personal hygiene on health and well-being.

Learning Outcome 2: Be able to support individuals to maintain personal hygiene

Assessment Criterion 2.1: Support an individual to understand factors that contribute to good personal hygiene

What does AC2.1 mean?

- The lead word **support** means that you must be able to **show through your work practices** how to assist an individual to understand factors that contribute to good personal hygiene.
- Your **observations of your work practices** must include you supporting an individual to understand these factors.
- For the key word **factors** you can think about aspects of washing before and after high-risk activities such as preparing food, using the toilet and eating, showering and bathing including frequency and equipment used, washing and grooming hair, cleaning and trimming nails, moisturising skin, washing and changing of clothes including frequency and equipment used, treating promptly and correctly any infections or skin allergies.
- For the key words **good personal hygiene** you can think about how you can support an individual to understand different aspects of keeping one's body clean and healthy.

Read the following **Real Work Setting** scenario and think about how it relates to your work setting and role:

Real Work Setting

Name: Scarlett
Job Role: Support Worker for adults who have learning disabilities
Scarlett has been working as a Support Worker for four years. Her responsibilities include: supporting individuals with daily activities including personal care, managing their money and taking part in social activities such as meeting up with friends, going to the pub and eating out at restaurants.
Factors that contribute to good personal hygiene: During Miranda's review of her support plan, Scarlett supports Miranda to share with her advocate and Scarlett's line manager how the plan of support that has been put in place to encourage her to maintain a good standard of personal hygiene is working in practice.

Evidencing AC2.1 to your assessor:

For AC2.1 you must evidence your skills in supporting an individual to understand factors that contribute to good personal hygiene.

Assessment Method:

Direct Observation of your work practices

- You can **show** your assessor or an expert witness how to support an individual to understand factors that contribute to good personal hygiene.

REMEMBER TO:

- Make arrangements for **observation** of your work practices.
- Include evidence of you demonstrating how to support an individual.
- Ensure your evidence relates to understanding factors that contribute to good personal hygiene.
- Think about **your work setting** and how to support an individual to understand factors that contribute to good personal hygiene.

Learning Outcome 2: Be able to support individuals to maintain personal hygiene

Assessment Criterion 2.2: Address personal hygiene issues with the individual in a sensitive manner without imposing your own values

What does AC2.2 mean?

- The lead word **address** means that you must be able to **show through your work practices** how to think about and deal with personal hygiene issues with the individual in a sensitive manner without imposing your own values.
- Your **observations of your work practices** must include you dealing with personal hygiene issues with the individual.
- For the key words **personal hygiene issues** you can think about aspects in relation to not washing, frequency of washing, inconsistency when washing, regularity of grooming hair and cleaning and trimming nails, frequency of moisturising skin, frequency of washing and changing of clothes, precautions taken with infections or skin allergies and body odour.
- For the key words **sensitive manner** you can think about how you speak with an individual, the language, pictures and words you use, where you meet to speak about this with an individual, and how you respond to an individual's questions and feelings.
- For the key word **values** you can think about how when dealing with personal hygiene issues with the individual you do not impose your personal thoughts, ideas, principles and beliefs on the individual.

Read the following **Real Work Setting** scenario and think about how it relates to your work setting and role:

Real Work Setting

Name: Scarlett

Job Role: Support Worker for adults who have learning disabilities
(See page 299 for a description of the role)

Sensitively addressing personal hygiene issues: During discussions between Scarlett, her line manager, Miranda and her advocate, Scarlett gently raises the areas of Miranda's personal hygiene that still require addressing, including ensuring she changes her clothes regularly, puts on clean clothes after having a shower in the mornings and wears deodorant when taking part in sporting activities that she enjoys.

Evidencing AC2.2 to your assessor:

For AC2.2 you must evidence your skills in addressing personal hygiene issues with the individual in a sensitive manner without imposing your own values.

Assessment Method:

Direct Observation of your work practices

- You can **show** your assessor or an expert witness how to address personal hygiene issues with the individual in a sensitive manner without imposing your own values.

REMEMBER TO:

- Make arrangements for **observation** of your **work practices**.
- Include evidence of you addressing personal hygiene issues with the individual.
- Ensure your evidence relates to you doing this in a sensitive manner and without imposing your own values.
- Think about **your work setting** and how to address personal hygiene issues with the individual in a sensitive manner without imposing your own values.

Learning Outcome 2: Be able to support individuals to maintain personal hygiene

Assessment Criterion 2.3: Support the individual to develop awareness of the effects of poor hygiene on others

What does AC2.3 mean?

- The lead word **support** means that you must be able to **show through your work practices** how to assist an individual to develop awareness of the effects of poor hygiene on others.
- Your **observations of your work practices** must include you supporting an individual to develop awareness of the effects of poor hygiene on others.
- For the key word **effects** you can think about the impact on others of individuals not caring for their body and keeping it clean and healthy in terms of physical, emotional, mental and social health and well-being.
- For the key words **poor hygiene** you can think about the effects of poor personal hygiene such as by not washing all parts of the body regularly, not washing hands using the recommended technique, and not changing clothes regularly.

Read the following **Real Work Setting** scenario and think about how it relates to your work setting and role:

Real Work Setting

Name: Scarlett

Job Role: Support Worker for adults who have learning disabilities
(See page 299 for a description of the role)

Developing awareness of the effects of poor hygiene on others: Scarlett also supports Miranda to talk about the occasion when she got a little upset because one of her friends made a comment about her appearance and her body odour when she went out one evening after playing badminton with another friend. Scarlett supports Miranda to understand the reasons why her friend may have made this comment and how she thinks that her not changing her clothes or not wearing deodorant may have affected her friend.

Evidencing AC2.3 to your assessor:

For AC2.3 you must evidence your skills in supporting the individual to develop awareness of the effects of poor hygiene on others.

Assessment Method:

Direct Observation of your work practices

- You can **show** your assessor or an expert witness how to support the individual to develop awareness of the effects of poor hygiene on others.

REMEMBER TO:

- Make arrangements for **observation** of your **work practices**.
- Include evidence of you supporting the individual to develop awareness of the effects of poor hygiene.
- Ensure your evidence relates to the effects of poor hygiene on others.
- Think about **your work setting** and how to support the individual to develop awareness of the effects of poor hygiene on others.

Learning Outcome 2: Be able to support individuals to maintain personal hygiene

Assessment Criterion 2.4: Support the preferences and needs of the individual while maintaining their independence

What does AC2.4 mean?

- The lead word **support** means that you must be able to **show through your work practices** how to support the preferences and needs of the individual while maintaining their independence.
- Your **observations of your work practices** must include you supporting the preferences and needs of the individual while maintaining their independence.
- For the key word **preferences** you can think about the different ways individuals keep their bodies clean and healthy, according to their background, beliefs, culture, faith and beliefs.
- For the key word **needs** you can think about the different support that individuals may require, depending on their strengths, abilities and preferences.
- For the key word **independence** you can think about how to provide support to an individual by assisting them to manage their personal hygiene, rather than doing it for them.

Read the following **Real Work Setting** scenario and think about how it relates to your work setting and role:

Real Work Setting

Name: Scarlett

Job Role: Support Worker for adults who have learning disabilities
(See page 299 for a description of the role)

Individuals' preferences and needs: After supporting Miranda in her review, Scarlett agrees to support Miranda with having a bath this evening. Miranda explains to Scarlett that she would like to have a soak in the bath and that afterwards would like to wash her hair under the shower, as she believes that this is more hygienic than doing so in the bath but would need Scarlett's help with this, because she finds the step to get into the shower difficult to manage. Scarlett suggests that she could attach a shower hose to the bath taps if this would make it easier for Miranda to use on her own and, therefore, maintain her independence while having a hair wash.

Evidencing AC2.4 to your assessor:

For AC2.4 you must evidence your skills in supporting the preferences and needs of the individual while maintaining their independence.

Assessment Method:

Direct Observation of your work practices

- You can **show** your assessor or an expert witness how to support the preferences and needs of the individual while maintaining their independence.

REMEMBER TO:

- Make arrangements for **observation** of your **work practices**.
- Include evidence of you supporting the preferences and needs of the individual.
- Ensure your evidence relates to maintaining their independence with maintaining good personal hygiene.
- Think about **your work setting** and how to support the preferences and needs of the individual while maintaining their independence.

Learning Outcome 2: Be able to support individuals to maintain personal hygiene

Assessment Criterion 2.5: Describe how to maintain dignity of an individual when supporting intimate personal hygiene

What does AC2.5 mean?

- The lead word **describe** means that you must provide an **account** that **details** how to maintain the dignity of an individual when supporting intimate personal hygiene.
- Your **account** must detail how to maintain the dignity of an individual.
- For the key words **maintain dignity** you can think about how this involves considering their privacy, being aware of abuse, building trust, showing your respect to the individual, empathising when individuals are supported with intimate personal hygiene, being professional and using a range of approaches including being gentle, not being patronising, averting eyes to avoid embarrassment, and using appropriate language that is suitable for the individual.

Read the following **Real Work Setting** scenario and think about how it relates to your work setting and role:

Real Work Setting

Name: Scarlett

Job Role: Support Worker for adults who have learning disabilities
(See page 299 for a description of the role)

Maintaining dignity when supporting intimate personal hygiene: While supporting Miranda with a bath this evening, Scarlett gives careful consideration to how she can maintain Miranda's dignity. Scarlett ensures that she respects Miranda's choice to wash herself and only uses verbal prompts to encourage Miranda to wash all over her body including her intimate areas and, as Miranda does so, Scarlett ensures she averts her eyes from Miranda to avoid embarrassment.

Evidencing AC2.5 to your assessor:

For AC2.5 you must describe how to maintain the dignity of an individual when supporting intimate personal hygiene.

Assessment Methods:

Oral or **Written** Questioning or **Discussion** or a **Personal Statement** or **Reflection**

- You can **tell** your assessor about how to maintain the dignity of an individual when supporting intimate personal hygiene.
  Or
- You can **talk** to your assessor about how to maintain the dignity of an individual when supporting intimate personal hygiene.
  Or
- You can write a **personal statement** or **reflection** about your experience of how to maintain the dignity of an individual when supporting intimate personal hygiene.

REMEMBER TO:

- Provide a detailed **account**.
- Include **details** and **examples** of how to maintain the dignity of an individual when supporting intimate personal hygiene.
- Ensure your evidence relates to supporting intimate personal hygiene.
- Think about **your work setting** and how to maintain the dignity of an individual when supporting intimate personal hygiene.

LD206C

AC 2.6

Learning Outcome 2: Be able to support individuals to maintain personal hygiene

Assessment Criterion 2.6: Identify risks to own health in supporting an individual with personal hygiene routines

What does AC2.6 mean?

- The lead word **identify** means that you must **make clear** the risks to your health in supporting an individual with personal hygiene routines.
- Your **list** must make clear the risks to your health.
- For the key word **risks** you can think about how to identify the potential danger, harm and hazards that may arise in supporting an individual with personal hygiene routines, such as in relation to personal and general health and safety, infection control and abuse.
- For the key words **personal hygiene routines** you can think about how to identify risks in supporting an individual with activities such as washing, showering, bathing, using the toilet, dressing, undressing and grooming.

Read the following **Real Work Setting** scenario and think about how it relates to your work setting and role:

Real Work Setting

Name: Scarlett

Job Role: Support Worker for adults who have learning disabilities
(See page 299 for a description of the role)

Identifying risks to your health: Prior to supporting Miranda with her bath this evening, Scarlett identified two areas of risk in relation to Miranda deciding halfway through her bath that she no longer wished to continue to have it and attempting to get out of the bath quickly and throwing her personal toiletries and materials at Scarlett owing to embarrassment at requiring support with personal care.

Evidencing AC2.6 to your assessor:

For AC2.6 you must evidence your knowledge of identifying risks to your health in supporting an individual with personal hygiene routines.

Assessment Methods:

Oral or **Written** Questioning or **Discussion** or a **Spidergram**

- You can **tell** your assessor about identifying risks to your health in supporting an individual with personal hygiene routines.
  Or
- You can **talk** to your assessor about identifying risks to your health in supporting an individual with personal hygiene routines.
  Or
- You can complete a **spidergram** of risks to your health in supporting an individual with personal hygiene routines.
- You can also use as a **supporting piece of work product evidence** a risk assessment you have completed at work that identifies risks to your health in supporting an individual with personal hygiene routines.

REMEMBER TO:

- Include a **list** of different risks to your health.
- Ensure the list relates to supporting an individual with personal hygiene routines.
- Think about **your work setting** and identify risks to your health in supporting an individual with personal hygiene routines.

Learning Outcome 2: Be able to support individuals to maintain personal hygiene

Assessment Criterion 2.7: Reduce risks to own health when supporting the individual with personal hygiene routines

What does AC2.7 mean?

- The lead word **reduce** means that you must be able to **show through your work practices** how to minimise the risks to your health when supporting the individual with personal hygiene routines.
- Your **observations of your work practices** must include you minimising the risks to your health.
- For the key word **risks** you can think about how to minimise the potential danger, harm and hazards that may arise in supporting an individual with personal hygiene routines such as in relation to personal and general health and safety, infection control and abuse.
- For the key words **personal hygiene routines** you can think about activities such as washing, showering, bathing, using the toilet, dressing, undressing and grooming and how to minimise the risks to your health that these may present.

Read the following **Real Work Setting** scenario and think about how it relates to your work setting and role:

Real Work Setting

Name: Scarlett

Job Role: Support Worker for adults who have learning disabilities
(See page 299 for a description of the role)

Reduce risks to your health: As part of Miranda's risk assessment, Scarlett ensures that Miranda is aware that she can choose to not continue with having a bath whenever she likes and can inform Scarlett of this if she begins to feel this way. Scarlett also ensures that she wears a disposable apron and gloves and stands close to the exit of the bathroom, should Scarlett attempt to throw any items at her so that she can then try to move out of the way and reduce any risks to her health.

Evidencing AC2.7 to your assessor:

For AC2.7 you must evidence your skills in reducing risks to your health when supporting the individual with personal hygiene routines.

Assessment Method:

Direct Observation of your work practices

- You can **show** your assessor or an expert witness how to reduce risks to your health when supporting the individual with personal hygiene routines.

REMEMBER TO:

- Make arrangements for **observation** of your **work practices.**
- Include evidence of you reducing risks to your health when supporting the individual with personal hygiene routines.
- Think about **your work setting** and how to reduce risks to your health when supporting the individual with personal hygiene routines.

Learning Outcome 2: Be able to support individuals to maintain personal hygiene

Assessment Criterion 2.8: Identify others who may be involved in supporting the individual to maintain personal hygiene

What does AC2.8 mean?

- The lead word **identify** means that you must **make clear** others who may be involved in supporting the individual to maintain personal hygiene.
- Your **list** must make clear others who may be involved in supporting the individual.
- For the key word **others** you can think about how people who can support the individual may include the individual themselves, your colleagues, individuals' families, Carers, friends or advocates, members of the public and other professionals.
- For the key words **personal hygiene** you can think about how others may be involved in supporting the individual with activities such as washing, showering, bathing, using the toilet, dressing, undressing and grooming.

Read the following **Real Work Setting** scenario and think about how it relates to your work setting and role:

Real Work Setting

Name: Scarlett

Job Role: Support Worker for adults who have learning disabilities
(See page 299 for a description of the role)

Identifying others who may be involved in supporting the individual: As part of Miranda's risk assessment it has also been agreed that although only one Support Worker is to enter the bathroom with Miranda, another Support Worker must also be available while Miranda has a bath and must wait outside the bathroom in case immediate assistance is required.

Evidencing AC2.8 to your assessor:

For AC2.8 you must evidence your knowledge of identifying others who may be involved in supporting the individual to maintain personal hygiene.

Assessment Methods:

Oral or **Written** Questioning or **Discussion** or a **Spidergram**

- You can **tell** your assessor about identifying others who may be involved in supporting the individual to maintain personal hygiene.
  Or
- You can **talk** to your assessor about identifying others who may be involved in supporting the individual to maintain personal hygiene.
  Or
- You can complete a **spidergram** of others who may be involved in supporting the individual to maintain personal hygiene.
- You can also use as a **supporting piece of work product evidence** a risk assessment you have completed at work that identifies others who may be involved in supporting the individual to maintain personal hygiene.

REMEMBER TO:

- Include a **list** of others who may be involved in supporting the individual to maintain personal hygiene.
- Ensure the list relates to **maintaining personal hygiene**.
- Think about **your work setting** and who may be involved in supporting the individual to maintain personal hygiene.

Learning Outcome 3: Understand when poor hygiene may be an indicator of other underlying personal issues

Assessment Criterion 3.1: Identify underlying personal issues that may be a cause of poor personal hygiene

What does AC3.1 mean?

- The lead word **identify** means that you must **make clear** the underlying personal issues that may be a cause of poor personal hygiene.
- Your **list** must make clear other issues that may cause poor personal hygiene.
- For the key words **personal issues** you can think about how these may be about an individual's physical, emotional or social well-being, abuse, financial or health issues.
- For the key words **poor personal hygiene** you can think about the underlying reasons that there may be for not caring for one's body and keeping it clean and healthy.

Read the following **Real Work Setting** scenario and think about how it relates to your work setting and role:

Real Work Setting

Name: Denzel

Job Role: Care Assistant for older people

Denzel has been working as a Care Assistant for older people for eight years. His responsibilities include supporting individuals with personal care, bathing, showering, eating and drinking, moving and handling and participating in social and leisure activities.

Identifying underlying personal issues: Denzel is meeting with his manager for his supervision and discusses with him his concerns over one of the individuals he supports, Ben. Denzel explains that Ben seems to not be very keen on buying any more toiletries, even though he has almost finished his shower gel and shampoo. Ben thinks that this may be due to him being concerned about how much money he has left in his bank account, as he disclosed to Ben that he is worried because he is soon going to run out of money.

Evidencing AC3.1 to your assessor:

For AC3.1 you must evidence your understanding of identifying underlying personal issues that may be a cause of poor personal hygiene.

Assessment Methods:

Oral or **Written** Questioning or **Discussion** or a **Spidergram**

- You can **tell** your assessor about identifying underlying personal issues that may be a cause of poor personal hygiene.
  Or
- You can **talk** to your assessor about identifying underlying personal issues that may be a cause of poor personal hygiene.
  Or
- You can complete a **spidergram** of underlying personal issues that may be a cause of poor personal hygiene.

REMEMBER TO:

- Include a **list** of underlying personal issues that may be a cause of poor personal hygiene.
- Ensure the list relates to **poor personal hygiene**.
- Think about **your work setting** and underlying personal issues that may be a cause of poor personal hygiene.

Learning Outcome 3: Understand when poor hygiene may be an indicator of other underlying personal issues

Assessment Criterion 3.2: Describe how underlying personal issues might be addressed

What does AC3.2 mean?

- The lead word **describe** means that you must provide an **account** that **details** how underlying personal issues may be addressed.
- Your **account** must detail underlying personal issues.
- For the key words **personal issues** you can think about how these may be about an individual's physical, emotional or social well-being, abuse, health or financial issues.
- For the key word **addressed** you can think about the different ways of how to deal with underlying personal issues, depending on what they are, the individual's needs and the agreed support in place.

Read the following **Real Work Setting** scenario and think about how it relates to your work setting and role:

Real Work Setting

Name: Denzel

Job Role: Care Assistant for older people
(See page 307 for a description of the role)

Addressing underlying personal issues: Denzel discusses with his manager how best to address these issues with Ben. Denzel's manager explains that they need to find out a little more about the reasons why Ben's personal hygiene has deteriorated and suggests for the three of them to agree to meet and discuss this together, including how Ben would like them to support him to resolve those issues that may be a cause of his poor personal hygiene.

Evidencing AC3.2 to your assessor:

For AC3.2 you must evidence your understanding of addressing underlying personal issues that may be a cause of poor personal hygiene.

Assessment Methods:

Oral or **Written** Questioning or **Discussion** or **Personal Statement** or **Reflection**

- You can **tell** your assessor about addressing underlying personal issues.

  Or
- You can **talk** to your assessor about addressing underlying personal issues.

  Or
- You can write a **personal statement** or **reflection** about your experience of addressing underlying personal issues.

REMEMBER TO:

- Provide an **account** that details how to address underlying personal issues that may be a cause of poor personal hygiene.
- Think about **your work setting** and underlying personal issues that may be a cause of poor personal hygiene.

Glossary

Active participation – is a way of working that recognises an individual's right to participate in the activities and relationships of everyday life as independently as possible; the individual is regarded as an active partner in their own care or support, rather than a passive recipient

Agreed ways of working – include policies and procedures where these exist, they may be less formally documented with micro-employers

Consent – means informed agreement to an action or decision; the process of establishing consent will vary according to an individual's assessed capacity to consent

Individual (in the context of safeguarding – Unit HSC24) – will usually mean the person supported by the learner but may include those for whom there is no formal duty of care

Individual (in the context of person centred working – Unit HSC36) – refers to someone requiring care or support; it will usually mean the person or people supported by the learner

Person-centred values – may include individuality, rights, choice, privacy, independence, dignity, respect, partnership

Policies and procedures – may include other agreed ways of working as well as formal policies or procedures

Preferences and needs – will include any particular requirements and personal hygiene determined by an individual's culture, faith, belief, religion

Stress – can have positive as well as negative effects, but in this unit (HSC37) it is used to refer to negative stress